GLIDING
THEORY OF FLIGHT

Note

While every effort has been made to ensure that the
content of this book is as technically accurate and as
sound as possible, neither the editors nor the publishers
can accept responsibility for any injury or loss sustained
as a result of the use of this material.

First published in 2002 by
A & C Black (Publishers) Ltd
38 Soho Square, London W1D 3HB
www.acblack.com

Second edition published in 2007

Copyright © 2002, 2007 The British Gliding Association

ISBN: 978 0 7136 8660 9

A CIP catalogue record for this book
is available from the British Library.

Text and cover design by Jocelyn Lucas
Cover photograph © Getty Images (Tony Hutchings)
All illustrations by Steven Longland

This book is produced using paper that is made from wood grown
in managed, sustainable forests. It is natural, renewable and
recyclable. The logging and manufacturing processes conform
to the environment regulations of the country of origin.

Typeset in Minion Display 10/11.5 pt by
Palimpsest Book Production Limited, Grangemouth, Stirlingshire

Printed and bound in Great Britain by
Biddles Ltd, Kings Lynn

CONTENTS

ACKNOWLEDGEMENTS

Graham McAndrew, for large parts of the text and a number of drawings.

John Gibson, whose tireless efforts and patient advice have helped clear up a number of fundamental points, and whose papers and drawings have provided the basis for much of the new material.

Peter Bisgood, for his advice and unflagging good humour when faced with lots of rather stupid questions.

Tom Bradbury, whose profound understanding of the weather has been invaluable in the meteorology section. I suspect that, like me, he thinks that trying to describe the weather in 30 pages or so is a mark of lunacy.

Andy Walford, for his knowledge, expertise and unselfish help.

Alan Dibdin, whose clarity continues to amaze me.

David Owen, John Dadson, Afandi Darlington, Dave Bullock and others who have offered pertinent criticism and helpful suggestions.

Andrew G. W. Lawrie, for his extremely helpful advice and his excellent explanations of some of the more abstruse aspects of fluid flow.

My thanks also to the various 'beta-readers' who have generously ploughed through various drafts of draft chapters to check their general comprehensibility, and to Graham Morris for helping with the tedious task of proofreading. No one seems to have been irretrievably brain damaged by their involvement.

Also to the BGA for allowing the use of some drawings and text, largely from *Sailplane & Gliding*.

Finally, to anyone who has contributed either wittingly or unwittingly to this marathon production, and who has again not been thanked by name, my apologies – and thanks.

INTRODUCTION

It should be stated at the outset that this book was never intended for beginners, it being loosely based on the British Gliding Association's (BGA) original Ground School; a lecture series aimed chiefly at instructors. If, like some, you were expecting the first edition to be a 'how to work the controls and go solo' book, the second edition still isn't it. Its purpose is precisely the same as for the first; general education and information for instructors, and for glider pilots who are solo and might like to know a bit more about how everything works.

Given the book's intention, it is inevitable that the text will veer off into areas not directly relevant to the basic theory of flight – there is, for example, quite a lot of historical background. Some readers may find the asides (and probably the history as well) irritating, but there's no requirement to read the whole thing, though, particularly not in one go.

WHAT DO YOU NEED TO KNOW?

It is debatable which parts of the theory a glider pilot ought to know, and in how much detail, but it does pay big dividends to have some understanding of the basic physical laws and how they work. Any pilot who tries to ignore them is speaking to the Universe using the sort of juvenile finger language that will get them into really serious trouble. Ideally everyone would be interested in, if not exactly ecstatic about, the theory, but sadly it is commonly seen as:

(a) difficult. It would be a lie to say it was always easy, but it is often very straightforward if you keep your head. Paradoxically, and very annoyingly if one is clearly failing to get the point, the extreme simplicity of some of the theory can make it difficult to grasp

(b) intellectual. In the most insulting sense, intellectual is tabloid-speak for useless. Arguing that this is untrue would be regarded by such publications as intellectual

(c) requiring a brain the size of a planet. Not really. A couple of attentive neurons is usually sufficient, plus a bit of imagination

(d) causing eruptions of spots and pimples. I can't say that I have any more than usual.

If you are interested in just how useful theory can be, the subject is discussed in chapter two as part of the Requirements for Flight.

The contents page of each chapter has been 'coded'. Items which glider pilots, instructors in particular, really ought to know about are marked with a ★. Items about which you should know something, but where detailed knowledge is not required, are marked with a ☆. Anything unmarked is there largely for interest. The Meteorology chapter has not been coded because you'll need to know all of it, and a great deal more besides if you want some understanding of how the weather works.

Regardless of one's best intentions, there will be errors in this book, and, being the second edition, some from the first will have been corrected and others slyly inserted. Changes have been made. Two chapters have been rewritten, so the scope for error is certainly there. Once again, this book makes no claim to be either perfect or the last word on anything.

Readers can remain assured that whatever the current theory happens to be, reality will continue to work as well or as badly as before.

CHAPTER 1
DEFINITIONS

CHAPTER CONTENTS ★ should know ☆ useful

1 DEFINITIONS

Skip this chapter if you are familiar with basic physics

Scary science

Whatever your views about what scientists do, what they think they're doing, and how and why they go about doing it, there is no question that science is the most powerful tool ever to come into the hands of the human race. No other way of looking at the physical world has anything even remotely approaching science's practical horsepower, and in terms of our understanding it has been both hugely successful and, it has to be said, occasionally woundingly destructive. Either way, it has changed forever how we look at and see the world and ourselves, and, like it or not, will continue to do so in ways we cannot even guess.

Scientists are not always science's best ambassadors, and non-scientists don't always take kindly to being told they don't really know anything. Worse, when mathematics is wheeled out to provide elegant and logical proof of something – it hardly matters what – many of us experience an overwhelming desire to become completely unconscious. In fact, a general understanding of how gliders work doesn't need anything more elaborate than the 'three apples plus two pears' variety of arithmetic. We do, however, need to understand basic physics as without it we have little chance of realising how a glider manages its tricks.

This first chapter looks at some of the basics, with many of the examples being taken from gliding. In fact, you can check out most of the physics for yourself by doing nothing more strenuous, mentally or physically, than going to an airfield and either taking a flight, or just pushing something around at the launch point.

PHYSICS IN THE FIELD

The list below contains a selection of airfield activities and some of the relevant physical laws, for the moment, stated without any explanation:

- helpers somehow manage to run a glider over your foot. The pain you feel is a result of the glider's *weight* (weight equals *mass* times *gravity*)

- you are momentarily distracted by something else on the airfield. Helpers run the glider into your back. The pain you feel is related to the glider's *momentum* (momentum equals *mass* times *velocity*)

- you land on a runway. Helpers come to push the glider. Even though the surface is smooth and flat, the effort you use to get the glider moving, particularly if this needs to be done in a hurry, is far more than what's needed to keep it moving once it's rolling. The difference is due to *inertia* (Newton's First Law of Motion)

- the effort you expend pushing the glider also demonstrates *energy conversion* (breakfast cereal into bodily movement) and illustrates something about *vectors* (force(s) applied in a specific direction)

- to manhandle a K13 with two people already on board up the launch queue, you first have to push down on the tail to lift the nose-skid off the ground. If you move closer to the wing you have to push down much harder to get the same result (*moments* and *levers*)

- you have a cable break on the launch. As you push over, you experience a reduction in your weight (*acceleration*, Newton's First and Second Laws of Motion).

We spend every minute of every day demonstrating these and other laws to ourselves, even if we aren't aware of doing so. What is important about all the examples given above is that the physical laws they illustrate describe things which, apart from the specific injuries mentioned, happen with a high degree of regularity and predictability; all of which suggests that the world has a natural and inherent order, as indeed appears to be the case.

Dimensions

We'll take it as read that the physical world exists. If we think about why it works in the way it does rather than in any other way, then most of what we take completely for granted turns out to be a bit strange, to say the least. Take the space around us. Each of us lives at the centre of a sphere of perception dotted with objects that are separated from each other by . . . well, by what exactly? Empty space? Nothing? Whatever it is, without it none of us would be anywhere.

It is useful to think of this space as either containing or consisting of three related physical *dimensions* (figure 1), at right angles to each other.

Despite the world's hills and valleys, we spend most of our life pinned by gravity to the surface of the two-dimensional *plane* represented by figure 1, example ②. As with so much of the natural toolbox bequeathed to us by nature and evolution, we are not aware that our existence is governed by the need for us to continually measure and calculate where we are within the surrounding space. True, we don't leap about saying '$x^2+y^2=z^2$', or '$d=r \times \alpha$', but if we weren't doing something similar we would not last very long. The information required by the brain for the necessary calculations and comparisons comes from two main sources:

(1) force information provided by the semicircular canals in each ear, and sensations from other parts of the body, particularly the feet and legs (tension in the muscles and so on)

(2) visual information from the eyes (directions, angles, distances).

An apparently coherent and fluid reality is conjured out of this information, but it takes time to create it, however short, so our perceived world trails a fraction of a second behind the real one. The brain also has an editorial function, and is masterly at ignoring things that 'don't fit'. Equally, faced with a contradiction, or a gap that 'should not be there', it will make something up. Just how much of our experience is sneakily extemporised in this way is obviously difficult to say.

Exactly how the brain decides whether a sensory input is worth including in its worldview or not is another matter. When flying in conditions of good visibility, pilots are well aware that when banked *they* are tilting, not the world. When circling in cloud or very poor visibility, visual input falls below some critical threshold, and 'up' becomes almost entirely dependent on the senses, or apparent direction of gravity. In a balanced turn this is straight down our spines, i.e. in the 'upright' direction.

In each ear we have three semicircular canals that lie at right angles to each other. They contain tiny lime crystals whose contact with sensory hairs projecting into the canals supply the brain with information about orientation and acceleration. During a constant and balanced turn the crystals settle onto sensory hairs associated with 'upright'. Without instruments or any other input to confirm or contradict this message, the brain takes it to mean, quite literally, upright as in 'not banking'. Still turning, we suddenly pop out of cloud, and the world appears to have fallen over. We feel distinctly sick while the brain readjusts itself.

The reason for mentioning any of these things is that (a) there can be serious discrepancies between how we see the world and what's really happening (this begs a few questions) and (b) our personal sense of where we are is, in the most general sense of

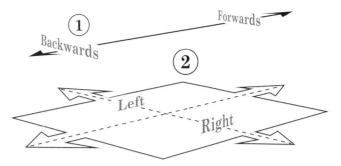

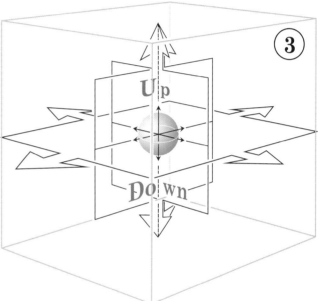

FIGURE 1 The three dimensions and associated planes

the term, self-centred, and it's difficult to see how it could be anything else. Some of the results of this can be confusing! You point at the sky and say 'that's up'. On the opposite side of the world someone else does the same thing. A remote observer would see two people pointing in completely opposite directions. What we take to be 'up' is a universal standard only in so far as everybody relates it to themselves. 'Up' is determined largely by our body's orientation, and the direction of any forces acting upon it. Since the major force to which we are subjected appears to be weight, and, by association, gravity, then 'up' normally means 'head at the top and feet at the bottom'.

GIVING DIRECTIONS – STARTING FROM WHERE?

If there was only one person on the planet, the self-centred view would be irrelevant. One could believe exactly what one liked. Suddenly, someone else appears and asks for directions. Once over the shock, what does one actually say? Not much if we don't know where we are in relation to this other place. If we do know, then in effect we have to create a map, which implies measurement.

Way back, the standard might have been the length of the ruler's foot. Systems based on one person's physical quirks, however regal, are hardly ideal. The ruler will die and the foot go with him, causing economic and social distress. Maybe the foot could be cut off and pickled, but far better to persuade him to sanction an accurate reproduction to be copied by the thousand. That way everyone has access to the foot, wherever the original, and it becomes an independent, neutral, and public standard of measurement.

In whatever way a measuring system/standard is set up, it must have:

- a consistent and agreed set of units (e.g. walk 35 paces)

- an imaginary and usually regular grid centred on a fixed *origin* (e.g. start from here)

- a location defined on the grid by at least two, possibly three unique pieces of information (e.g. go east until you meet the river, then walk one mile north).

COORDINATES (YOU ARE HERE)

To pinpoint the position of anything on a map, or a graph – both two-dimensional grids – a minimum of two *coordinates* are needed, one for each dimension. There's a left/right coordinate, and a forwards/backwards coordinate, each defined in relation to the grid's origin. For example, if you stand at position A in figure 2, your coordinates are *forwards eight, left nine*. At position B your coordinates would be *backwards two, right three*.

While two coordinates are enough to define a position on the surface of a map, a minimum of three are needed to describe any position above it (figure 3). There's no point adding extra dimensions if all they do is duplicate information you already have, so on that count alone the third dimension must be at right angles to the other two.

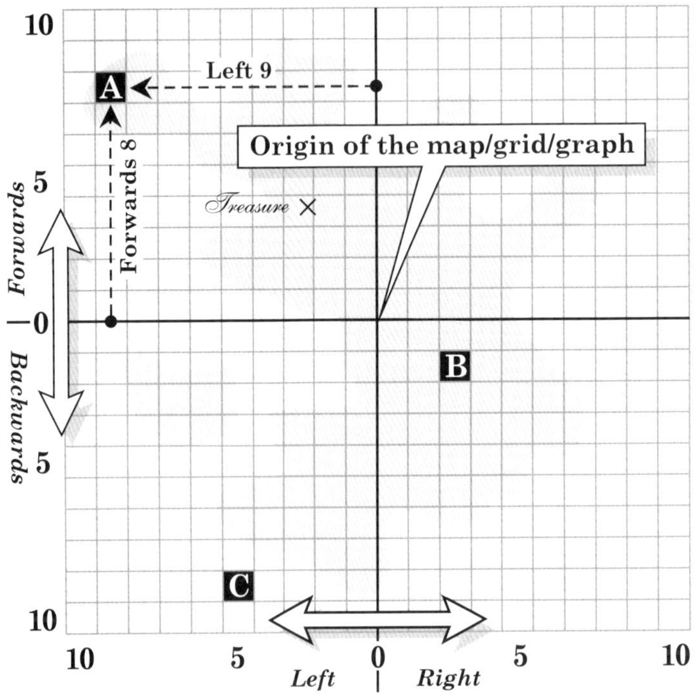

Positions can also be defined using a *bearing* and distance from a known point, e.g. five miles south west of Aston Down. Our height will need describing in terms of another angle, an *elevation*, or as a vertical distance above the end of the line from the origin.

FIGURE 2 Maps – two-dimensional coordinates

ALGEBRA AND BEING LOST

Describing a position in terms of coordinates is straightforward if you happen to know where you are. 'I am three miles due west of the Long Mynd at 3,500ft,' you might say. But what if you're lost?

Most of us associate numbers with specific things: there are three apples in the fruit bowl and minus two hundred pounds in the current account. Easy stuff, yet confront us with numbers which aren't stuck like flags to objects, or flash us arithmetic with alphabetical bits – the cursed algebra – and the IQ gauge falls to zero. This is a very odd reaction because a lot of what we say (and do) is suspiciously algebraic. For example, we might recall that there was fruit in the bowl, but not how much or even what sort. We wouldn't think twice about saying, 'I know there's some fruit in the bowl,' but though essentially the same thing, we would not say 'there are X fruit(s) in the bowl, where X is a number.' A mathematician might describe the situation thus, but go further and lop off anything even a whisker beside the point, leaving us with a fruit bowl contents probability-function such as X_{FRUIT}, or something equally cryptic.

Whether lost in flight or not, our position requires three coordinates to describe it, either exactly (we know the numbers), approximately (we know some of the numbers), or abstractly (we haven't the faintest idea what the numbers are, but we know they're needed). If asked, we could describe our uncertain location as 'at coordinates XYZ,' where X is along, Y is up, and Z is at right angles to X and Y (figure 3). Without the numbers, this is about as helpful as saying 'Hello, I'm somewhere.'

TIME'S ARROW

Time is also a dimension and a coordinate. A four-dimensional position report would be something like: 'I knew where I was at four o'clock.' Even though we are aware of time, it's probably true to say that no-one really knows quite what it is that clocks are actually measuring. St Thomas Aquinas put his finger on the problem when he wrote that he knew perfectly well what time was, until someone asked him to explain it.

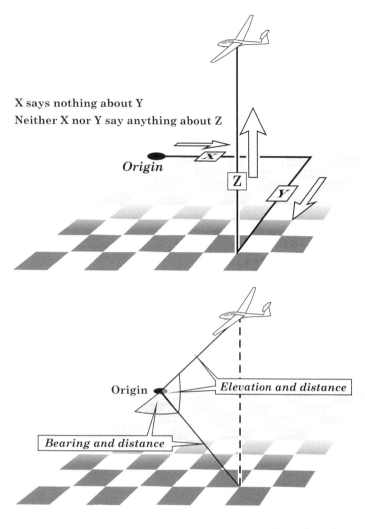

X says nothing about Y
Neither X nor Y say anything about Z

FIGURE 3 Three-dimensional coordinates

Forces, vectors, loads

Whereas objects are visible, *force* and *energy* are only so indirectly. Like many biological and biodegradable entities, we are in the unusual position of being aware of the expenditure of energy ('what an effort'), and can sense force ('I was hit'), without being able to see either of them. In order to apply forces ourselves ('move this'), we have to burn some of the energy stored in our bodies, and then eat to replenish the store. On that basis we might conclude that only biological organisms have energy and can apply force, but

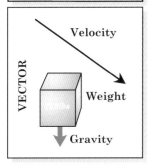

FIGURE 4 Quantities

inanimate objects can have plenty of both. You can prove this by dropping a brick on your foot!

Volume, length, depth, width, mass and speed are *scalar* quantities. A *vector*, on the other hand, is a quantity which has both magnitude and direction. *Velocity*, which is speed in a specific direction, is a vector, as are gravity and weight (figure 4).

Loads are the internal response of a material to an applied force, and have no independent existence. For example, if you hold a rod just touching a wall (figure 5), no pressure or force is applied until you push the rod against it. The 'push' then becomes a load, which is transferred through the rod's material to the wall. Loads are vectors.

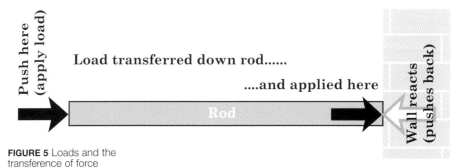

FIGURE 5 Loads and the transference of force

Equilibrium

Equilibrium is a condition in which all the forces involved balance out, but that doesn't necessarily lead to things being steady in the conventional sense of the term. An object can be in equilibrium when it is motionless, and when it is ripping along at several hundred miles an hour and tumbling crazily end over end. Equilibrium can be very deceptive and hide extreme forces. For example, out of reach in the flames of the garden bonfire is an empty aerosol can. The contents are expanding in the heat and the internal pressure is rising; yet nothing appears to be happening. Suddenly the can explodes. Shrapnel and fragments of bonfire fly all over the place. So much for equilibrium!

Weight, gravity and mass (W, G and m)

It is doubtful whether, in our everyday lives, any of us make a distinction between mass and weight, and there's no reason why we should. Had the distinction been crucial to our survival, then natural selection would have shaken out sense organs capable of disting-uishing between the two, but it didn't. Nor did it equip us specifically for flight, which is an area where the distinction between mass and weight is more obvious and, in some respects, far more critical. Pilots are familiar with how manoeuvring in flight can alter their weight to zero, or become so heavy they cannot move. That these changes occur at all is significant enough, but even if we momentarily weigh nothing we don't as a result wink out of existence. Pinch yourself at the appropriate weightless moment during a vigorous pushover after a cable break and, yes, you are still there. This implies that even if weight is an inconsistent and, indeed, an unreliable quantity, there is something else that is not.

That 'something else' is *mass*, and could be defined as 'the stuff left over when you've taken weight away'. Mass creates the force we know as gravity, and gravity creates weight. Anything with mass will attract anything else which has mass, so weight depends to a certain extent on who is having the greatest effect. We attract the Earth towards us, but with little result given the scale of its effect on us. It is convenient, therefore, if not strictly accurate, to think of the Earth as being the only source of gravitation at its surface.

Since the Earth's mass is effectively acting upon itself, the planet's natural shape is a sphere. A falling object will accelerate towards the Earth's centre at a constant rate of 32 feet per second, every second (32ft/sec² or 9.8m/sec²), but if already on solid ground, it can't get to where it is being drawn. Weight is the result, and it can be seen as the frustrated acceleration of mass. That's not to suggest that weight is an illusion – try lifting a grand piano on your own – just that it isn't quite what it seems.

Two further points need to be made about gravity and mass:

(1) two objects of dissimilar mass but similar volume, dropped together, will fall in tandem. The effects of air resistance are considerable, so this is hard to demonstrate! Assuming no air resistance, a large ball of expanded polystyrene dropped from a high tower will accelerate downwards at the same rate as a lead ball of identical volume, and they will reach the ground simultaneously, i.e. at the same velocity. Here's a practical tip: air resistance or not, if you are going to be hit by either, make sure it isn't the lead ball (see *inertia* and *momentum*, below)

(2) when we stand on any solid surface it pushes passively upwards against us with a force exactly equal and opposite to our weight (figure 6). If the ground's reaction were anything else we would either sink out of sight or be hurled into the air. The normal passive reaction has consequences for flight in that, if aircraft are to fly at all, an upward force must act upon them which is at least equal to that provided by the ground when they are sat in the hangar.

Since the strength of Earth's gravity is broadly constant at the Earth's surface and within the wafer-thin layer of the atmosphere where we conduct most of our activities, it is treated as a *constant,* and, for convenience, 32ft/sec² is regarded as 1G. Comforting to know, because, everything else being equal, the glider which injured us earlier will always weigh the same amount no matter how often it is run over our foot.

Inertia

The same cannot always be said of *inertia*, which is the irritating thing that makes any object, particularly a large one like a glider, difficult to get moving and then equally hard to stop. Even though mass and weight are related (see box), an object's inertia is dependent solely upon its mass; the greater the mass of an object, the greater the effort required to start it moving or bring it to a halt.

Measuring inertia is not straightforward. Experimenters are constantly

On the face of it, the pain suffered in the first two examples of airfield activities on pages 3–4 –the helpers running the glider over your foot then into your back – have an identical cause. Yet even though weight was responsible when the glider ran over your foot, it had nothing to do with your pain when the glider ran into your back.

Weight = Mass × g, or W = mg. If g = 1 then W = m

FIGURE 6 Ground, gravity and weight

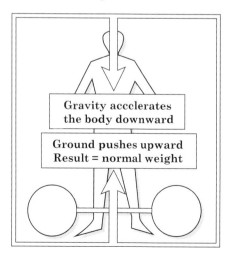

Gravity accelerates the body downward

Ground pushes upward Result = normal weight

faced by nature's prodigal habits, and detail, which they would like to study, is surrounded by equally insistent detail jostling for attention, and simply getting in the way. The cleverest part of experiments aimed at measuring something specific often lie in avoiding measuring anything else! For example, try to measure inertia by moving a glider on soft ground and the wheel will dig a deep hole and want to stay in it. Most of our effort goes into trying to shove the glider up an effectively endless hill, and has nothing to do with inertia.

There are easier ways of observing inertia at work than pushing a glider all over the place. Take a spring balance and hang a large object from the hook (figure 7). The result is a minimalist model of a glider at rest on the ground. Normally we wouldn't attempt to lift a glider straight up into the air, but that's what a wing has to do, so the following experiments will tell us something about the mechanics of flight.

By lifting and lowering the balance and the suspended object several times in the ways indicated, we can come to the following conclusions:

- when lifted very slowly and steadily the scale reading remains constant

- when the balance is lifted abruptly the scale indicates briefly that the suspended object became heavier – the more so the quicker we try to raise it

- if we lower the balance very suddenly and quickly the scale reading reduces and may briefly register zero

- the same momentary loss of weight occurs if we suddenly stop moving the balance upwards.

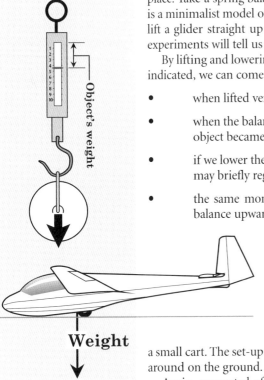

The majority of these examples demonstrate inertia, and how weight is affected by acceleration. It could be argued that weight was responsible for some of the effects, but to prove otherwise we'd have to get rid of it. Impossible as that might sound, it can be done. If weight is a direct result of gravity acting on mass, and gravity acts vertically downwards, then that is the direction in which weight acts. All we have to do is support the weight in, say, a small cart. The set-up is now as illustrated in figure 8, and analogous to moving a glider around on the ground.

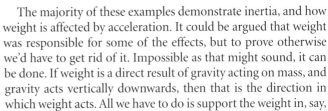

Again, unwanted effects like *friction* can make nonsense of the results, but when allowance has been made for them, we note that a sudden horizontal pull on the spring balance produces a marked positive reading on the scale. The swifter and harder we pull, the larger the initial reading. Scales normally measure weight, but because the cart and the ground have taken care of that, what we are measuring is the object's mass and inertia. Interestingly, the scale would indicate the object's weight if we accelerated the trolley sideways at 32ft/sec[2]!

FIGURE 7 Spring balance, and balance and glider at rest

Momentum

Momentum is the energy possessed by a moving object. The speed and direction (*velocity*) of an object add energy to the object's mass.

A rifle bullet may only weigh a few ounces, but fired at point blank range into a plank it will pass straight through at upwards of 600mph. If the gun subsequently misfires and the bullet falls out of the barrel and bounces off the plank onto the ground, it will be clear that (a) something has gone seriously wrong, and (b) no damage has been done. The only relevant difference between the shots was the speed of the bullet which, in one case, added lethal amounts of extra energy to the bullet's small mass, and turned the other into feeble slapstick.

In terms of the clumsy helpers mentioned earlier, the very practical result of the above is that if they run the glider into your back very slowly, it won't hurt nearly as much as it would if they do it quickly.

Chucking one's weight about

Map coordinates help us locate where things are, but the basic principles extend to objects moving through 3D space. The flight of a ball can be treated as two-dimensional because only two coordinates are needed to describe it: a horizontal and a vertical component of velocity at right angles to each other (figure 9).

Any *ballistic object* is clearly influenced by gravity because if you throw a ball straight up it eventually comes straight down again. What is not so obvious is that this up and down motion, the vertical component, is unaffected by any horizontal component you give the ball when you throw it. The ball's vertical velocity in free flight is gravity driven and will change at a constant rate. Ignoring the considerable effects of air resistance, the horizontal velocity is dependent on how hard and at what angle the ball is thrown. Once in free flight nothing accelerates or decelerates this component – it remains constant. The result is that regardless of whether the

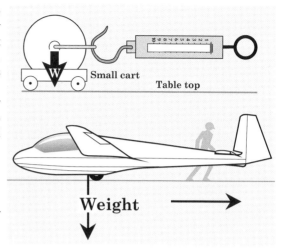

FIGURE 8 Measuring inertia

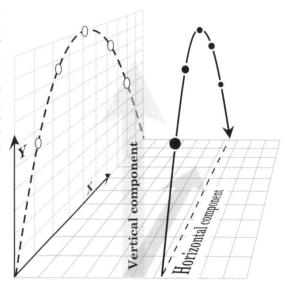

FIGURE 9 Flight path components of a ball

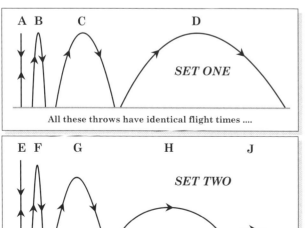

FIGURE 10 Parabolic, free fall curves

ground is flat or not, the flight time of any ballistic object is dependent solely on the vertical component of velocity, i.e. on gravity.

Ballistic objects trace out *parabolic curves*, and figure 10 (see previous page) shows two sets of these. The vertical lines A and E represent a ball thrown vertically upwards and coming straight down again. There are differences between the two sets, but they have nothing to do with the angle of any of the throws, only with the initial force. In set one, for example, regardless of the angle, the ball is always thrown hard enough to reach the same height, and the more angled the throw the more effort has to be made (figure 11). In set two, each throw has the same initial impetus put into it. As the angle of the throw becomes shallower, more of the impetus goes into the horizontal component and less into the vertical one, so each time the ball goes less high and hits the ground sooner.

Ballistic objects in flight trace out a *freefall* parabola, and because the vertical velocity component is influenced solely by gravity (forgetting air resistance again), they are *weightless*. This probably doesn't sound quite right, so let's take a really surreal example. We've just fallen out of a glider at altitude and happen to have with us a pair of bathroom scales. As we accelerate downwards at 1G we are weightless, or at least, that's the theory we will now check out. We try to sit on the scales. What do they read? A lot, a little, or nothing? Contrary to everything we might expect, the reading will depend entirely on what we do with the scales. For example, if we just slide them underneath us, they will read zero. If we pull them up against our backsides and make a very determined effort to be 'sat down', all they will measure is how hard we are trying!

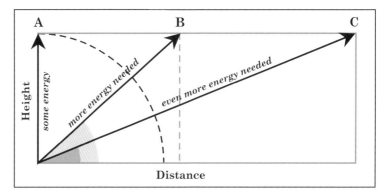

FIGURE 11 Angled throws and velocity/energy input

Accelerations not due to gravity

On those rare occasions when we think about acceleration, we tend to associate it with pressing down on a car accelerator and being pushed back into our seats (figure 12). Similar sensations occur at the start of a winch launch. Despite what we feel, we are not being thrust back by some unseen force from ahead, but being pushed from behind and proving rather reluctant to go forwards (inertia).

Cars and winch launches provide examples of 'fore and aft' acceleration, reinforcing the notion that acceleration is just a process of 'speeding up'. In fact, acceleration can occur in any direction and is fundamental, not only to changes of speed brought about by putting your foot down, but to changes of direction where, confusingly, we can accelerate without altering our speed in the slightest.

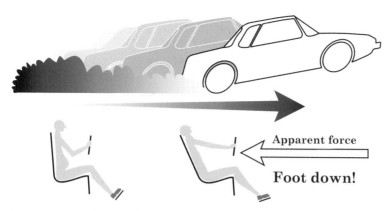

FIGURE 12 Normal view of acceleration

Apparent force

Foot down!

For instance, we are driving home at 50mph from the airfield, and reach a corner we have rounded uneventfully many times before. When we turn the wheel now, though, the car ploughs straight on through the hedge and into a field. The thought least likely to have passed through our heads is that on every corner, anywhere, the car has *always* wanted to go straight on. There is nothing odd about this. Ploughing straight on is the option involving the least effort, and 'least possible effort' is a majestically lethargic principle that dominates the material world. We may sweep round the corner at a constant 50mph, but our direction keeps changing, so a force (an acceleration) must act towards the centre of the circle whose circumference we are attempting to follow (figure 13).

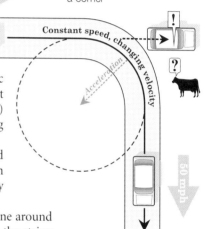

FIGURE 13 Acceleration round a corner

Normally, when the steering wheel is turned, friction between the road surface and the tyres provides the into-turn force, but this time there was ice on the road, so turning the wheel had no effect. Unable to alter our velocity in any way whatsoever, we bowed to the principle of least effort and quit the road.

There's no need to wreck a car to understand what happened. Whirl a stone around on the end of a string (figure 14). As you whirl the stone faster the force in the string increases. If the stone normally weighed a quarter of a pound and the force in the string was three pounds, then that would be the stone's current effective weigh. Three pounds is a twelve-fold increase, so the stone was being subjected to an acceleration of 12G (3/0.25). The equivalent of 'ice on the road' here is to remove the inward accelerating force by letting go of the string. Viewed from above, the stone instantly flies off in a straight line (C).

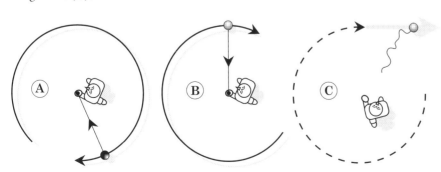

FIGURE 14 Stone on a string

FIGURE 15 Direction of gravity

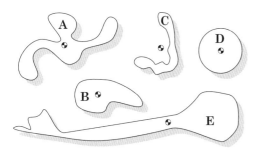

FIGURE 16 CG of
two-dimensional shapes

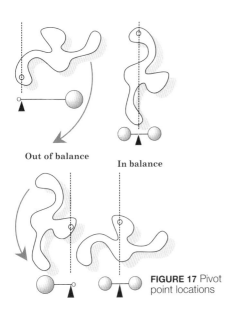

Out of balance

In balance

FIGURE 17 Pivot
point locations

Centre of gravity (CG), centre of mass

The centre of gravity of a body is its centre of mass. Because the Earth is more or less a sphere, its CG is in the centre. It can be located by noting in which direction gravity appears to be acting at various points on the surface, and then extending these *lines of action* downwards to their meeting point. Gravity acts at right angles to the surface, and so we are able to stand anywhere upon it and be in no danger of either falling or sliding off into space (figure 15).

Finding the CG of a two-dimensional shape cut from card, like those in figure 16, can be done by trial and error. Pin shape A to a vertical surface, making sure it can rotate freely. With the pin placed in an arm, or along an edge, the shape will always try to hang as shown in figure 17. This is because in the starting position, there is always more of its weight/area to one side of the vertical line through the pivot than to the other. (The dumbbells represent the approximate distribution of weight to each side of the pivot line. The arrows show the direction the shape will swing when released.)

After some experimentation you'll find a *pivot point* where the shape doesn't swing whatever the position in which it begins – or, if you spin it, however fast, each and every position in which it stops will be a balanced one. This indicates that the pin is at the shape's CG, as in figure 18.

In point of fact, what has just been described is a longwinded way of locating the shape's CG. The easiest method is to pin it up by an arm, as shown in figure 19, and with a pencil draw a vertical line down from the pivot pin. Using a different pivot point, preferably as far away from the first line as possible, draw another line in the same way. These two lines will cross at the CG. How you would pin up a shape with an external CG (figure 16, example C), is anybody's guess.)

The CG of a two-dimensional shape is the geometric centre of its surface area, but the same principle used to find its CG can be applied to certain types of 3D object. Gliders aren't spherical, they contain lots of empty space, have no appreciable gravitational effect on anything, and their mass tends to be concentrated in particular places. Even so, working out a CG position is fairly straightforward because, like most aircraft, gliders have a vertical *plane of symmetry*, i.e. left mirrors right (figure 20). Providing the glider is weighed with wings level, it can be treated as if it were a two-dimensional object, and this is what CG calculations assume (see Appendix B, p. 293).

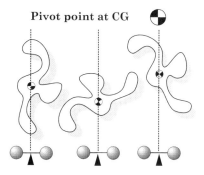

FIGURE 18 Pivot at CG

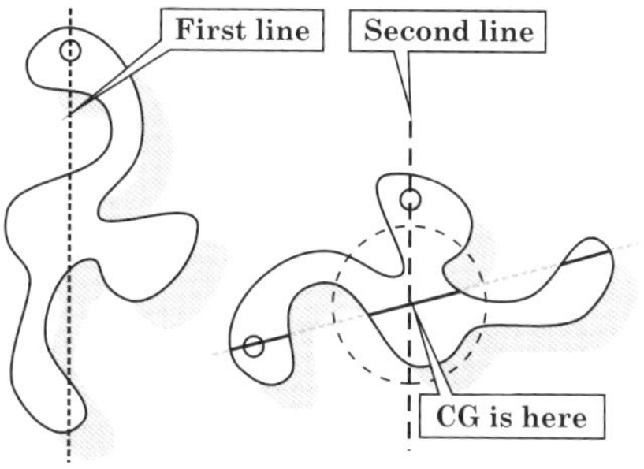

FIGURE 19 CG, the simple way

FIGURE 20 Plane of symmetry

FALLING OVER

Things topple when the *line of action* of their weight – vertically downwards from the CG – goes beyond some edge or place on the object which will act as a *pivot point* (figure 21). A ball on level ground doesn't and can't fall over because, being circular, the pivot point is always directly underneath the CG (figure 22, see over).

As far as the box in figure 21 is concerned, it can be in one of four basic states:

(1) *Equilibrium.* The box's weight acts straight down through the middle of the base.

(2) *Positively stable.* The weight's line of action remains to the side of the initial equilibrium position, giving the box a tendency to tip back towards it.

(3) *Neutrally stable.* At some point the weight's line of action falls straight through a ground contact/pivot point, such as the box's edge. There is the same weight/mass each side of the pivot. The box is in fine balance and can fall either way.

(4) *Unstable* or, depending on how you look at it, positively stable. The weight's line of action is well to the side of the pivot point and pulls the box over. If we think of the box as falling towards another equilibrium state [5], then [4] can be seen as positively stable.

CG WHEN THERE'S NO G

In zero gravity there would be no CG as such, so the in-balance and out-of-balance cases at which we've looked wouldn't seem to apply. However, the object still has a *centre of mass*, at the same place as the CG, and even if it cannot be located by any of the methods previously described, you only have to spin the object to realise the importance of where you put the pivot.

With the pivot in the wrong place the object jumps around, much as a washing machine does if it is put onto the spin cycle when the clothes inside aren't distributed evenly. Any rotating object will try to spin about its centre of mass, and any attempt to make it do otherwise produces an imbalance leading to the kind of behaviour just described.

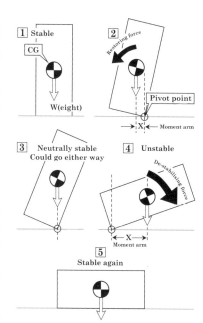

FIGURE 21 The toppling box

FIGURE 22 Pivot point of ball

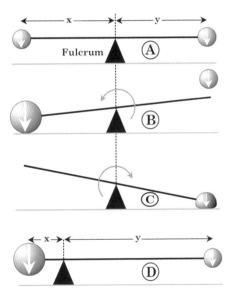

FIGURE 23 The see-saw

Moments and levers

Moments and *levers* are fundamental to balance and crucial in relation to glider stability (see chapter 6). Moments and levers haven't been mentioned in previous sections, but they've been there, by implication.

We've all had a go on a see-saw. When someone of our weight sat on the opposite side (example (A), <u>figure 23</u>), everything balanced out and a joyful time was had by all. Put the inevitably heavier playground bully on the other end, and when he sat down we shot up in the air (example (B)). After a bit of teasing, off he would leap and down we would crash (example (C)). The practical solution to this problem is not a contract killing, but something that gives us at least an equal influence on the see-saw's behaviour.

The *moment of a force* is its distance from a pivot or *fulcrum*, multiplied by its *magnitude*. For the see-saw to balance, our two moments about the fulcrum must be equal. At the same distance from the fulcrum as ourselves, the heavier bully had the greater moment (effect), so we took off when he sat down. If he inches nearer to the pivot and we stay put, he arrives eventually at a position where his moment about the fulcrum is the same as ours, and the see-saw balances. Alternatively, the fulcrum can be moved towards him (example (D)), which puts more of the see-saw on our side and gives us some extra *leverage*. The effects are the same.

A similar see-saw act is needed to move a two-seat glider around when the pilots are already strapped in. We first have to lift the nose-skid off the ground, otherwise we aren't going to go anywhere. The usual way to provide the appropriate moment is to push down on the lifting handles at the tail – line 4 in <u>figure 24</u>. If the pilots are very heavy, we may have to use most, if not all, of our weight, but there is then so little friction between our feet and the ground that by ourselves we cannot provide any useful push.

If the combined weight of the people sitting in the cockpit is 308lb (22 stone), then their mutual fulcrum is the CG of their combined weights. This acts along line 1, three feet ahead of the glider's fulcrum, the wheel (line 2). The setup is identical to almost all the weight being on the bully's side of the seesaw (<u>figure 23 (B)</u>).

The formula which works out how hard you are going to have to push down on the tail ②, 11 feet behind the fulcrum, to exactly balance the people in front, is:

$$W_P \times A = W_Y \times B$$

or the left hand moment must equal the right hand moment.

What is the minimum downward force (W_Y) needed at the tail to lift the nose? Grit your teeth! $W_Y = W_P \times A/B$, which is $308 \times 3 \div 11 = 84$lb (6 stone). This only just balances the pilot's weight, so a bit more is needed to lift the glider's skid clear of the ground. If you push down just behind the wings, about four feet behind the fulcrum ③ the balancing force rises to 231lb (16½ stone). Two feet closer and it is 308lb (22 stone). Six inches from the pivot it is 1,848lb, about three quarters of a ton.

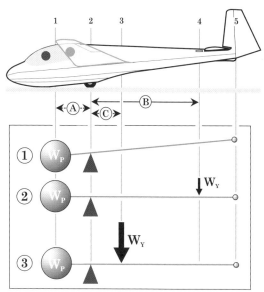

FIGURE 24 Raising the nose, easy or difficult?

Vectors and the resolution of forces

It is not unusual for groups of people to work against each other when they think they're cooperating, and moving gliders around is no exception. How often have you seen three people pushing on one wing and one on the other, with the wingtip holder trying desperately to keep such a lopsided set-up going in a straight line? Even two helpers can combine to successfully thwart each other's efforts, and yours.

In figure 25 (A), we have two such helpers. They are very reliable and will push consistently, or not at all. In example (B), helper H_1 always pushes eastward with a force of 100 units (lb, oz, kg, whatever), while helper H_2 is set on pushing blindly north with a force of 50 units. Both will act upon the glider through the same point – where the wheel contacts the ground – and the glider will respond to both their efforts.

Before these helpers even begin you can work out where the glider is likely to end up. This involves a process known as *resolution*, which can be done either mathematically or graphically. The graphical method involves drawing what is in effect a scale model of the forces involved, and uses something known as a *parallelogram of forces*.

Draw the forces out at scale lengths (1mm = 1lb, for example), ensuring that both lines start from the same point and have the correct angle between them. Complete the parallelogram then measure the diagonal – the result, or *resultant*. Both the maths and the graphics say that when H_1 pushes the glider one foot to the east, H_2 pushes it six inches to the north. Their efforts result in a roughly north-easterly force on the glider of 111.8lb (example (B)). Example (B) shows H_1 and H_2 acting at right angles to each other, but more likely they'll act at some other angle. (C) shows them becoming hopelessly confused and pushing away from each other. As you might expect, the useful result(ant) is less than before (approximately 80lb), but still in a roughly north-easterly direction. In the extreme case (example (D)), they are pushing in completely opposite directions. The resultant is 50lb in an easterly direction, with the helper on the left being dragged backwards. It is easy to see what a desperately inefficient way this is of returning a glider to the launch point.

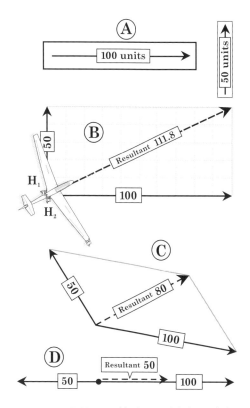

FIGURE 25 Vectors and their resolution

The reality

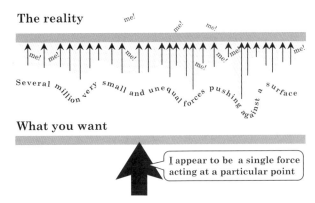

What you want

I appear to be a single force acting at a particular point

FIGURE 26 Reducing multiple forces to one

Graphical resolution becomes more inaccurate the more vectors involved, and only works well for very basic situations where the forces are neither too different in magnitude, nor too alike in direction. As a way of sketching out a likely resultant, however, it will give a rough idea of what is likely to happen, and can serve as a useful cross check for any arithmetic.

When hundreds, even trillions, of small forces are acting on a surface, resolving them becomes complicated. At sea-level pressures each molecule of air is about a millionth of a millimetre from its nearest neighbour. How each behaves is critical to whether something like a wing works or not, but it would be insane to try and deal with the effect of each in turn. Yet, for aerodynamic and structural reasons, we must know where the resultant force is acting. In other words (figure 26), never mind the individual, how's the crowd behaving? If the object was, say, a wing, we could place it into a wind tunnel and measure the *acting forces* at a small selection of points on its surface. Using simple arithmetic (levers and moments again) we could then calculate the single and more manageable resultant.

It is possible, and often desirable, to work backwards from a resultant (or any single force for that matter) and, within certain limits, split it into any number of forces acting in whatever directions we choose. Both creating more or fewer vectors is called resolving or resolution. Either way, this book will regard more than two, perhaps three at a pinch, as a bit of a waste of time.

ODD COUPLES

Well-coordinated or not, at least the previous helpers were pushing through a common pivot point, but in the majority of cases the *line of action* of a force being applied to an object won't act through the object's CG or its pivot point. This offset and the unbalance it creates is known as a *couple*.

In figure 27, H_1 and H_2 represent two remote and equal forces failing to act directly through the glider's pivot point. Our helpers remain both obstinate and consistent, and examples ① to ③ represent the ongoing results of their efforts.

There are far more complicated couples than the one illustrated, but most share similar dynamics. In the first two stages illustrated, the line of action of forces H_1 and H_2 are, so to speak, kinked in relation to the pivot point. This is not tolerated in a dynamic system and, in an effort to literally straighten things up, H_1 and H_2 try to rearrange everything so that they can act in a straight line through the pivot point, as they do finally in stage ③. Once everything is lined up the rotation ceases.

The figure shows one helper tripping over the tailplane and the other walking off into the distance, but in a real situation where H_1 and H_2 remain hands-on to the object, what happens next depends on whether the forces are equal or not. It may be, of course, that the straight line sought by the dynamics of the system is impossible, in which case the object being acted upon will continue to rotate, or at least try to do so.

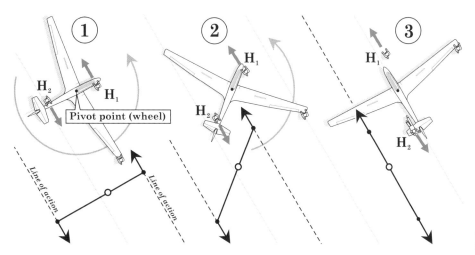

FIGURE 27 The effects of a simple couple

Energy and energy conversion

Nobody is quite sure what energy is, but, rather like mass, it can be identified through its effects, and we're pretty clear about how it is transferred. Pushing a glider is an example of energy being transferred from one object (a person) to another (a glider). Ultimately, everything is assumed to be composed of energy, and luckily most of it is very securely locked up. In the small number of forms readily available to us, energy can appear far from energetic. Coal is dark, dull and inert. We have to set it alight to persuade it to release small quantities of radiant heat, but if all the energy calculated to be in one lump could be persuaded to let rip instantaneously, it could flatten a moderate sized town. By comparison, burning the coal releases tiny amounts of energy, a very small proportion of which warms us. Most of the rest goes up the chimney to help with global warming.

The ratio between what's put into a process and what comes out is a measure of its *efficiency*. A ratio of 1:1 would be 100 per cent efficiency, unobtainable in reality. Something is always lost, somewhere. Most energy conversions are very inefficient, and made more so by the cumulative losses that can occur in a multi-stage conversion like, say, generating electricity. We burn fuel to work an engine, which drives a generator, which turns the rotational energy of a coil into electricity. The National Grid then brings the electricity to our homes where, at the flick of a switch, a heater element glows and warms the air. *Convection* spreads the heat throughout the room, inevitably warming the ceiling more than the floor. The 'from there to here' process has at least four distinct stages, with energy irretrievably lost at each.

Energy conversions in gliding are far simpler and rarely involve physically destroying one thing to get at another, but unrecoverable losses still occur. Even so, in comparison to aircraft efficiency in general, the majority of gliders are models of supreme excellence.

POTENTIAL AND KINETIC ENERGIES

Potential energy is energy due to position, which usually means height. *Kinetic energy* is energy due to speed. Within certain limits these two energies can be swapped one for the other.

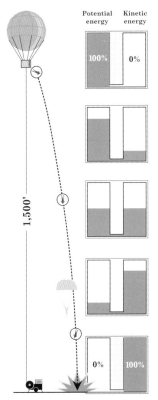

FIGURE 28 A parachute jump

A parachutist dropping from, say 1,500ft (<u>figure 28</u>), begins his fall with zero kinetic energy and 1,500 units worth of potential energy. He accelerates as he falls, so kinetic (speed) energy increases and potential (height) energy decreases. In theory, the sum of the two energies ought to be the same at any point during the fall, and for a few seconds during the initial acceleration that's near enough the case. We could record this as 'height plus velocity equals a constant', or H + V = C. However, air resistance does eventually set a limit, and somewhere between 120 and 180mph it exactly balances the parachutist's weight, so he doesn't go any faster (*terminal velocity*).

At this point, if not before, the energy equation appears to spring a leak. Kinetic energy stops increasing (speed constant), but potential energy continues to decrease (person still falling), so the total amount of energy is decreasing. When the parachute is deployed, kinetic energy abruptly decreases by a further notch or two, and remains at a very low value as the parachute drifts earthwards. The potential energy continues to diminish, but at a very much slower rate. In terms of the initial amount of energy, large quantities of it seem to have vanished. However, in the same way that you never really get anything for nothing as far as energy is concerned, so too it doesn't disappear. Energy cannot be created or destroyed, but it can be converted from one form to another. In this case almost all of the missing energy went into accelerating the surrounding air into vigorous but useless swirls and whirls.

In gliding terms it is easier to think of the total amount of available energy as being credit held by a bank. If you are flying at 4,000ft and 58kt your Energy Bank statement says that your potential account contains 4,000ft units, and your kinetic account 58kt units[1]. Forget for the moment that the exchange rate is not one to one. Each time you manoeuvre the glider there is a fee for transferring energy from one account to the other. The more energy needed for the manoeuvre, the more you pay for the privilege. Even though the trivial adjustment of putting the string in the middle helps to reduce overall losses, it still costs something. Roll left – sorry, there's a charge. Lower the nose and, sorry, there's a charge for that, too. The trade-off in manoeuvring is between what is quick and what is the most energy-efficient. They are rarely the same. Sadly, even if you do absolutely nothing there is still a small charge. If there wasn't, you could stay airborne forever.

The concepts of potential and kinetic energy are very helpful to understanding some aspects of variometer usage (see chapter 9, pp. 241–56), and are fundamental to a proper understanding of how gliders actually manage to fly at all. The most important point is that whatever changes and energy swaps are involved, conversion processes always involve a bill. How much this comes to and how quickly it has to be paid is another matter altogether.

Packets and parcels

Reality may be seamlessly smooth, but thought appears to operate in a series of discretely disconnected jerks. Partly because of this rather on/off way of operating, thought is not at its best when attempting to isolate the significant detail of such a fluid and obviously nonstop physical process as the weather.

[1]Ignoring air resistance, 150 ft = 58kt, i.e. if you fell from that height, that's the speed you would hit the ground. Likewise, to reach a height of 150ft you would have to jump upwards at 58kt!

One way to discover how something works is to take it to bits. Remove the mainspring from a wind-up watch and it stops working, so the spring must be important. Cog wheels are important, too, because if you remove any of them the watch will very likely stop telling the time, even if it doesn't actually stop ticking. Just about everything in a watch is functional – nothing is redundant – but in the end we would have to conclude that the spring was the critical component because without it the watch would never work, no matter how many cogs and wheels it contains.

Taking the weather apart is, of course, nothing like dismantling a watch. The sheer immensity of all that's involved is daunting. As it happens, many of the processes which power the weather are used elsewhere by nature on far more manageable scales. Conducting 'experiments' on these processes does not require a vast laboratory, prodigious levels of government funding, or perilous bouts of crocodile wrestling with venture capitalists. The effects of temperature on the behaviour of gases – a process vital to weather generation – could be investigated using a jam jar in the garden shed.

If experiments on vapours in jam jars can provide insight into the ameboid mechanics of the weather, there are equivalent jam jars in the mind. *Packets* and *parcels* of air are referred to in later chapters; they are 'jam jars', convenient 'as ifs' to allow you to exclude effects you don't want to consider.

FIGURE 29 A packet or parcel

Frames of reference

At its simplest, a *frame of reference* is literally a point of view; this is what such and such a thing looks like from here, but from somewhere else it looks like this. Some items in this book make no sense unless seen from a particular point of view. A few, particularly the second of the examples that follow, are difficult to grasp because what we think is happening, and seems completely obvious, isn't! The problem arises, in part, from the way in which the brain puts a comfortable spin on otherwise confusing situations. Unfortunately, such well-meaning interference can and does lead to real and often fatal spins.

Two gliders on a gently converging collision course (figure 30) are an example of a very simple frame of reference. From A's point of view, B is converging on him, whereas B sees A as converging on him. Arguments over priority could kill them both, so the Rules of the Air make the decision for them – even though both are right.

There are far more subtle and complicated frames of reference. The following old chestnut pops up regularly in the letters pages of aviation magazines, if not perhaps in quite the same words, and can provoke heated debate. You observe an aircraft flying on a windy day. As it turns into wind it decelerates, and when it turns downwind it accelerates. The writers then go on to say something more or less like this:

FIGURE 30 Frame of reference – relative movement

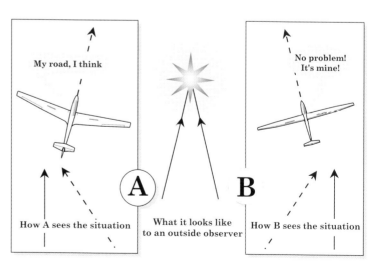

FIGURE 31 The acceleration problem (an inertial frame-up?)

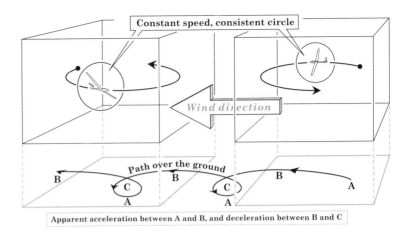

Constant speed, consistent circle

Wind direction

Path over the ground

Apparent acceleration between A and B, and deceleration between B and C

(a) if you accelerate something you need energy, so where's it coming from?

(b) there is obviously a serious danger of stalling when turning downwind, so shouldn't we fly faster upwind to allow for this?

In this instance, seeing is not believing! If the aircraft is clear of wind gradient effects, then all of its so-called accelerations *in relation to the ground* are irrelevant (figure 31).

Those which do occur, such as the G increasing during a turn, are relative to the block of air through which the glider and pilot are both travelling. For example, we are able to move around inside a steadily moving railway carriage without having to accelerate anything except our own mass; the significant point being that the carriage is not accelerating or decelerating in relation to the rest of the world, any more than is the block of air through which the aeroplane moves. The carriage is the passenger's *inertial frame of reference*, and the block of air is the aeroplane's.

This may strike no chords, so consider the following: were the effects described by (a) and (b) to be real, they would occur at any altitude. For argument's sake, you are thermalling a glider at a steady 55kt. The stalling speed in the turn is 42kt, and you are at 4,500ft with a 30kt wind blowing. If (a) and (b) are correct, the glider should stall out each time it turns downwind (figure 32). Check this out on a suitable day and you will find that nothing of the sort happens.

Question (a) is impossible to answer because the acceleration doesn't occur, whatever it looks like, and extra energy isn't needed from anywhere. As for question (b), the most likely explanations for stalling and spinning off a downwind turn in the circuit are:

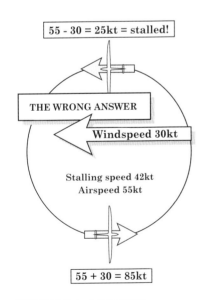

55 - 30 = 25kt = stalled!

THE WRONG ANSWER

Windspeed 30kt

Stalling speed 42kt
Airspeed 55kt

55 + 30 = 85kt

FIGURE 32 Not what happens

- not having sufficient speed to begin with, or

- the pilot sees his speed over the ground increasing and unconsciously raises the nose and/or throttles back to slow down.

Summary of chapter one

Page	Subject	
11–3	**Acceleration**	rate of change of velocity.
18	**Acting forces**	those which influence an object.
–	**Attributes**	physical characteristics of an object. **Local**: size, shape and colour. **Universal**: mass, gravity and inertia.
6	**Bearing**	**Location**: horizontal angular relationship between two things. **Mechanical**: e.g. a ball race.
11	**Ballistic object**	object without motive power of its own that, once projected, cannot influence its own path e.g. artillery shell. A glider is not a ballistic object even though it can occasionally act as if it were one.
14, 15	**Centre of gravity (CG)**	centre of mass of a body such that all moments about it are zero. Point of balance. Also point about which the mass of body appears to act.
15	**Centre of mass**	as CG.
19	**Conservation of energy**	(First law of thermodynamics.) Energy cannot be created or destroyed, only changed from one form to another.
9	**Constant**	unchanging quantity or quality within a given frame of reference.
6	**Coordinates**	location of an object or point in relation to an origin.
18	**Couple**	a pair of (equal) forces acting on an object in opposite and parallel directions to each other.
–	**Datum**	reference point from which measurements are made. Not necessarily the origin.

Page	Subject	
4	**Dimensions**	(1) length, breadth and depth of an object (2) spatial dimension, including time.
6	**Elevation**	location; vertical angular relation between two things.
8	**Equilibrium**	state of balance, but not necessarily lack of motion.
–	**First law of thermodynamics**	(*see* conservation of energy).
12	**Freefall**	object 'falling' with gravity – weightless.
7	**Force**	energy acting in a direction.
10, 14	**Friction**	resistance to sliding between two objects which are in contact. The direction of the friction force is parallel to the plane of contact between the two surfaces.
16	**Fulcrum**	support about which a lever moves.
8, 9	**Gravity (G)**	property of mass. At the Earth's surface, a constant acceleration of 32ft/sec^2 directed towards the planet's centre of mass.
9, 10	**Inertia**	inherent property of mass. Resistance to acceleration or deceleration (defined in terms of Newton's Laws of Motion). See chapter 2 summary p. 53.
21	**Inertial frame of reference**	an exclusive 'frame' in relation to which a change occurs.
–	**Inverse square law**	change inversely proportional to the square root of a quantity $(1/\sqrt{\times})$.
19, 20	**Kinetic energy**	energy due to velocity $(\frac{1}{2}\,mV^2)$.
18	**Line of action**	direction in which forces act.
8	**Load**	internal response of material to applied force.
8, 9	**Mass**	property of matter.
16	**Magnitude**	strength of a force.
16	**Moment**	force $\times$ distance.
10	**Momentum**	mass $\times$ velocity (mV).
6	**Origin**	the zero point of a coordinate system (i.e. 0,0 on a graph).
17	**Parallelogram of forces**	graphical method of working out a resultant (see same) force.
12	**Parabolic curve**	(parabola) path traced out by a ballistic object (see same).
20, 21	**Parcel**	also *packet*. Theoretical entity allowing examination of selected effects.

Page	Subject	
4	**Plane**	two-dimensional surface, e.g. a sheet of paper.
14	**Plane of symmetry**	axis about which an object is 'mirrored', i.e. left = right.
19, 20	**Potential energy**	energy due to position or location, e.g. height.
–	**Properties**	*see Attributes.*
–	**Reference point**	(1) imaginary point used for judging the approach and landing (2) also 'datum'.
17	**Resolution of forces**	(1) the net result or resultant of several forces acting on the same object (2) the splitting up of a single force into several components.
17, 18	**Resultant**	the combined effect of any number of forces.
8	**Scalar**	quantity with magnitude but not direction, e.g. speed, mass, volume, etc.
–	**Science**	rational belief system.
–	**Second law of thermodynamics**	(in its simplest form) no energy conversion is 100 per cent efficient. Can seem to contradict the first law of thermodynamics (conservation of energy) but no 'system' is completely closed. In terms of energy, it would appear that everything leaks, without exception.
20	**Terminal velocity**	velocity of vertical dive where weight and drag exactly balance (genuinely terminal in a glider).
8, 17	**Vector**	force or quantity acting in a specific direction. Can be represented graphically and mathematically. Gravity and velocity are vectors, as is weight (*see Scalar*).
8	**Velocity (V)**	speed with a directional component. A vector quantity. E.g. *30mph NW* is a vector but *30mph* is a scalar.
8, 9	**Weight (W)**	object's mass (m) influenced by gravity (G) or acceleration (W = mG). If G = 1 then W = m.

CHAPTER 2
FALTERING STEPS

CHAPTER CONTENTS ★ should know ☆ useful

2 FALTERING STEPS

Aviation is now such an integral part of most people's mental furniture that it probably seems about as miraculous as a cheap toaster, and is equally taken for granted. Once so new, aviation has become a truck; a means of picking things up from one place and dropping them off at another: bombs, cans of Coca Cola, people, the ferrying of fascinating and deadly diseases to new and more promising locations, you name it and aviation has, or probably will, transport it. As for sporting aviation, that may not be about transport – the Cambridge Gliding Club annually award a trophy for 'going nowhere by the most tedious route' – but the fact that almost anyone can take part, given minimal entry criteria, is a mark of just how unexceptional it has all become.

As the twentieth century tottered to its disruptive and slightly demented conclusion, a few scientists became convinced that humanity is on the verge of constructing a Theory of Everything[1]. The implication is that eventually there will be an 'answer to everything'; a universal formula which, like a Swiss Army penknife, will fulfil all philosophical, scientific and psychological functions. The belief that there actually is an 'answer to everything', never mind a theory, is as old and treacherous as the human race. For a time that is boiling over violently with spectacular science and technology, and likely to become the victim of the unhinged and self-destructive notions that seem to accompany rather too much of it, the idea has an especially seductive gleam.

By comparison with the reckless scope of such cosmic conceits, the scale of the problems faced by aviation's pioneers seem inconsequential, to say the least. Yet they were attempting to make one of the biggest leaps mankind has ever made, and the territory into which they ventured was almost completely unmapped. Their efforts to master it demonstrate both the free and far-sighted and the entrenched and narrow-minded in human behaviour, and show that in one way or another much human progress takes place entirely by accident, happy or otherwise.

Today, we have three advantages denied to the earliest pioneers. First, and most obvious, we can see with our own eyes that heavier-than-air flight is possible; that something as enormous as a Boeing 747 can stagger into the air with 400 or more people aboard. Our second advantage is that we do not have to teach ourselves how to fly. The third, and by far the most significant, is that we know more or less how 'flight' works.

---

[1] This 'everything' is what physicists find interesting, i.e. the unification of the four fundamental forces of Nature, Nuclear (weak and strong), Gravitational and Electromagnetic.

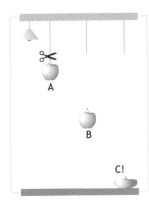

Requirements for flight

Regardless of the differences between the pioneers' situation and our own, we need, as did they, machines which meet certain fundamental structural and aerodynamic criteria. In the late 1700s, when the idea of being able to fly was starting to change from 'can't be done' to 'maybe', the inevitable question was 'what are the requirements?'

SUPPORT

It was once a common view that air was, literally, nothing. How sailors thought the wind propelled their ships, one can only guess, but perhaps the 'what and why' were irrelevant. When the wind blew you raised a sail and off you went, whatever the explanation. To be able to fly, much more is needed. The first and minimum requirement is to buoy your flying machine up in the air, a medium which is one of the thinnest and least supportive of all. To do this you need a vertical lifting force, at least strong enough to support:

(1)   the lift-producing structure itself

(2)   the weight of any other bits which are necessary but don't actively contribute to the lifting force, e.g. the pilot

(3)   the weight of an engine and fuel, unless it is a glider.

MOTIVE POWER

A major headache in the early days was the lack of a suitable engine. Until the invention of the first steam engine in 1711 by Thomas Newcomen, there was only the horse with its poor power to weight ratio and disobedient controls, or wayward natural forces like wind and water. As for using human muscle, in those days there wasn't the slightest chance of manpowered flight of any sort becoming a reality. Paul MacCready's Gossamer Condor of 1977 (figure 1) was the first really successful manpowered aircraft and required modern materials and the clever application of late twentieth-century aerodynamic know-how for its success.

By 1775 James Watt had improved upon Newcomen's original and hugely inefficient design by several hundred per cent, but it was still not enough. Steam engines burn their fuel outside the driving cylinders (*external combustion*), and use it to heat water in an

external boiler. For power to be produced, the boiler, the driving cylinders, and all the in-between pipework must be capable of withstanding the high steam pressures involved, so the complete unit tends to be very heavy. Early steam engines were industry/railway orientated and ground-based, and had no need to be light, as indeed they were not. In addition, the amount of energy which can be extracted by normal means from fuels like coal and wood is low in relation to their weight.

In 1876 Nickolaus Otto produced the first petrol engine. An *internal combustion* engine – fuel is burnt in the driving cylinders – the petrol engine is more efficient, lighter, and with a better *power to weight ratio* than the steam engine.

But why bother with an engine at all? Why not tap into all that

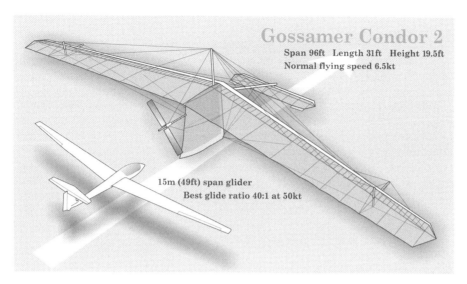

FIGURE 1 Paul MacCready's manpowered aircraft

free energy in the air, as glider pilots do? First, you have to know it's there. The Frenchman, Louise P. Mouillard, the author of an inspirational book called *The Empire of the Air*, wrote in an article in *Cosmopolitan* in 1894:

"Inventors, and seekers for light motive power, were therefore quite nonplussed until a new aspect of the question (the problem of aerial navigation) was presented, some years ago, by a few observers who had been watching the large soaring birds perform their evolutions. These observers maintained that, when once under way, soaring birds expended no muscular power whatever; that they sailed on indefinitely with rigid wings, deriving from the wind all the energy required, not only to sustain their weight, but also, paradoxical as it may seem, to advance against the wind itself . . . These assertions were at first treated as rankest heresy. The larger soaring birds being very rare in those temperate regions where human activity most prevails, many able men, who had not seen the performance, simply denied the fact that any tropical birds could accomplish what was claimed . . ."

Mouillard's beautifully written article is well worth reading in full because, in addition to the problems quoted above, it shows that many pioneers had a conceptual problem to do with relative motion and frames of reference. For example, if a sailing ship is blown along by the wind then, logically, one can't sail directly into wind. How, therefore, can birds that aren't flapping manage to do the aerial equivalent, and often climb away at the same time?

The goal of the early experimenters was very definitely powered flight, but lack of suitable engines pushed them incxorably towards gliders. Their attitude towards them, such as they were, was anything but 'leisure-sporty', but gliders were to serve as one of the few practical research tools available. Most pioneers would have been perfectly happy to strap on any old engine and simply launch themselves into the blue, never mind any research. For such trusting souls the results would have been calamitous. Still, if it is powered flight that you're after, the engine needs to:

(1) be light

(2) be powerful

(3)   be fuel efficient (more fuel means more weight, and more power is needed to support it)

(4)   have an effective means of translating the engine's power into motion, either via a propeller of some sort or jet or rocket propulsion.

Reliability is not included because most of the pioneers would, one suspects, have felt that anything which fulfilled the 'engine' criteria listed above, however intermittently, was better than nothing. Unreliable engines tend to have less catastrophic consequences than structural failure or suspect aerodynamics.

STRUCTURAL STRENGTH AND INTEGRITY

Pre-aviation engineering understood the need for things to be strong, but when aeroplanes, however ineffective, began to arrive, their structures needed to be light as well. To a greater extent than a ship, an aeroplane is going to be kicked about in an environment which is the natural home of capricious and irregular gusts, often of considerable violence. If structural failure is to be avoided, the aeroplane's designer/builder must have a reasonably clear understanding of the forces and loads involved, which include:

(1)   the movement of the air

(2)   manoeuvring. The effects of this and item ① were either grossly under estimated or simply not taken into account in the early days

(3)   heavier than normal contact with the ground. Landing, takeoff and taxiing loads tend to be a lot sharper-edged than flight loads

(4)   the way in which the entire structure and the materials out of which it is made react to loads. For example, which parts can be allowed to bend, and which not?

(5)   Keeping the bits together. Early glues weren't strong; lashing parts together added weight, and nailing, screwing or bolting any of the light materials available, like bamboo, was an invitation for them to split and break. It was also dawning on nineteenth century engineers that the path of a load through a structure wasn't always the most obvious one, and that failure of seemingly unimportant items could lead to a cascade of failures ending in total disintegration.

STABILITY AND CONTROL

These two items are so closely linked that in some respects they are the same thing. From a pilot's point of view a stable aeroplane needs neither constant attention nor fails to respond when the pilot decides he'd like to go somewhere else. Stability and control ought to have been a major concern for the early pioneers but, in an oversight that seems to have bordered on the certifiable, the majority spent their time chasing stability and paid little or no attention to control. Most early heavier-than-air machines, whether they were capable of becoming airborne or not, were little more than unguided missiles. Though hardly a byword for controllability, even balloons can steer by climbing or descending to make use of the changing direction of the wind. This may not count as complete control, but it is surprisingly effective. Control requires:

(1)   a modest amount of inbuilt stability which is not unduly sensitive to differences in pilot weight

(2)   some means of allowing the pilot to influence the progress of a flight

(3)   a good balance between (1) and (2); this was, and still can be difficult to get right.

THEORY

Our attitude to any machine, be it a horse or a motorcar, is straightforward: 'I want to do this. Will this thing do it, and how can I make it do it?'. It isn't usually 'how does it work?'. The modern car requires the activation of minimal levels of intelligence and operational skill and anything difficult has been quietly tidied out of sight. Users have no views on this because generally they don't notice, but they would be very upset if the designers were equally unaware.

Having said that, humanity has survived for thousands of years in total ignorance of many things upon which its existence depends, so failure to grasp even the minimum technical details of how something works obviously can't be that critical. Reality's default setting, so to speak, seems to be that the risks inherent in everyday situations are small, but the real message of that is not that life is safe, but that biology and behaviour which did not fit more or less self-destructed. Humanity's default reality never took flying into account.

The function of theory in all of this is twofold. First, it helps us literally to model how things work. You might wonder why we have to do this at all, but sheer curiosity and the apparently irrepressible urge to fiddle have something to do with it. Second, theory helps us to assess degrees of risk, appreciation and understanding of which varies hugely from person to person.

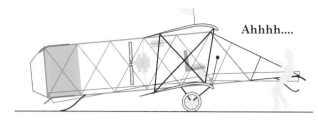

Ahhhh....

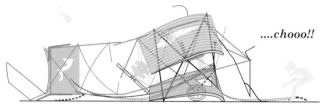

....chooo!!

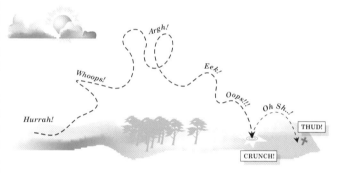

Theory as model-making

There are two main categories to model-making, the first of which is mental model-making, thinking, ideas, notions and the like. The second category is physical model-making; which can be subdivided into historical models of things that already exist, e.g. Chartres Cathedral painstakingly recreated out of several million matchsticks, and test models counting as practice runs for something larger – a wind tunnel model of Concorde, perhaps, or an architectural model of a new housing development.

The advantage of making what are, in effect, proof of concept models, is that we don't have to put ourselves at risk, nor convince someone else that they should be put at risk.

Oh yes it is

Oh no it isn't

Etc etc

Besides, the model is often far cheaper and easier to deal with than the real thing. Nevertheless, despite the benefits that result from doing-it-small before making-it-big, there are some exasperating drawbacks. When the model finally grows to full size, as it must, things often don't work out in quite the way we were led to expect.

The first not-what-we-expected is related to the structure. Doubling the external dimensions of a model does not result in something twice as strong. If you make a wing twice the linear dimensions of the original model (i.e. twice the span, width and depth), then the wing area increases by four times, not two, and the volume by eight times (figure 2). The structural weight and aerodynamic loads also alter by nonlinear amounts.

The second area where things can go awry is more subtle. To creatures as large as ourselves, air is something through which we can walk as if it weren't there. For a very small insect, forces that we don't notice become much more significant – their flight becomes the equivalent of us swimming through a roomful of tennis balls. The smaller the model relative to the full-size machine (and the air molecules), the greater the aerodynamic differences between them. When early aircraft failed to perform as well as models had predicted, or not to perform at all, such *scale effects* were baffling. Now we are better at allowing for them, but since they are rooted in how the world works, they're unlikely ever to go away.

Theory as risk assessment

Aviation is one area where ignorance and trusting to luck are impressively dangerous strategies. Rolling the dice, as it were, is an unavoidable consequence of any new technology, but as a long-term approach it is about as sensible as assuming that every throw will yield a double six – awkward if you have only one die. Were we immortal such an attitude would not matter; crash here, crash there, who cares.

What we understand about an environment is, broadly speaking, inversely proportional to the risk factor, so for something new the risk is high. Once safely past the by-guess-and-by-God stage, we develop a feel for what to avoid, and why. The knowledge may be sketchy and inaccurate, but it is an essential link to the stage where we can begin

FIGURE 2 Effect of doubling linear dimensions

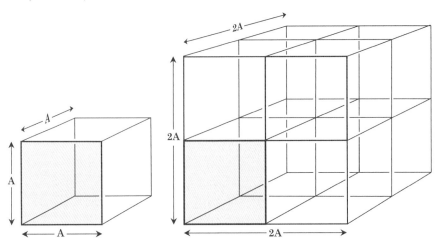

to make informed guesses about the likely outcome of various courses of action, and in a position to make genuinely realistic choices between them. Such guesses are, in effect, theories whose basic purpose is predictive. Like tea leaves and animal entrails – but with at least a foot in reality – one of theory's functions is to help us cheat death, even if it occasionally does exactly the opposite.

Birds, kites and paper darts

Birds are superb flyers, who, without being especially bright (apparently), have solved the major problems associated with flight. No surprise, then, that our first faltering steps consisted of stumbling after them. What we did not know at the time was that over the years they would lead us a merry and largely meaningless dance. In 1505 Leonardo da Vinci wrote that:

"A bird is an instrument working according to mathematical law, which instrument is within the capacity of man to reproduce in all its movements."

True, but as it was to turn out, beside the point. Even though birds' flight and our own rigid version of it make use of the same aerodynamic laws, birds have advantages over us. Their brains are linked directly into the flying apparatus; a major plus because the bird that spins in has either been injured, or was dead before it hit the ground. They also have the muscular strength and appropriate supporting skeletal structure.

Da Vinci believed that with each downstroke of their wings, birds compressed the air beneath them, so he designed flapping mechanisms to do exactly that. Suspecting arms alone might not be enough, he invented complicated pulley and lever systems to allow flappers to use their legs as well. Sadly, it was a wasted effort. Though obsessed with flight, many of da Vinci's ideas about it were wrong. Working model *ornithopters* (flapping wing flying machines) can be made – a few fluttered around late nineteenth-century drawing rooms – but are small and seem to rely on scale effects for their success.

In 1680 the Italian mathematician Giovanni Borelli looked at the human muscle problem and proved that we weren't strong enough to fly by flapping. If not for quite the same reason, myth had already hinted that the birds would lead us astray. Around 1700BC, Icarus and his father Daedalus are alleged to have escaped from the Cretan Labyrinth on wings made of eagles' feathers bound together with wax. Ignoring his father's warnings about going too close to the sun, Icarus fluttered dazedly upward like some adolescent moth, suffered a structural meltdown, and fell to his death in the sea.

What is striking about the bird followers is not their ill-founded courage, admirable conviction and high fatality rate, but their surreal logic. In 1507 an ambitious gentleman named John Damian coated himself with chicken feathers and leapt from the walls of Stirling Castle. His bone-crushing but luckily non-lethal impact shortly afterwards prompted a gloriously convoluted explanation for the accident. 'I could not fly', he later explained, 'because I used the feathers of a flightless bird.' He could equally have blamed his fall upon the religion or art of the time. Today he would have sued the poultry farmer.

Damian would probably have crashed even had he known that in 1080BC the Chinese had cracked some of the problems associated with flight, and invented the kite. The first

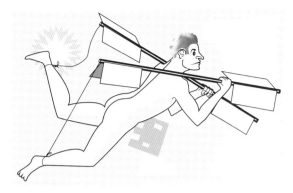

FIGURE 3 Besnier's flying machine

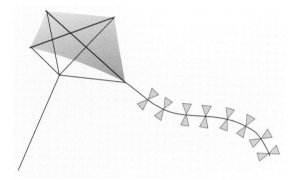

FIGURE 4 Kite

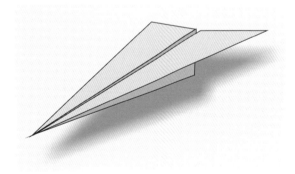

FIGURE 5 Paper dart

direct mention that people had flown – though not by their own choice – came to Europe in AD1300, via the slightly dubious reportage of Marco Polo, who wrote:

". . . when any ship must go on a voyage, they [Chinese merchants] prove whether its business will go well or ill . . . find someone stupid or drunken and . . . bind him on the hurdle [kite]; for no wise man nor undepraved would expose himself to that danger, and this is done when a strong wind prevails. The proof is made in this way, namely that if the hurdle going straight up makes for the sky . . . the ship . . . will make a quick and prosperous voyage."

The fate of the luckless passenger(s) was never recorded.

The Chinese also invented the rocket and used it both as a weapon and for celebration. The West's values would interpret their failure to follow through on such revolutionary technologies as a lost opportunity. However, one could argue that our uncontrollable appetite for fusing technological change with maximum velocity, profit, and frustration, suggests that we probably aren't quite right in the head.

In 500BC the Greek Archytus of Tarentum designed and built kites (whether influenced by the Chinese or not isn't known), and was reported to have made a mechanical pigeon driven by steam. In the sixteenth century the paper dart, almost certainly not in the form illustrated, first appeared. Viewed, perhaps, as a child's toy and not a grownups' plaything, it had no influence on anything.

However haphazardly we wove our way towards the aeroplane, success did depend on us starting to think methodically and rationally about what was involved. Simply believing that you can fly, through the force of a disordered will or the exercise of great faith, leads inescapably to disaster. Equally, many strands have to come together at the same time, and the right people have to be interested enough to pull them all together. Priorities were different in the past, and leisure time far more limited, so one reason for aviation's early non-development may be no more complicated than the fact that in any society where merely keeping alive is a full-time job, racking one's brains about how to fly would have been the kiss of death.

A change of direction

No matter how miraculous the birth of new ideas in the human mind, they are rarely quite as virginal as they are subsequently made to appear. There is always some background, however tenuous or oblique, to groundbreaking insight, and without it many things are impossible to invent, not because they cannot or will not be invented, but because at the time they are quite literally inconceivable.

Flight's toolkit, so to speak, was virtually empty until the arrival of two important components: physics and mathematics. Some of the key physics came with Sir Isaac Newton. His main contribution to flight was the three laws of motion (*see* chapter summary p. 53) published in 1687. They clarified the manner in which physical forces acted and interacted, and helped change the attitudes of the proto-aviators, as it were, from a wishful 'I will only be able to fly if I am a bird (or dress up and flap like one),' to the practical and attainable,' I wonder if there are underlying principles which I can use, just as a bird does?'. After that it was just a matter of finding out what these principles were.

One factor that has given science its power is not so much a dedication to 'truth' as an ability to get measurable, repeatable and practical results. Western society is almost entirely based on a technology with roots in scientific practice, principally the notion of experiment. A number of individuals throughout history conducted genuine scientific experiments, but the techniques were nowhere near as standard as they are now. It wasn't so long ago that most people's views on just about everything were based on the writings of worthy souls like Aristotle (384–322BC) or Plato (428–347BC), and holy books of one persuasion or another.

For centuries Aristotle was held in such reverence that if he hadn't mentioned a subject when he was alive, then nobody felt it worth discussing after he was dead. In some respects his legacy stifled debate, which was ironic considering his views. The best way to answer any significant question, he believed, was logical discussion among a group of intelligent people. Truth could not fail to court such company. Argument and discussion are still vital, but the idea and practice of experiment – which offers the best chance of separating the likeliest explanations of how and why things work from those which are completely off the wall – has placed the burden of proof, not on talk, however dazzling, but on real-world results.

Experimentation

Let's say that we want to find out the way in which a ball bounces or a cookie crumbles. We can drop the ball and say, 'it bounces' (or not), crumble the cookie into fragments, and then leave it at that – and be little the wiser. But what if we wished to produce a ball that bounced incredibly well, or wanted to create a mouth-watering cookie that cried out to be consumed the instant it was removed from its yummy packaging? Equally, we might just be curious to know why some things bounce and others don't, and why we like one brand of cookie and detest others.

There are, broadly, two ways to proceed. We can guess, fiddle about and jump to conclusions. This is a common, wasteful, but sometimes unavoidable way of doing things, whose chief snag tends to be mountains of information. It isn't easy to extract rules and general principles from this colossal midden because we probably hadn't the faintest idea what we were looking for in the first place.

The best method is more organised. From the essential 'I wonder if . . .' we form some very likely half-baked ideas about whatever it is we're wondering about. Do these ideas form a comfortable fit with reality or not? We might have theorised that squashy things

ARCHIMEDES' PRINCIPLE

When a body is completely or partially immersed in a fluid, the fluid exerts an upward force on the body equal to the weight of the fluid displaced by the body.

bounce, only to discover that while true of a rubber ball, it most definitely isn't of a marshmallow or a tomato. We experiment with the ball (it's less messy), dropping it again and again from different heights onto the same solid spot, using the same measuring equipment in an environment that remains in every other respect as unchanged as it is possible to make it. Likewise, the cookie is crumbled in an incremental and controlled fashion.

Following the passage of an indeterminate length of time, perhaps after modifying the original theories out of all recognition, we discover the general principles behind 'bounceability' and 'yumminess' (if X, then Y), or exactly why something works in the way it does (because P hits Q), and so on. If the theoretical structure, so to speak, fits the physical evidence, or near enough as makes no difference – a fudge labelled 'within the limits of experimental error' – it may then enter the canon of 'Laws, Universal', or more likely slip quietly into the much larger category of 'other less monumental but nevertheless useful discoveries'.

That's not the end of it. An important but not always clear distinction between scientific experiment and childish monkeying about is that our peers must independently replicate our results. If they can that does not mean that our theory is right, just that no-one can show that its wrong.

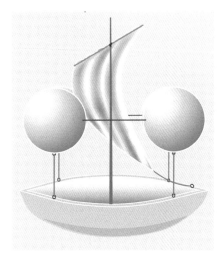

FIGURE 6 de LanaTerzi's 'balloon'

The rise (and fall) of the balloon

With the flapping avenue effectively closed by our own feebleness and the aeroplane no more than a dotty idea, it was inevitable that the first real flights would be made in balloons. Ships floated on water – Archimedes had outlined the principle years before – so the idea that one could build ships which floated in the air was a sideways rather than an upward step of the imagination. One of the earliest designs (figure 6) was put forward in 1670 by Francesco de LanaTerzi. He envisaged the craft being supported by evacuated copper spheres. Apart from the sail, the basic concept was sound, but any sphere which is light enough made of metals known to us would be crushed flat instantly by the pressure of the atmosphere.

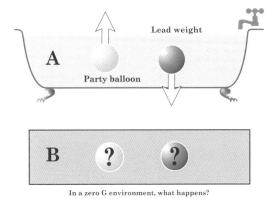

FIGURE 7 Buoyancy

BUOYANCY

The *buoyancy* of lighter-than-air craft depends on the difference between their overall density (weight divided by total volume) and that of the surrounding air. The principle is easy to demonstrate. Take an inflated party balloon and try to submerge it in a bath or basin full of water. The effort required is surprisingly large because we are using the balloon's low mass and large volume (low *density*), to push out of the way (displace) an equal volume of water which has a far greater mass (high density).

Assume that the inflated balloon plus the air inside weighs an eighth of a pound, and takes up the same amount of space as five pounds (half a gallon) of water. The difference between the two is an apparent negative weight in the balloon's favour of four and seveneighths of a pound, and that's how hard you have to push to keep the balloon submerged. Replacing the balloon with a lead ball of the same volume also displaces five pounds of water, but this is now only a small fraction of the ball's weight. Let go of the balloon and it will shoot to the surface. Do the same with the lead ball and it may punch a hole in the bottom of the bath (figure 7, see page 38). However, here's a question: the balloon is far less dense than the water, but if the water presses in equally from all directions, what makes the balloon rise to the surface?

Buoyancy can't exist without gravity and weight. By submerging the balloon we push it down the length of what is, in effect, a column of water extending from the surface to the bath's base. The deeper the balloon goes the more of this column there is above it – distance A in figure 8. Gravity gives the water weight, so the further down the column the balloon happens to be, the greater the weight of the water above it. Because the increase continues all the way to the bottom of the bath, there is a pressure difference between the top and the bottom of the balloon (distance B). The base of the balloon is at the weightier end of column B, so to speak, and the 'pressing in' forces of the water there are stronger than they are at the top of the balloon. This difference provides the upward force which pushes the balloon to the surface.

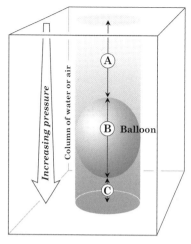

FIGURE 8 Water/air column above and below object

HOT AIR BALLOONS, CAPTIVE THERMALS

The envelope of a hot air balloon is of fixed volume, open at its base via a short neck, below which hangs a burner or brazier. When the burner is turned on it heats the air within the envelope (figure 9). The air expands, some of it spilling out through the neck, and the envelope now contains fewer air molecules by volume (less dense). When the internal air is warmed sufficiently the balloon's overall density will

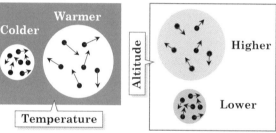

FIGURE 9 Density changes

become less than that of the surrounding air. The balloon then has positive buoyancy, and will rise. As the internal air cools and contracts, it draws some of the cooler outside air back in through the neck, increasing the balloon's overall density. When the internal and external densities are the same, the balloon has neutral buoyancy and neither rises nor falls. If the air in the envelope continues to cool to the same temperature as the outside air, the weight of the balloon itself will give it negative buoyancy, and it will descend.

Going, going, gone with the wind

The first recorded balloon flight was in 1709. Father Bartholomew de Gusamoa demonstrated an indoor model of a hot air balloon to the King of Portugal. Courtiers had to destroy the balloon before it set light to the royal curtains, so the flight was rather short. It is not known if the Montgolfier brothers, Joseph and Jacques Etienne, were aware of that earlier flight, but in 1782 they also made several model balloons, the very first of which was tiny and made out of silk. Encouraged by the fact that everything seemed to work, they increased the size of the balloons and gave their first public demonstration in June 1783. The unmanned balloon took off from the town square of Annonay, south of

FIGURE 10 The Montgolfier's 1783 balloon

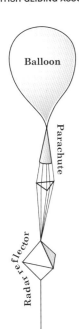

Balloon

Parachute

Radar reflector

Instrument package
and transmitter

FIGURE 11 Modern radiosonde balloon

Lyon, and rose to nearly 6,000ft, remaining aloft for ten minutes and covering a distance of almost two miles.

The news spread rapidly, rousing great interest, though a few educated people wondered how two mere papermakers could have done such an extraordinary thing. After a number of setbacks, including heavy rain wrecking their balloon just before a launch, the Montgolfiers were ready to give their most important demonstration. In September of 1783, in the presence of the King and Queen of France, the first package tour passengers, a cock, a duck and a sheep, took to the air (figure 10, see page 39). The flight was entirely without untoward incident, apart from the cock being slightly injured by a kick from the sheep.

On 15 October 1783, Françoise Pilâtre de Rozier became the first man to fly in a tethered Montgolfier balloon, and on the 21 November 1783 he made the first free flight, accompanied by the Marquis d'Arlandes. Everything went well, but on landing several miles away from the Bois de Boulogne, where they had taken off, overexcited spectators tore de Rozier's jacket from him and ripped it to pieces for souvenirs.

GAS BALLOONS

In 1766 the English chemist and physicist Henry Cavendish discovered 'inflammable air', and in 1783 the French chemist Antoine Lavoisier renamed it as hydrogen. In August 1783 the French physicist Jacques C. Charles launched the first (unmanned) hydrogen filled balloon. In December, he and a Mr Noël Roberts entered the gondola of another hydrogen balloon, rose from the garden of the Tuileries in front of an enormous crowd, and sailed majestically to a field some 20 miles north of Paris. As Charles later wrote, voicing a sentiment felt by many aviators since, but regarded in our own perfunctory times as rather 'purple' and verbose:

"Nothing will ever equal that moment of joy which filled my whole being when I felt myself flying away from the earth. It was not mere pleasure, it was perfect bliss."

The basic principles of buoyancy are the same for gas balloons, but hydrogen, apart from being highly inflammable, is very susceptible to temperature changes. The sun shining on the envelope can set the balloon climbing, and extensive cloud shadow have the opposite effect. The envelope can be of a fixed size, like most early balloons, or elastic, like the modern radiosonde balloon (figure 11). In either case there is always the potential for the balloon rising until the envelope bursts. With a radiosonde this is supposed to happen and allows the transmitting equipment to be parachuted back to earth. Controlling altitude is obviously important in a gas balloon and requires one to juggle the release of gas or ballast.

Needless to say, someone had the innovative and potentially lethal idea of using hydrogen and hot air in separate but adjacent envelopes (figure 12). By using the hot air section to gently warm the hydrogen in the other, such a composite balloon ought to use less fuel, be generally more efficient, and less at the mercy of changes in air temperature and warmth from the sun[2].

[2]A history of accidents would probably show that the desire for efficiency – usually in terms of saving money – has had a major and often crucial part to play in most of them.

Whether or not de Rozier originated the idea of the composite balloon now named after him, he found himself captaining the first on its maiden flight, a cross-Channel attempt from Boulogne. Bad weather caused weeks of delay, and everyone sagged gradually into fatalistic gloom. De Rozier's English fiancée, Susan Dyer, tried to dissuade him from making the flight. This would be his last, he promised her, but as a matter of honour he would rather die than give up the venture, and so it turned out. When the balloon finally took to the air it first drifted out to sea, then swung back inland, rising as it did so to about 5,000ft, at which point it caught fire and plunged to the ground. De Rozier was killed instantly and his fellow crew member, Jules Romain, died soon afterwards. In a faintly operatic twist to the tragedy, Susan Dyer, seeing the balloon falling in flames, collapsed and died.

Discounting Icarus, de Rozier – by all accounts intelligent and likeable – holds a unique and unrepeatable double first in the history of aviation: the first person to take safely to the air, and the first to die in a flying accident. As to what killed him and his companion, it may not have been the obvious culprit. Evidence suggests that in their attempts to rip open a metal panel in the top of the balloon and descend, the aeronauts inadvertently created a large static charge in the envelope. The escaping gas was ignited by an electrical spark.

Nobody wanted to know about composite balloons after that, but the idea wasn't daft, just premature. There are balloons around today, such as the round-the-world Breitling Orbiter, that use the same general principle, but have replaced hydrogen with non-flammable helium – something not available until 1895 and not in any great amounts until very much later.

Despite their early successes, hot air balloons quickly fell out of favour. Hydrogen became cheaper and more readily available, and in some respects provided a greater and more controllable lifting force. In addition, the rubberised silk envelopes of the early hydrogen balloons were far more robust than the hot air balloons' flimsy paper-lined linen envelopes.

THE PERILS OF PIONEERING

Early ballooning was hazardous, but even so, there were only eight serious accidents in the first 1,000 flights, or one every 125 launches. These days nobody would tolerate such a rate, but at the time (as indeed at any time) not all the dangers were, or could be fore-seen, and the more responsible and intelligent of the aeronauts knew this perfectly well.

A clearly understood problem with the early hot air balloons was that they frequently caught fire, so the pre-flight checklist included sponges and buckets of water. Other hazards were much less obvious. By the mid-1800s it was known that there was less oxygen at altitude, but ground experiments on the likely effects failed to take into account the cold at altitude, physical exertion, and the effortless ease with which anoxia subverts good judgement. Modern oxygen systems are provided with a closefitting face mask and most automatically balance the amount of oxygen being fed to a pilot against the ambient air pressure; less of one, more of the other. By contrast, the early aeronauts had first to feel in need of revival, and then pick up a tube and suck in some of the air/oxygen mixture contained in an attached bladder.

During a French flight in 1875 to test out this new breathing equipment, the balloon and its crew of three reached about 23,000ft, and stopped. Feeling pretty ropey, the aeronauts sucked at the mixture, and having perked up as a result, decided to go higher,

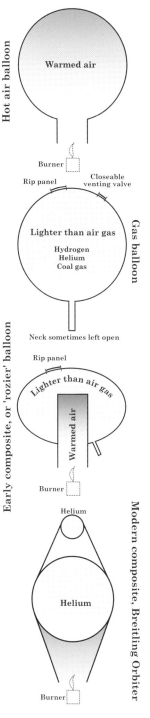

FIGURE 12 Types of balloon

41

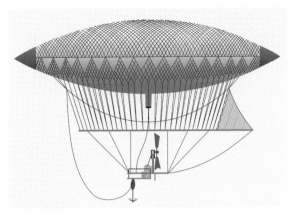

FIGURE 13 Henri Giffard's 1852 dirigible

intending to beat a previous height record set by the British. They dropped ballast and the balloon began to ascend. Shortly afterwards they were all unconscious. When they came to, the balloon was descending at tremendous speed. In the ensuing scramble to avoid being smashed against the ground, they threw out far too much ballast, sending the balloon rocketing skywards, so high that once again everyone fell unconscious. When the balloon descended, two of them were dead. The survivor, Gaston Tissandier, had the wit remaining not to repeat the previous mistake, and managed to land safely.

SUCCESS, AND THE SEEDS OF DISASTER

Henry Ford's remark that customers could have cars any colour they liked, providing it was black, applies to balloons; you can go anywhere you like as long as it's downwind. Balloons were a dead end as far as flexible and effective transport was concerned, but not useless. Tethered balloons were first used by the military for artillery spotting, in 1795. They served as a somewhat random postal destination and personnel escape service for cities like Paris, in the grip of siege during the 1870 Franco-Prussian war. They have always been involved in atmospheric and meteorological research; it was data from an unmanned balloon in 1902 which suggested the atmosphere was arranged in layers.

To move independently of the wind requires an engine. There was the inevitable flapping, and the equally ineffective 'row yourself along'. There were hand cranked propellers, though whether these did anything more than exhaust the operators is debatable. A few balloons were even equipped with sails.

Attaching an engine to a round balloon is just as likely to spin it round like a top as drive it forward. The envelope of a navigable balloon, or *dirigible*, is best elongated and tapered in the intended direction of motion, like the hull of a ship. Henri Giffard was the first to apply these principles in his hydrogen filled airship of 1852 (figure 13). Fitted with a small 3hp steam engine and a propeller, the dirigible puffed along at a stately 5mph, steered with modest effect by the cloth-covered rudder at the tail.

As for heavier-than-air-flight, there were some partially successful attempts in the early 1800s, as we'll see, but by comparison with the elegant simplicity of balloons and dirigibles, aeroplanes were contrived and crass, and they simply didn't work. Even as late as the 1920s, it was still felt by many that the future of air transport belonged to the airship. Two spectacular accidents, the first being the destruction of the R101 at Beauvais in France in 1930, put paid to that idea.

In any event, in terms of development potential and payload, the airship has a crippling weakness which is apparently without solution. The density difference between hydrogen and air is far less than it is between air and water. By comparison with an ocean liner made of steel, weighing thousands of tons and able to move massive amounts of people and cargo, the carrying capacity of an airship of roughly the same volume is microscopic. The ill-fated airship *Hindenburg* (figure 14), destroyed at Lakehurst, New Jersey in 1937, was one of the largest airships ever built. But by comparison with today's Boeing 747, its payload to bulk ratio was abysmal. Aeroplanes are also much faster than the great airships, which belonged to more leisurely times when we still had a good chance of arriving at our destinations at the same time as our brains.

Whatever their vintage, aircraft are far too dense to float in air even though they do have some residual buoyancy, so the necessary lifting force must be generated by means other than hot air or gas.

An early start

One of the first people to realise that we didn't have to flap to fly, was the Yorkshire baronet Sir George Cayley, a man of awesome intelligence and breadth of interests. During his early studies of birds Cayley came to the same conclusion as Borelli, that we lacked the muscle power to flap and fly. Yet, rather than give up – which most people would have regarded as the sensible thing to do – he went on to work out the basics of fixed wing heavier-than-air flight. One of his most important contributions was the realisation that if we treated the need to support and move an aeroplane as separate items, we wouldn't then need to tackle the problems associated with flapping. Even so, he thought that flapping might provide motive power, or *waftage*, as he called it.

The press can be criticised for having an hysterical view of the world, but one of the more reputable contemporary journals unknowingly prompted Cayley to publish the first part of his treatise 'On aerial navigation'. Excited by a report in *Nicholson's Journal* in November 1809, he wrote:

"Sir, I observed in your Journal for last month, that a watchmaker at Vienna, of the name of Degen, has succeeded in raising himself in the air by mechanical means. I wait to receive your present number, in expectation of seeing some further account of this experiment . . ."

At the time Cayley did not know that the journal had misreported the flight. Mr Degen had strapped wings to himself, but the article neglected to mention, and the accompanying illustration to show, the crucial fact that he was also strapped to a balloon. The wings' usefulness may be judged by what happened when Degen arrived in Paris to demonstrate his invention. As the engineer Octave Chanute later observed:

FIGURE 14 Relative sizes of Montgolfiers' balloon, the Hindenburg, and a Boeing 747

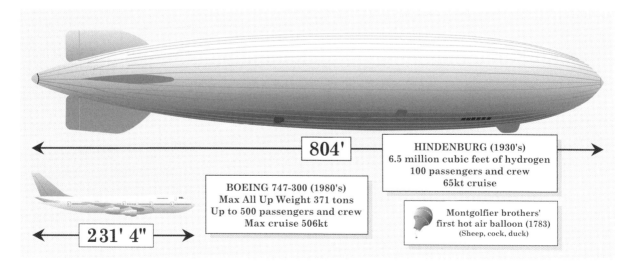

804'

231' 4"

BOEING 747-300 (1980's)
Max All Up Weight 371 tons
Up to 500 passengers and crew
Max cruise 506kt

HINDENBURG (1930's)
6.5 million cubic feet of hydrogen
100 passengers and crew
65kt cruise

Montgolfier brothers'
first hot air balloon (1783)
(Sheep, cock, duck)

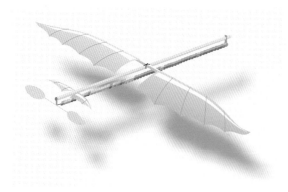

FIGURE 15 Penaud's 'Planaphore'

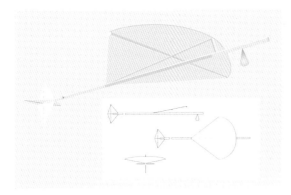

FIGURE 16 Cayley's 1804 model glider

". . . unfortunately for him, as there was wind upon each occasion, he was blown away, and on the third attempt he was attacked by disappointed spectators, beaten unmercifully, and laughed at afterwards as an imposter."

Rather a high proportion of aviation's pioneers fell foul of press and public in one way or another. De Rozier's jacket got its comeuppance after the first Montgolfier flight, but even before that, when J. C. Charles' first unmanned balloon came to ground at Gonesse, near Paris, the locals decided the twelve foot 'thing' was a bit much, and cut it to pieces with their billhooks and pitchforks. The public would turn up in truculent thousands to see balloons perform, and as Degen found out, were capable of turning nasty if promised events failed to materialise. This led to a number of aeronauts being beaten up, or even dying, as a result of attempting flights in totally unsuitable conditions.

There were other ways to be trashed. The brilliant Frenchman Alphonse Penaud, designed and built an influential rubber-powered model aircraft, the 'Planaphore' (figure 15), and also came independently to many of the same conclusions as Cayley had done, 50 years earlier. Unlike Cayley, though, Penaud had no financial security and suffered throughout his life from chronic ill health. In 1880, at the age of 30, worn out by his circumstances and public and press ridicule of all things aeroplane, he shot himself.

The list of Cayley's aeronautical accomplishments[3] is extraordinary, given that genuine sustained man-carrying, heavier-than-air flight wasn't achieved until nearly 50 years after his death. Cayley:

- laid down the scientific principles behind heavier than airflight

- used a whirling arm machine to carry out aerodynamic research into aerofoils

- made models for research purposes

- made and flew the first proper aeroplane in the shape of the 1804 model (figure 16)

- realised the importance of streamlining, and outlined the shape of a body with least resistance

- demonstrated and discussed the movement of the Centre of Pressure (CP) of a surface in an airflow

- discussed the problems of stability and drew attention to the effects of dihedral and of a moveable tailplane (to all intents and purposes an elevator and a rudder)

[3]This list, penned originally by Captain J.L. Pritchard, is taken more or less verbatim from Charles H. Gibbs-Smith's excellent book *The Aeroplane, an historical survey*, published by HMSO and regrettably now out of print. I am indebted to HMSO for allowing its inclusion here.

- suggested the use of superimposed wings (biplanes or triplanes) to provide maximum lift (and strength) for minimum weight

- drew attention to the importance of limiting the weight

- designed a lightweight spoked undercarriage wheel for aeroplanes

- built and flew a man-carrying glider

- realised that curved surfaces create lift more efficiently than flat surfaces[4]

- suggested an internal combustion engine for aircraft (he made a small gunpowder motor) and drew attention to the importance of the power/weight ratio and the need for any engine to be light

- suggested jet propulsion (in relation to airships)

Cayley continued to write about aeronautical matters after the flights of his model in 1804, but his many other commitments took first place. In 1849 his interest in the experimental side was reawakened, possibly due to the collapse of Henson and Stringfellow's Aerial Transit Company, an event to which we will return later. At about this time Cayley built a triplane glider large enough to carry a ten-year-old boy. Three years later, in 1852, he designed and had built a much larger machine with a kite-like wing and a boat-like fuselage (figure 17). By now 76 years old and too frail to be a test pilot, he gave the job to his coachman, John Appleby. The glider was launched by six strong men, flew 500 yards across a small valley near Castle Brompton in Yorkshire, and crashed resoundingly on the other side. No doubt afraid that Sir George might wish further life-threatening trials, Appleby told him that he had been 'hired to drive, not to fly', and resigned.

In 1980 Anglia Television commissioned the building of a replica machine for a programme about Cayley. The idea was to return to the original location and re-enact the flight. The well-known Derek Piggott was approached to be the test pilot. On the day he was wired for sound and asked to provide a running commentary. As it happened he said nothing during the flight, and due to the general ineffectiveness of the controls, crashed much as John Appleby had done all those years before. The sound tape of the flight is largely

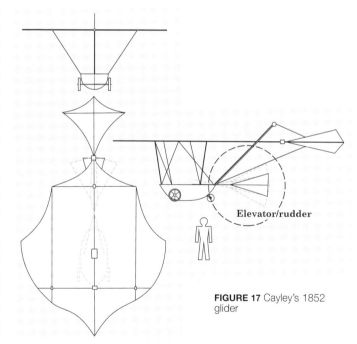

Elevator/rudder

FIGURE 17 Cayley's 1852 glider

[4]In June of 1866, F.H. Wenham reported to the newly formed Aeronautical Society of Great Britain that curved surfaces lifted more effectively than flat ones, and that long, narrow wings were more efficient than short, broad ones. In 1884 H.F. Phillips was the first to realise that there is low pressure over the top of an aerofoil, helping to generate lift.

airflow noise suddenly interrupted by the crack of impact, and after a brief pause a single, 'Oh dear!'

The big question mark about Cayley revolves around the true extent of his influence, not around what he discovered, about which there is now no argument. At least one modern commentator believes he had no influence on anybody, but Cayley's writings on aerial navigation were published privately, and translated into French, so despite limited circulation this seems unlikely. Had his writings sparked the interest they deserved, mankind would have mastered flight very much earlier than it did, and the history of the world would have been, not better (that would be expecting too much), but different.

Even if Cayley's influence on the more important figures in aviation's early history was indirect, that wasn't so with two of his contemporaries, William S. Henson and John Stringfellow. Based upon Cayley's writings and researches, Henson's Aerial Steam Carriage (figure 18) was designed and patented in 1842. Quaint as it now looks, the general layout is that of a modern aircraft. Among other forward-looking features, the 'Ariel', as it was called, had a properly braced wing with a cambered aerofoil, a tricycle undercarriage, twin pusher propellers, and a tailplane and fin. Depending on the reference book, the Ariel had (or didn't have) moveable control surfaces. It had no ailerons, but may have had an adjustable tail similar to Cayley's 1804 model. Henson and Stringfellow must have known about the model and understood the tail's purpose. If so, the Ariel was at least theoretically controllable.

A cartoon circa 1843, attributed to the novelist William Thackeray, shows Ariel attempting to land on top of an Egyptian pyramid. The cartoon would have been based on contemporary illustrations in *The London Illustrated News*, or images printed on promotional handkerchiefs as part of the publicity for the Aerial Transit Company, which the pair had formed in 1842 to capitalise upon the design.

Not unsurprisingly, almost all the pioneers underestimated the size of the task they were undertaking. Cayley had an inkling of the true scale of the enterprise, and predicted that the technical problems dogging heavier-than-air flight would initially allow balloons to make all the running – as they were doing already, and continued to do so for over 60 years. But Henson and Stringfellow's enthusiasm had got the better of them. Swept away by visionary hype of modern marketing proportions, their company was promising flights to India and China ('twenty four hours certain') when nobody had yet built and flown a powered model, let alone anything with the Ariel's projected span of 150ft (about 40ft less than a standard 747).

A 26hp steam engine was intended to power the Ariel but neither was ever built, although in 1844 Henson and Stringfellow did construct a 20ft span steam powered model. Of its testing, Chanute wrote later:

"A tent was erected upon the downs, two miles from Chard, and for seven weeks the two experimenters continued their labours. Not, however, without much annoyance from intruders. In the language of Mr Stringfellow, 'there stood our aerial protégée in all her purity – too delicate, too fragile, too beautiful for this rough world . . ."

The tests had their farcical aspects. The intrusive and disruptive nature of public interest led to test flights being

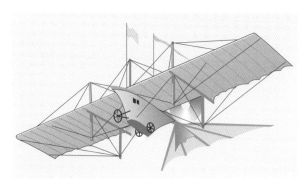

FIGURE 18 Henson's 'Ariel' (1842)

attempted at night. As Chanute noted drily, (they had) 'still less success as a result'. Nature conceived subtle ways of fouling things up, as Stringfellow discovered:

"*I soon found, before I had time to introduce the spark, a drooping in the wings, a flagging in all the parts. In less than ten minutes the machine was saturated with wet from a deposit of dew, so that anything like a trial was impossible by night.*"

There were other problems. Besides being structurally weak, the model was very unstable and the slightest puff of wind tipped it to the ground. 'The steam engine', Stringfellow wrote, 'was the best part.'

The notable failure of this pair, coupled with their heroic claims, did nothing for the progress of aviation in the UK. A bill introduced into the House of Commons to help finance the company was loudly jeered and thrown out. Elsewhere, outraged investors made the usual strangled noises that escape from people who have just guessed wrong with their money. The company collapsed, and a good start along broadly the right lines went straight into the bin.

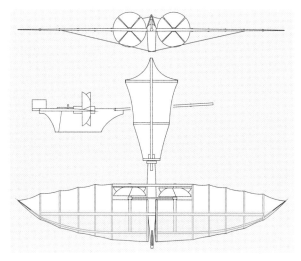

FIGURE 19 Stringfellow's 1848 steam-powered model

The Ariel's inspired design would never have worked in its original form, and the model, as Chanute remarked politely, 'failed to support itself when liberated'. Nevertheless, had the project been less ambitious and more discrete, there is a good chance that after initial hiccups, Henson and Stringfellow might have succeeded, not in flying to China – that was not to happen for nearly 100 years – but in demonstrating that powered man-carrying heavier-than-air flight was not only possible, but inevitable.

Deeply upset by the humiliating failure, Henson married and emigrated to the United States, where he maintained an interest in aviation but not in further practical, and as he probably saw it, embarrassing experiment. An engineer by profession, and probably less temperamental than his partner, Stringfellow continued doggedly, but ultimately fruitlessly, to experiment on his own. Beginning in 1846, he built other models (figure 19) powered by improved engines whose original design had, incidentally, been Henson's. It is recorded that one of these models flew in the open air for some 45 yards, but there is doubt among modern commentators as to whether this was a genuine flight or a teasingly prolonged bout of simply failing to hit the ground.

Publicity and progress

As always, the public's appetite for comical failures remained robustly heartless. But surprises were in store, and heavier-than-air-flight was about to receive unusually good publicity from an unforeseen and accidental ally, the camera.

The first paper negative was made in 1816, but until the invention of the halftone printing process in 1881 it wasn't possible to reproduce photographs in books, magazines and newspapers. Early cameras were bulky, and the glass photographic plates required long exposure times. Human subjects were obliged to stay completely still for many minutes on end, often actively restrained by implements more at home in a torture chamber than a photographer's studio. There was no way one could ask a flying man to 'try and keep still, for God's sake!' Inevitably, the technology improved, and in 1884 George Eastman produced the first roll-film. The first Kodak box cameras appeared in 1888. They were small, portable, easy to use, and the light sensitive emulsion of the new film was sufficiently fast to freeze most movement and allow quick consecutive snaps.

Otto Lilienthal was the first successful flyer to be photographed in flight. Small beer these days, perhaps – just snaps of a hang-glider floating down uneventfully from the top of a small hillock – but the interest created by these pictures was enormous.

Sacrifices must be made

Like Cayley, Lilienthal invented a whirling arm machine on which he tested various aerofoil shapes. Quieter aerofoils, he noted, were generally more effective, and by this slightly oblique route he concluded that a modestly curved plate, which was the quietest, was best. In his paper of 1893, entitled 'The carrying capacity of arched surfaces in sailing flight', he wrote:

"Today, . . . it is easy, in investigations on air resistance, to take curved surfaces like the wings of a bird instead of flat plates, and to develop in succession those wonderful effects, the first discovery of which was, after all, not quite so simple and selfevident as some may be inclined to assume now . . . it took much time and study to arrive at the conclusion that the slight curvature of the wing was the real secret of flying . . . a conclusion . . . some noted investigators are not willing to admit even at this late day. I must confess, however, that to us who abandoned flat wings fully two decades ago, it seems almost inconceivable that experimenters should cling so tenaciously to the aeroplane[5] . . . even to the present hour the majority of aviators expend much painful effort in attempting the hopeless task of trying to fly with flat wings."

Lilienthal knew there was no point in waiting for a suitable engine (Giffard's was far too heavy), and tackled other issues, such as control. The gliders which he and his brother Gustav built were hang-gliders, controlled by weight shift (figure 20). Weight-shift is fine, but not ideal; with the glider in some attitudes the pilot may be unable to move his body to the position needed for recovery. Unfortunately, Lilienthal's ideas about lift and how it was generated weren't entirely correct, and to fit his theories the gliders grew in size and unwieldiness. During a flight in 1896 his glider was hit by a gust of wind and pitched up. Before he was able to regain control, it stalled and side-slipped violently into the ground. He died shortly afterwards.

A QUESTION OF EVIDENCE

Unlike Cayley's data, Lilienthal's was fairly readily available to anyone who bothered to look for it. Lilienthal had flown successfully so many times that no-one dreamt there was anything fundamentally wrong with what he had been doing, yet a series of cumulative errors – many of them not his – had been building up, and a good chunk of what many pioneers and researchers were taking as fact was incorrect, either wholly or in part.

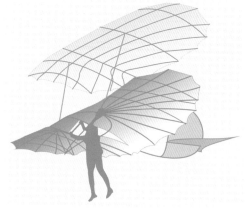

FIGURE 20 Lilienthal's biplane glider

[5]Lilienthal uses the word 'aeroplane' in the sense of a flat sheet, literally an aero plane.

Everything is obvious when you know the answers. Our ancestors were no more stupid than we are. The fact is that each day what will be self-evident to tomorrow stares us in the face and we don't notice it. Less happily, it is very easy to be right for completely the wrong reasons! The Montgolfier brothers provide a classic example. Fire, they believed, produced a lighter-than-air gas. Modestly called 'Montgolfier gas', its lifting power was proportional to the amount of smoke produced, so it made perfect sense to fuel a balloon with anything which created huge amounts of it. Their first unmanned balloon was fuelled by an evil-smelling mixture of old shoes, rotten meat and straw.

After Lilienthal's death there was a period in which progress, such as it was, appeared aimless. There were hopeful hops and jumps aplenty. One of the brighter stars, the Englishman Percy Pilcher, who had sought Lilienthal's advice and flown one of his gliders, was on the brink of adding a small 4hp motor of his own design to his hang-glider in 1899, when he too was killed in a flying accident. Europe seemed to have lost its way, but things appeared to be looking up in America.

AN EXPENSIVE CUL-DE-SAC

Samuel P. Langley was an astronomer, civil engineer and one-time secretary of the renowned Smithsonian Institution in Washington DC. Structural problems seem to have dogged all his experiments. For example, in his paper 'Story of experiments in mechanical flight', he wrote (describing one of his early model aircraft):

"(It was) . . . not likely to be launched at all, since there was a constant gain in weight over the estimate at each step. . . . The wings yielded so much as to be entirely deformed under a slight pressure of the air, and it was impossible to make them stronger without making them heavier, where the weight was already prohibitory."

This seems to have been a fairly constant refrain. Describing a later model he wrote:

"The flexure of the wings under these circumstances must be nearly that in free air, and it was found to distort them beyond all anticipation . . . the wings were strengthened in various ways, but in none of which, without incurring a prohibitive weight, was it possible to make them strong enough."

By 1896, one model had made several very successful flights, the best slightly less than a mile. Langley's original intention had been to reach this point and then call it a day, which suggests that, though interested in flight, it was hardly his passion. Hearing of the successes, the US President asked that Langley build a full-size aircraft. Funded by a $50,000[6] War Department grant, he set to again, and in 1901 built and successfully flew a quarter-scale petrol engined model of the proposed man-carrying aircraft, to which he was to give the strange name 'Aerodrome' (figure 21).

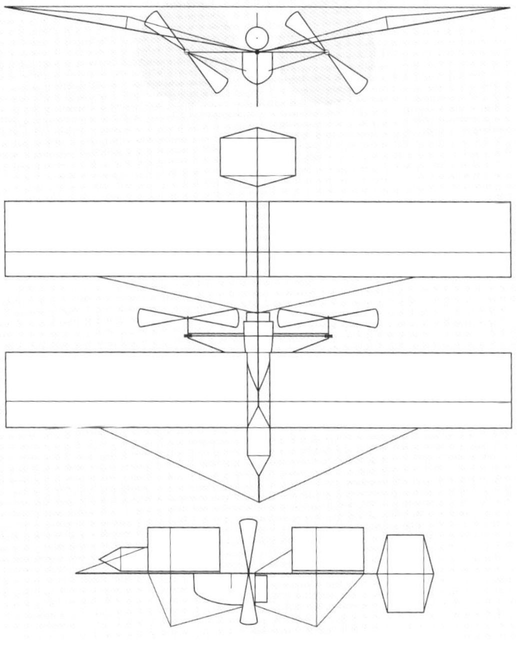

FIGURE 21 Langley's model 'Aerodrome'

[6]$2,000,000+ (or about £1.5 million) in 2007.

The full-size machine had a wingspan of 48ft and was powered by a very efficient 52hp radial engine made by his engineer and test pilot, C. M. Manly, based on an original and initially not very successful design by a Mr Balzar. All the previous flights made by the models had begun with a catapult launch from a houseboat in the middle of the Potomac river. Exactly why isn't clear, but this is how Langley intended to launch the full-size machine.

On 7 October 1903, Manly took his place and the engine was started. The machine was catapulted off and broke up almost immediately, falling into the river. Manly escaped drowning, and did not appear to believe himself to be in any further danger, because, after the machine had been rebuilt, he was once more aboard, if not exactly in control. On 8 December of the same year, the Aerodrome again broke up during the launch, and this time Manly was lucky to escape with his life.

The Government had poured huge sums of money into Langley's experiments. As was to happen in Britain in the 1930s with the R101 airship, there were strong pressures brought to bear for results. They were not forthcoming. In the case of the R101, political pressure to 'put up a good show' led to a major air disaster, but for Langley his failure was bitter. In 1903 a US War Department report on his project commented:

"We are still far from our ultimate goal . . . years of constant work and study by experts, together with the expenditure of thousands of dollars, would still be necessary before we can hope to produce an apparatus of practical utility along these lines."

In December of the same year, days before the Wright brothers made their first powered flight, the New York Times remarked in a thoroughly pompous editorial:

"We hope that Professor Langley will not put his substantial greatness as a scientist in further peril by continuing to waste his time and money involved in further airship [sic] experiments. Life is short, and he is capable of services to humanity incomparably greater than can be expected to result from trying to fly."

Following the Wright brothers' success, the financial plug was pulled on Langley's experiments. His main contributions to flight were, first, the extremely successful models and, second, the engine. Current opinion of the Aerodrome is that even if it had flown, it was virtually uncontrollable. Later events reinforce that view.

Airborne and under control at last

What flight needed was the rare combination of enthusiasm to fly and iron dedication to accurate and meticulous research. Oddly enough, it was again two brothers who fitted the bill. In 1878 Bishop Milton Wright, father of Orville and Wilbur Wright, brought home a Penaud helicopter model as a present. Fascinated by it, they tried to make a larger version, which didn't work. Nevertheless, they were hooked, but it was not until 1900 that they began experimenting in earnest. They corresponded with people like Octave Chanute, institutions like the Smithsonian, and with Langley. They read everything about aviation they could lay their hands on. They studied and checked out the available research, including Lilienthal's. Discovering that most of the available data wasn't correct, they devised their own experiments and collected and collated their own data.

In all of their endeavours the Wrights were encouraged and, to some extent, advised by Octave Chanute, and they valued his friendship. Following a successful career as an engineer, he took early retirement and made aviation his hobby, having some notable successes with gliders. He became a generous promoter and publicist of aircraft and their development, and was in contact with people of similar interests around the world. Several of the quotes in this chapter are from his book *Progress in Flying Machines*, a collection covering the history and then current aspects of heavier-than-air flight.

The brothers' aim, unlike that of everyone else, was a neutrally stable aircraft which depended on its pilot for adequate control. They placed the tail in front of the wings to prevent it from being damaged during landing, but due to an excessively aft CG the configuration was unstable. When stalled, the Flyer would fall flat to the ground. They afterwards claimed this was a safety feature to prevent stall fatalities such as Lilienthal's, whose glider had the tail at the rear.

They built a small wind tunnel and other test equipment, switching between indoor research and the crucial testing with gliders on the bleak and windswept dunes of Kitty-hawk, North Carolina. They learned about piloting, and crashed fairly frequently, but without serious injury. They found out about stalling and worked out the recovery procedure. They realised why lateral (roll) control needed the provision of a moveable rudder.

Their solution to roll control was typically ingenious. Observing that birds banked by twisting their wings, the brothers built this feature into their aircraft in the form of *wing warping*. Unfortunately, wing warping requires the wing to be flexible along an axis that should be rigid. Though used successfully in many early aircraft, as airspeeds rose and loads increased, it became clear that as an engineering solution, it teetered precariously on the edge of structural failure. After a few years, ailerons replaced wing warping[7].

By the time the brothers made their historic twelve-second flight on 17 December 1903 they had succeeded, with the help of C. E. Taylor, a bicycle shop associate of theirs, in producing a powerful and lightweight petrol engine attached to a pair of efficient propellers. The aircraft structure was also strong and light. Of crucial importance, in view of the highly unstable layout, they also had control in all three axes, and were by now excellent pilots; though this didn't stop Wilbur over-controlling the Flyer (figure 22, see over) during an attempt three days beforehand, and stalling in and causing minor damage. All four flights on the 17th ended with a loss of control.

PROMISE FULFILLED, SUCCESS TARNISHED

A few locals attended the first flights, but Wilbur was determined to keep details of the machine from leaking out. The only report that did appear was made up by a reporter who had been tipped off by the telegraph operator who had sent the message signalling their success to their father. The editor of a local Dayton paper, told by the Wrights' younger brother Lorin about the four flights, one lasting 55 seconds, said, 'fifty-five seconds? If it had been fifty-five minutes it might have been a news item'.

Through a variety of circumstances, some of the brothers' own making, it was a few years before the world as a whole said 'Hurrah'. Sorting out the patents for their inventions took them until 1906. Meanwhile, they were reluctant to give public demonstrations for fear of giving away their secrets. France, having long regarded itself

[7]Esnault-Pelterie's 1906 monoplane was fitted with ailerons, although it never flew. He is generally given first claim to their invention, but M.P.W Boulton did patent something similar in 1868.

FIGURE 22 The Wright 'Flyer'

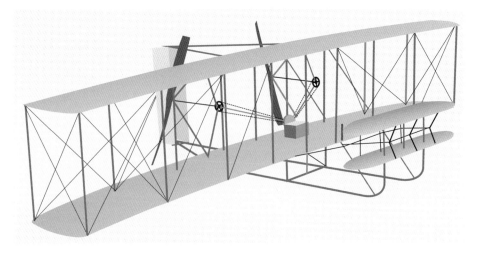

as the cradle of flight, was deeply suspicious of the Wrights' claims, particularly since the brothers seemed unwilling to back them up. Besides, pipped at the post, most people outside the USA found it hard to believe that two bicycle mechanics could have done what was claimed. Until Wilbur arrived to fly in France in 1908, and, as the phrase goes, knocked their socks off, Europe remained huffily unimpressed.

There was the usual sour collection of wrangles. One extremely vocal group believed that the Frenchman, Clement Ader, had made the first real flight in 1890, though at the time Ader himself made no such claim for what was, according to the evidence of witnesses, an uncontrolled hop. There was plenty of litigation about who had invented what, which dragged on for years. Preposterously, even when the rest of the world finally acknowledged the remarkable nature of the Wrights' achievement, the Smithsonian Institute turned its back on them and awarded Langley the honour of 'first', despite the fact that his Aerodrome had been wrecked every time it was launched.

In 1914, at the request of Glenn Curtiss (later to become famous as an aircraft manufacturer), the Aerodrome was removed temporarily from storage at the Smithsonian – Langley had died in 1906. Curtiss's stated intention was to check whether the machine had been capable of genuine flight. For reasons best known to himself he rebuilt it with a number of fairly major modifications, including adding floats, and whatever he believed he had done, the machine was no longer Langley's. The new Aerodrome flew a number of abbreviated and more or less out-of-control hops, none more than five seconds in duration, from Lake Keuka in New York State, and was then returned to the Smithsonian. The Institution's secretary knew what Curtiss had done, but proceeded nonetheless to make a number of disingenuous statements about the Aerodrome, including that 'it was the first (powered) aeroplane capable of sustained free flight with a man', and that is how it was displayed. The Wrights weren't mentioned.

In 1948 the Smithsonian retracted all of its previous claims and statements. Orville (Wilbur had died of typhoid fever in 1912) allowed the Flyer to be moved from the Science Museum, London – where it had been on display and where he had threatened to leave it – back to the USA, where it belonged. On 17 December 1948, 45 years after the epoch-making flight, the installation ceremony took place at the Smithsonian. Orville had died in January.

Summary of chapter two

Page	Subject	
38	**Archimedes' Principle(s)**	(1) a body immersed in a fluid displaces its own volume (2) when a body is completely or partially immersed in a fluid, the fluid exerts an upward force on the body equal to the weight of the fluid displaced by the body.
38	**Buoyancy**	upward force exerted on a body by the fluid in which it is immersed (*Archimedes' principle*). Buoyancy only works with gravity and weight.
38	**Density**	mass of an object divided by its volume (usually defined as mass per unit volume) m/V.
40	**De Rozier**	composite hot air and gas balloon; alleged to have been invented by Pilâtre de Rozier (1754–1785).
42	**Dirigible**	navigable balloon (steerable).
30	**External combustion engine**	fuel is burnt outside the driving cylinders (steam engine and boiler).
30	**Internal combustion engine**	fuel is burnt inside the driving cylinders (petrol engine).
37	**Newton's laws of motion**	(1) a particle not subjected to external forces remains at rest or moves with constant speed in a straight line (2) the acceleration of a particle is directly proportional to the external forces acting upon the particle and inversely proportional to the particle's mass (3) for every action there is an equal and opposite reaction.
35	**Ornithopter**	flapping wing flying machine.
30–35	**Requirements for flight**	(1) support (lift) (2) motive power (thrust) (3) structural strength and integrity (4) stability and control (5) theory (includes physics and mathematics).

Page	Subject	
34	**Scale effect**	**aerodynamic**: changes to airflow behaviour due to relative sizes of object and air molecules.
33–5	**Theory**	description/explanation/assumption about how/why things are, what they are, and do/don't work.
51	**Wing warping**	Method of roll control involving twisting the wings to alter their relative AoAs (see *Angle of Attack*, chapter 3, p.63 for explanation of AoA).

CHAPTER 3

LIFT, DRAG
AND THE
BOUNDARY
LAYER

CHAPTER CONTENTS ★ should know ☆ useful

CHAPTER CONTENTS ★ should know ☆ useful

3 LIFT, DRAG, AND THE BOUNDARY LAYER

Viewing the invisible

BACKGROUND

Air is both a fluid and a gas. The simple definition of a fluid is that it flows, to which we might add that fluids tend to be splashy and wet, like water. Not the best definition, as it happens, because air's not particularly splashy or wet, and under certain circumstances materials like sand, rocks, snow, can all behave exactly like fluids. Like most gases, air also has one paradoxical property by which we probably know it best – we can't see it. This transparency allows slightly peevish comments like "why are the best clouds always miles away?", but for something like aerodynamics the same property is rather unhelpful.

Seeing may not always be believing, but it can alter the interpretation of a given set of facts, sometimes radically, and make the difference between a useful theoretical model, and one that isn't. In the 18th and 19th centuries it became increasingly important to assess the likely behaviour of mechanical objects before you built them. The old wet finger up to the wind approach, 'Yes, my grandfather made one like that and it worked perfectly. Can't say why this one didn't! ... Let me sell you another', is far too hit and miss, and potentially very expensive. Prediction, with all its pitfalls, required a more rigorous and scientific basis. Rather unfortunate, then, that naval architects and ordnance designers were becoming increasingly puzzled by serious discrepancies between the predictions of fluid theory, and what was clearly happening in defiance of them. Yet even if the engineers had been able to see how flow was behaving, as one might have expected of naval architects, the theory/reality mismatch would not necessarily have been resolved. Good ideas can come a cropper because of the way they're subsequently interpreted, occasionally by the very people who had them.

As a consequence of his laws of motion, Newton had suggested that birds were able to fly because of a transfer of momentum, by impact, between their wings and the molecules of the air. The repetitive 'clack, clack' of the executive toy which is little more than a train of suspended steel balls, demonstrates momentum being transferred in this way (figure 1). As explanations go, *impact theory* is simple, logical, and seems to explain everything, which is part of its problem[1]. Start. X hits Y. Transfer of energy. Finish.

Simple. Well, 'yes' to the transfer of energy and 'not quite' to the simple, as we later found out. Down here, at the bottom of the atmospheric pond, there's no such thing as **one** air molecule hitting a surface. The reality is trillions of them in endless collisions with each other and with any surface they contact. In terms of the transfer of momentum the results are far more complicated than Newton realised.

If you'll pardon the pun, impact theory had a further knock-on effect. When Cayley, and later Lilienthal, made whirling arm machines to test the efficiency of various lifting surfaces, their aim was to measure and compare lift and drag forces. Newton's reputation and influence would have lent considerable weight to an almost inevitable assumption of impact theory,

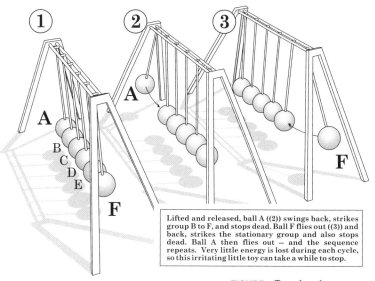

Lifted and released, ball A ((2)) swings back, strikes group B to F, and stops dead. Ball F flies out ((3)) and back, strikes the stationary group and also stops dead. Ball A then flies out – and the sequence repeats. Very little energy is lost during each cycle, so this irritating little toy can take a while to stop.

FIGURE 1 Transfer of momentum in an executive toy'.

that lifting surfaces would present only their undersides to the airflow, and that this essentially single surface effect was all that really mattered; which might go some way to explaining why, in the early days, hardly anyone seems to have given much thought to what was going on over a wing's upper surface.

In fairness, people like Cayley realised that impact theory was flawed when all their measurements of lift produced far higher values than it predicted. Langley, in about 1890, found that a flat plate could produce twenty times as much. This wasn't because the plate was particularly efficient, just that impact theory's predictions were hugely pessimistic and that, by implication, it couldn't be right.

A further and inadvertent consequence of impact theory was to convince many scientists that heavier-than-air flight was impossible, and that the 'measurement errors' that kept occurring were down to problems with the accuracy of the experiments! As a part of the search for accuracy and dependable data, in 1871 F. Wenham and J. Browning built the world's first wind tunnel. The tunnel was crude, the test objects were flat plates, and there was still no direct observation of flow. Flight's biggest problem – how to get airborne at all – was solved at about the same time that researchers started trailing thin streams of smoke (literally '*streamlines*' (figure 2)) into wind tunnel airflows, which revealed often surprising information about how flow streams really behave. Even so, the miniaturised world wasn't quite the perfect environment researchers had hoped for.

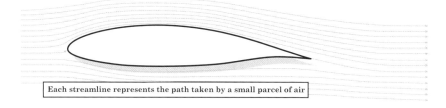

Each streamline represents the path taken by a small parcel of air

FIGURE 2 Streamlines

[1]If everything has been explained, what other explanations could there possibly be?

Early wind tunnels and the models that went into them were very small. Scale effects (see chapter 2, pp 34) weren't understood, and the experimental environment frequently yielded results which bore almost no relation to anything happening in the larger world outside. This can happen with today's wind tunnels, though to a far lesser degree, but even though we understand the problem and make allowances for it, full-sized aircraft can still fail to work as well as the models predict. One early 'avoid the wind tunnel' solution to looking at flow was to tuft the full-size airframe with short lengths of wool, and during flight – or whatever passed for it – to use either direct observation by onboard observers, or cameras, to record how the tufts fluttered about and in which directions they were pointing.

These days the costs and complexities of most aircraft have become so gargantuan that crunching the multi-million pound prototype, or having it perform badly, can put the manufacturer out of business. What used to be thrashed out by good old-fashioned 'try-it, fly-it and probably die-in-it' methods – rather unpopular in self-obsessed cultures – is now 'number-crunched' (virtually crashed) by computers first. Structural design is likewise electronically drafted and, as computing power continues to increase and the software algorithms improve, more and more of the critical airflow modelling is done in the digital hinterland. On the basis of the practical results, particularly in aerofoil design, some of the computational models would seem to be rather good. Nevertheless, the smoke and tuft of more traditional analogue methods remain in use as a reality check.

FLOW AND ENERGY

One of the first people to be interested enough in flow to record his observations, drawing them in excruciating detail, was Leonardo da Vinci in the 15th century. Leonardo started much and finished less, but he was fascinated by flight, and sketched out a design for a hang-glider. Gifted with a bit more focus, he might well have flown, and made the crucial connection between what he could see swirling in the water and what he couldn't see doing the same thing in the air. This wouldn't count as a theory of fluids exactly, but others certainly had a stab at creating one; two of the more famous being Archimedes back in the BCs – probably splashing about in his bath again – and Newton, who wrote about fluids and flow in book two of the *Principia Mathematica* (1687).

Flow is about the transfer of energy, and ruled by a rather dispiriting physical law whose ultimate consequence, some billions of years hence, is that the entire Universe will have fizzled out into a featureless wash of energy, rather like a very weak cup of cold grey tea. An earlier chapter described the principle behind it as 'universal lethargy', but it sounds less frivolous when referred to by its more usual title, the *second law of thermodynamics*. Equilibrium, states this law, is the natural state. Or, to put it another way, everything runs down and/or wears out in the end.

This can't always have been true, otherwise we wouldn't be here. Energy imbalances have occurred, and still do occur (there's more, or less, energy here than there is over there), and in a sea of relative uniformity these island peaks are responsible for flow. What's normal is that, in terms of the second law of thermodynamics, such states aren't normal at all. Turn on a tap and the water tries to pool and level itself off at the lowest possible point – least effort to reach the least (and most uniform) energy state – and when you turn off the tap there isn't a pillar of water left standing up in the sink. Likewise, air will flow down the pressure gradient from an area of high pressure (a hill) towards an adjacent area of lower pressure (a valley) (<u>figure 3</u>), and try and fill it up. This levelling off process is another consequence of the 'you don't get something for nothing' principle which is so important in aerodynamics but can be seen in action just about everywhere; it is one of the major forces driving the weather, for example.

Air's natural state, like that of all gases, is one of disorder, but if energy is pumped into the right places by, let's say, the sun, a transient order emerges in the form of a thermal (see chapter 10). Similarly, when an aircraft elbows its way through billions of air molecules, it imposes upon their aimless fidgetings an equally transient order which leads to the production of aerodynamic lift.

EASY ON THE SOURCE

One critically important aspect of flow, which we'll look at in greater detail later under *viscosity* and *boundary layer* (pp. 69–71), is what takes place in the exceedingly thin interface between a stationary fluid (air) and a moving object (aircraft). For the moment, though, we can say that in terms of flow, the most energy efficient results are usually obtained when it is *laminar*, or layered, like a series of horizontal sheets lying together like the pages of a book (<u>figure 4</u>) or a pack of cards. While these 'thin sheets' of energy suggest an inherent order, which is there, down at the molecular level it's nothing like as clear cut as the word suggests. There is sufficient irregular movement amongst the air molecules, enough 'noise', to smudge the energy sheets together, and given the right trigger – not that difficult to provide, unfortunately – our nice neat 'book' will start randomly to disorganise itself. The pages curl over and into each other (<u>figure 5</u>, see over), until finally there's no way of distinguishing between any of them. Trying to read and make sense of the result would waste a great deal of our time and energy. Similarly, *turbulence*, which is so disorganised as to be almost organised, usually wastes more energy than *laminar flow*, but in some circumstances it can waste a lot less and is deliberately invoked to do just that (p. 84).

Almost by definition, flow is not about the life and travels of a single air molecule, but the cumulative result of countless interactions between trillions of them. Like most crowds, encouraging air molecules to behave is quite difficult, even at the comparatively low speeds at which gliders move. Air molecules en masse dislike abrupt changes in velocity or pressure, and may decide not to travel smoothly round even relatively gentle corners[2]. We might want them to follow a particular surface, but they can readily detach themselves and fly off elsewhere. Avoiding a riot with this ill-disciplined gaseous mob requires the aerodynamic equivalent of much 'there, there' patting and 'let us address your issues' sedation! Amazing that we ever had the patience.

[2]At supersonic speeds they will go happily round quite sharp corners, but the only glider likely to be affected by that is the Space Shuttle

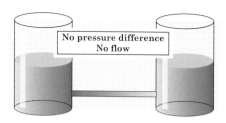

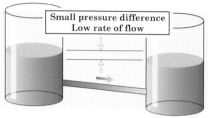

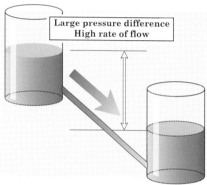

FIGURE 3 Seeking equilibrium

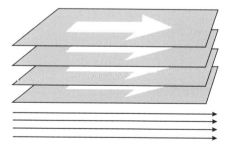

FIGURE 4 Laminar (layered) flow

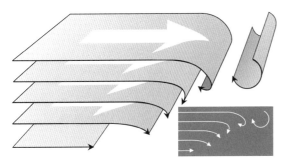

FIGURE 5 Start of turbulent flow

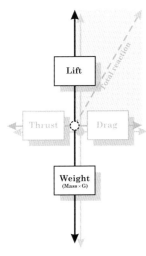

FIGURE 6 Basic forces

Lift

In an environment where gravity is ever-present and ever-downward, it is impossible to keep weighty objects airborne without creating a constant force acting in the opposite direction; chapter 4 deals in more detail with the basic forces illustrated in figure 6. We know the supporting force as Lift (usually written simply as 'L'). Highly desirable as L is, it comes linked inextricably to drag (usually written as 'D'), often in quite subtle ways. Don't be fooled into thinking that drag is useless and ought to be abolished. It belongs to a very large category of apparently wholly negative forces without which almost nothing would work.

It is the convention that L always acts at right angles to an aircraft's flight path, with D acting at right angles to L and parallel to, but against the direction of flight (see figure 9). L is usually the force we want, but since D is unavoidable, the best we can aim for is the most energy efficient ratio between the two. This is the Lift to Drag ratio, better known as L/D. We'll look at D in more detail later.

FLAT PLATES AS AEROFOILS

Creating L isn't that simple, but the precise shape of an *aerofoil* – sometimes referred to as a *section* – is key. The most basic section of all is a square-edged flat plate of the sort you see on model chuck gliders (figure 7). Kites appear also to have flat plate wings, but they aren't quite what they seem (Appendix G). At chuck glider scales a flat plate wing works well enough, and at larger scales too, one might think, given that the tailplane and fin sections of many light aircraft are flat plates with rounded edges (figure 10, see page 64). So why don't full-sized aircraft have flat plate wings? The main reason is that at larger than chuck glider scales, and when required to do any real work, flat plates are the energy equivalent of turning the central heating on full blast in the dead of winter, and then throwing open all the doors and windows; they are incredibly inefficient. A simple(ish) experiment, less complicated than anything Cayley or Lilienthal might have

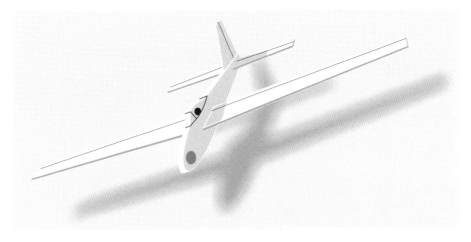

FIGURE 7 A chuck glider

done, gives clues as to why, and has the big advantage that we don't have to be very exact about any of it!

On a windy day, arm yourself with a large sheet of very stiff card – our uncomplicated version of a flat plate wing – and go outside. Hold the card in front of you, at right angles to and facing the wind (figure 8 (B)). Note the strong force acting towards you, as if the wind were trying to push the card out of the way. This is the 'all drag' situation. Now hold the card horizontally (A), and when you've aligned it exactly parallel to the wind, note the very small force straight back towards you. This is the 'no lift and almost no drag' situation. If you then tilt the nose of the card upwards slightly (C) you'll note a strong upwards force, and may also be aware of a somewhat smaller one towards you. This is the 'plenty of lift, not much drag' situation. Tilt the card further (D) and not only will the force towards you increase markedly, but there may be some vibration as well, and the up force may be less strong. The experiments are very crude, and because we're not making any measurements – just trying to get a general idea – it can be hard to separate out what counts as an 'up' or a 'back' force.

The first comment to make, fatuous as it will sound, is that if no air flows over the card, nothing happens. The second is that if you hold the card at a constant angle – say very slightly nose-up – running into wind produces more of an upward force than does standing still. If you run backwards and downwind fast enough there is no airflow over the card and again no force. Complete the sequence by standing still, facing directly into wind, and simply altering the angle of the card. Try many different angles. You'll see again that the forces change, often significantly.

These experiments suggest that the strength of the resulting forces depends on two things:

(1)   changes to the speed of the airflow (whether you ran or not, or if the wind gusted), and

(2)   the angle at which the card sits in relation to the general airflow, or its *angle of attack* – AoA for short – (you stood still and changed the card's tilt angle).

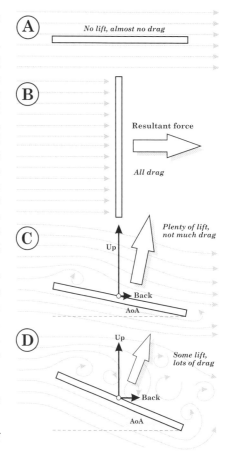

FIGURE 8 Flat plate

ANGLE OF ATTACK (AOA) AND RELATIVE AIRFLOW

Since every part of an airframe has an effect on local airflow in terms of velocity and pressure, it is very important that any definition of AoA takes account of this. For a flat plate, what's known as the *geometric chord line* is the longest possible straight line between the leading and trailing edge, and AoA is defined as the angle between that and the *relative airflow*. The definition of AoA for an aerofoil has one important difference; the aerofoil's chord line is defined as the straight line between the trailing edge and the point where the *mean camber line* meets the leading edge (see figure 52 for *camber*). For some aerofoils this may not be the longest possible line.

FIGURE 9 Angle of attack, (AoA), flight path and attitude

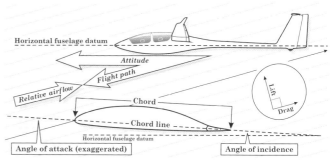

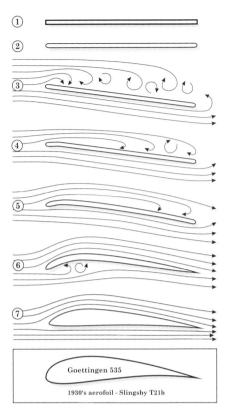

FIGURE 10 From plate to aerofoil

An aircraft's *flight path* is defined as the direction in which it is travelling in relation to air just far enough away from the airframe to be outside its influence; hence the phrase 'relative airflow' (figure 9). 'Just far enough away' may be a considerable distance (yards rather than inches), and can change during flight, depending on what the aircraft is doing at the time. One very important point to note about the flight path is that it may bear no relationship whatsoever to the aircraft's *attitude*, or *pitch angle*, which is the orientation of the fuselage in relation to the horizontal. The AoA is regarded as negative when the relative airflow approaches from above the chord line, and positive when it approaches from below. AoA is sometimes measured as the angle between the relative airflow and the *zero lift line*, a definition which we'll look at later.

Most of us don't have access to a wind tunnel, nor probably much desire for it either, but one equipped with smoke streamers is worth dozens without. Our previous experiments with the card hinted at the upper surface's role in lift generation. When the AoA was greater than a certain quite shallow angle, let's say +3°, the card could start to vibrate, sometimes quite violently. Vibration usually means an imbalance, but without a visible airflow nothing which we saw would look, or be, physically out of balance; odds on, therefore, that it was something we couldn't see. Put the card into a wind tunnel with smoke streams and all (almost) is revealed. The plate's AoA is the critical factor, not only in generating lift and drag, but to any associated vibration. While air striking the leading edge of a slightly tilted plate can continue on over the top surface without an alarming degree of disorder, a few degrees more and there's a riot; the airflow breaks away at the leading edge and a large and chaotic wake tumbles away downstream (figure 8 (D)). The turbulence is one cause of the vibration, the other is *vortex shedding* (see p. 72).

UNEXPECTED BENEFITS OF CURVATURE

How to get what you want without having to pay through the nose for it, if at all, is not a problem confined to aviation, but early research by people like Cayley and Lilienthal had demonstrated that while rounding off the edges of a flat plate made it somewhat more efficient, curving it in particular ways (figure 10 (4–6)) had a dramatically positive result. First, the lifting effect was far greater, and second, as a completely unexpected bonus, the drag (sometimes referred to in the early days as 'drift') was much less.

At a given AoA a curved plate will present a smaller effective area to an oncoming airflow than a flat plate, so it ought to work less well. A bit of a surprise to find it works a lot better. The improvement has to be due to the curvature and . . . well! . . . while we can all say truthfully that aerofoils work, having made much use of them, it is at this point that ideas about exactly how seem occasionally to diverge. Flying's basic forces are governed by Newton's Laws of Motion (see chapter 4 p. 101), which we'll refer to in this chapter as NL. Nobody familiar with physics disputes NL, but every so often there's a bit of Punch and Judy with what is sometimes made out to be a competing explanation.

CREATING L

Aerodynamicists have for years been utilising explanations based upon *Bernouilli's Principle*. The formula in <u>figure 11</u> is not Bernoulli's, but the mathematician L.Euler's (1707-1783) 'realisation' of the principle, which we'll refer to simply as BP. It's worth remembering the following:

(1)   the effects about to be described do occur

(2)   the answers to what's doing what seem to boil down, not to the facts themselves, but to their interpretation – nothing new there

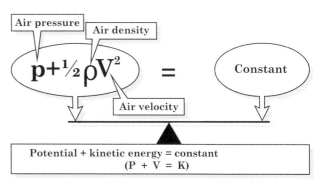

FIGURE 11 Euler's formulation of Bernoulli's Principle

(3)   assuming that BP and NL have nothing in common is like arguing that a 'planeur' and a 'sailplane' can't be the same thing because the words are different!

The tool best suited to a particular job tends to be the one that's used the most, and aerodynamicists generally prefer BP based explanations because measuring pressures is often far simpler than trying to measure anything else. What's then done in terms of design and airflow tweaking on the basis of pressure correlations works because, when velocities and pressures are altered, there's no way on earth you can avoid altering mass flow and momentum as well . . . and vice versa. Throughout any discussion that follows, bear in mind that BP and NL are at heart **the same thing**, and that in any normal situation they can't be anything else!

Chapter 4 has a fuller discussion of Newton's Laws, but we need to look at one of them here. The third law states that 'for every action there is an equal and opposite reaction'. In terms of something like a rocket or a turbojet engine, say, this law amounts to 'throw to go'. A large mass of heated air is expelled at a high velocity (action) and the attached vehicle responds by whistling off in the opposite direction (reaction). In terms of an aerofoil, where flow is very obviously diverted by the simple fact that the wing is in the way, and less obviously by reactions which result from the flow stream being made to go round a corner which, given the chance, it would not, the principle is more like 'bend to ascend'. The Harrier jump jet in <u>figure 12</u> illustrates hovering flight, with the aircraft supported on the downward pointing jet efflux, and cruising flight, where the engine takes the more conventional role of pushing the aircraft along fast enough for the wing to provide the support. In both cases the shifting of a large mass of air is providing the L force required to support W.

BP requires fairly lengthy explanation because it isn't in the slightest bit obvious. It's worth pointing out here that pressure forces are NL, so once again, any distinction

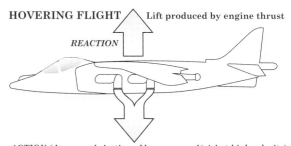

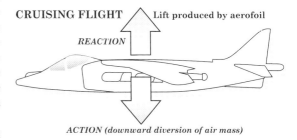

FIGURE 12 Action and reaction

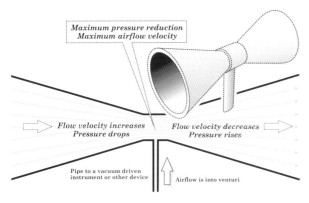

FIGURE 13 Velocity and pressure changes within a venture

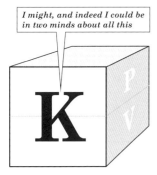

FIGURE 14 Energy parcel

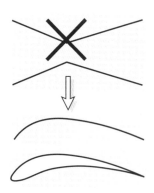

FIGURE 15 Venturi to aerofoil

between NL and BP is more apparent than real. We'll spend some time talking about BP because later there's a useful extended version of the formula in figure 11.

VENTURIS

A *venturi* (figure 13) is a narrow-waisted tube. Air going out the back leaves at more or less the same velocity and pressure it went in at the front. Pointlessly, nothing appears to happen in between. Appearances mislead, because a useful effect does occur inside, and has been harnessed to drive mechanical turn and slip indicators (T/S), among other things[3]. It's also a very useful way of explaining how BP works!

The principle of conservation of energy says that within any given and leakproof frame of reference (think of it as a closed box), the sum of potential and kinetic energies should always be the same. If you think of pressure as a form of potential energy rather than height per se, then the BP formula in figure 11 is effectively a 'conservation of energy' equation. The constant referred to is only so under certain conditions, which we'll take as read. As we can see from figure 13, the visual squeeze which the venturi's shape imposes on the flow lines implies that in the narrowest part, the throat, the pressure rises. In fact, the pressure there is lower than atmospheric, which isn't what our eyes are telling us, but there's worse. Instead of slowing down as the tube narrows, the airflow accelerates; the faster it goes the lower its pressure.

All of which might suggest there's more energy at the throat than elsewhere, but that's not the case. The internal energy (we'll call it K) of a parcel of air travelling through the venturi remains constant, but the proportions of the two separate yet interdependent components (figure 14) that comprise it, don't. They are 'P', which is the *static pressure* or static energy of the air within the parcel – initially the pressure of the atmosphere – and 'V' (shorthand for V[2] in the equation), which is the *dynamic pressure* or energy due to the parcel's velocity, and what you feel when the wind blows against you.

As a constant, K can't pinch energy from outside of itself, with the result that if P increases, V will decrease, and vice versa, but they don't split 50/50 in the compartmentalised way in which, for convenience, figure 14 shows them as doing. Providing the venturi does no 'outside' work, then energy in equals energy out, near enough. With a working T/S attached, however, air will be drawn into the venturi through the attached pipe (figure 11), K will change, and in this instance 'in' and 'out' won't match up. The difference is the work done (energy used, effort made) to drive the instrument.

The pressure and velocity changes that occur in a venturi are related to the difference between the cross-sectional area of the inlet and the throat. Aerofoils can be thought of as one-sided venturis (figure 15), with the 'other side' provided by air molecules doing their usual trick of not wanting to get out of the way. Higher flow speeds, or more

[3]Most aircraft and virtually all glider T/S are now electrically driven. A venturi needs to be out in the airstream, but the pressure and velocity changes within it make it very susceptible to ice formation. Once the throat is blocked, an attached mechanical T/S will stop working. This is most likely to happen in a modestly damp environment i.e. when you're in cloud and using the instrument!

accurately, accelerating flows equal lower, or decreasing pressures, and decelerating flows equal higher, or increasing pressures. While that's true, the simplistic 'suck and blow' explanation of how lift is created – that at a positive AoA higher pressure underneath the aerofoil pushes it upward, and the lower pressure over the top surface pulls the aerofoil upwards (figure 16) – is very dodgy, and certainly not the whole story. We'll look later at *circulation theory*, which is a more sophisticated application of BP.

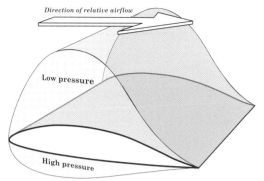

FIGURE 16 Aerofoil

PRESSURE PROFILES

By attaching *manometers* to sample the local pressure through tiny holes in the surface of a section, a pressure signature, or *pressure profile*, can be created. Despite appearances (figure 17), the profile doesn't tell you how far out the pressure changes extend from the aerofoil surface, simply how marked they are: longer = stronger. The largest reductions in pressure occur where the flow speed is greatest, and the position of the low pressure peak in relation to the aerofoil's *chord* (i.e. nearer the front or rear) depends on several factors, one of which is the AoA. The figure illustrates the *pressure coefficient* profile around an early laminar flow aerofoil, at three different AoAs. Note how the peak of the low pressure curve gradually shifts back and decreases as the AoA decreases. In common with most profiles this one seems to show that the top surface usually does most of the work; compare the area lying between each curve and the 'atmospheric pressure' line. The inevitable corollary is that if a large part of the upper flow is misbehaving, for whatever reason, the aerofoil's efficiency will be reduced significantly.

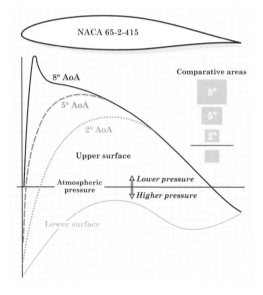

FIGURE 17 Pressure coefficient profile

STAGNATION POINT

Most aerofoils have a forward pressure peak at high AoAs – not as exaggerated as the NACA section's spike, perhaps – and the peak is the result of the top surface leading edge airflow being enormously accelerated. At any AoA (figure 18 ①, see over), some of the air approaching an aerofoil will strike the surface at right angles and come to a stop, forming what's known as a *stagnation point*. Stagnation points can occur elsewhere. The streamline that halts at the leading edge and marks the dividing flow line between air that continues on over the aerofoil's upper surface, and air that goes via the lower surface, is called the *central streamline*. The upward kink to this streamline just before it reaches the stagnation point is due to reduced upper surface pressure drawing upwards some of the air that might otherwise have passed underneath. Looking at the leading edge of ③ in terms of a venturi, one can imagine a larger and larger volume of air being drawn through an increasingly narrow slot, or throat. The higher the AoA the greater the acceleration of the upper surface flow, the nearer the maximum flow point moves to the leading edge, and the farther back along the undersurface the stagnation point. There are limits to how far the AoA can be increased, however.

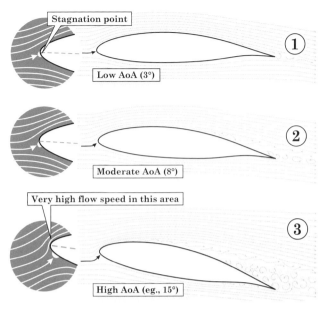

FIGURE 18 Stagnation point and leading edge flow

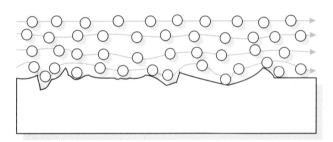

FIGURE 19 Skin friction (Viscous drag)

STALLING

Stalls and stalling are dealt with in detail in chapter 7 (pp. 205–33), but since the stall is mentioned several times before then, it's worth mentioning briefly here. Aviation has various structural and aerodynamic 'limit conditions' at the edges of the normal everyday working range of values, be they G loading or AoA. Stalling is a limit condition in that when the AoA reaches a high enough value, typically about +15°, the aerofoil won't produce any extra lift even if the AoA is increased further, although drag will continue to rise. Technically speaking, this lift peak is the stall. Whatever the impression given by the aircraft's behaviour at this point, the aerofoil doesn't instantly stop working. By comparison, and not entirely unexpectedly perhaps, a flat plate's stall is extremely abrupt.

Viscosity and skin friction

No explanation of lift can work without taking account of *viscosity* and *surface* or *skin friction*. Skin friction (also known as *viscous drag*) is resistance produced by contact between the air molecules and the glider. A surface may feel smooth to the touch, but there is always a microscopic roughness present (figure 19), both in the surface finish and as a result of minute particles of dust becoming trapped by, among other things, electrostatic forces. Air molecules at the aerofoil surface are caught in, or at least slowed, by the surface 'landscape', and then dragged along with the airframe. The more contact surface, or *wetted area* the glider has, the greater the skin friction.

Viscosity is *internal friction* in a fluid, and works in a slightly different way to skin friction. Every air molecule looks and behaves exactly like every other air molecule. But let's say that molecule X manifests a spark of individuality and sets off to travel from A to B (figure 20). In energy terms the journey turns out to be a very long haul indeed, because, on the way, vast numbers of collisions between other air molecules and X speed it up or slow it down, and each impact pings it off in a different direction. This sounds like hell, but it's also viscosity; effectively a measure of the effort X must make to go from A to B. Viscosity is occasionally described as air's 'stickiness'. In the *boundary layer* (see next page) 'get in your way' or 'sticky' behaviour is far more significant than it is outside of it.

In the real world air molecules sit there, fidgeting mindlessly. Suddenly this solid thing comes bowling out of nowhere, thrusts them aside by a combination of its immediate physical presence and the pressure wave that precedes its arrival – like the bow wave of a ship (figure 21) – and then disappears again, leaving behind a considerable disturbance. Without viscosity and surface friction, all that would happen to the air molecules being pushed over the top, say, of the intrusive aerofoil, is that they would go up as it went by and then sit straight down again after it had gone, ending up more or less where they started. This is exactly what early fluid theories predicted, and what the practical experience of contemporary engineers showed wasn't happening.

The boundary layer

It was the discovery of the boundary layer by a German professor, Ludwig Prandtl (1875–1953), and the publication of his paper on the subject in 1904, which solved the engineers' problem; the rather hubristically titled perfect fluid theory had taken no account of viscosity, friction, or anything even remotely resembling a boundary layer[4].

The boundary layer (figure 22, see over) can be thought of as a mini wind gradient, roughly similar to the one created by the interaction between the ground and the wind. On a modern aerofoil operating at peak efficiency this layer is extremely shallow; about 0.5mm deep at the leading edge, thickening to between 5.0mm and 6.0mm at the trailing edge.

Air molecules not trapped at the leading edge stagnation point continue onward, with those closest to the aerofoil surface being gradually slowed by skin friction. Eventually they will stop. Each succeeding layer of air molecules above those stuck to or creeping sluggishly along the aerofoil, is speeding up in relation to the one beneath, until, at some distance from the aerofoil, there is a layer which in effect doesn't even know the aerofoil is passing by. This layer is referred to as being at the *free stream velocity*[5]. It's worth noting that changes in the flow stream velocity continue out from the top of the boundary layer to the free stream at a far more leisurely rate of change than in the boundary layer, and for a far greater distance than the figure shows.

Any individual air molecule in a layer which is not at the extreme top or bottom of this energy layer 'stack', is influenced by an adjacent layer on the free stream side trying to speed it up, and another on the aerofoil side trying to slow it down (figure 23, see over). Viscosity helps make energy transfers between the layers smooth by not being very obstructive, or

[4]Perfect fluid theory is still used to describe the behaviour of airflow outside the boundary layer

[5]In a wind tunnel the free stream velocity is the velocity of the air pushed in at the front. In real flight, the airframe goes to meet the air, and the free stream velocity is zero. Likewise, in a wind tunnel the air decelerates to the stagnation point, but accelerates to it on an aircraft in flight. Confused? No matter. Airflow makes no such distinction, and any measurement problems are usually down to the tunnel.

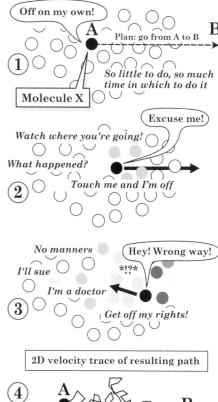

FIGURE 20 Viscous tribulations

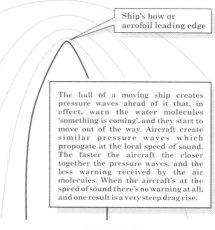

FIGURE 21 Pressure waves

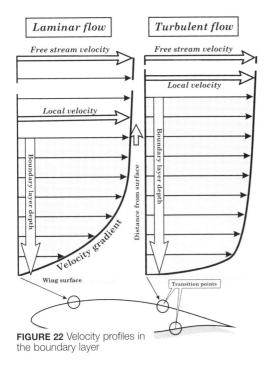

FIGURE 22 Velocity profiles in the boundary layer

sticky, and allowing a considerable amount of slip and slide, but not too much. This is important because none of the energy levels of these microscopically thin layers quite match up, and due to the random jiggling of the air molecules, they are also slightly 'fuzzy'. If one thinks of the air molecules as solid balls, a top/bottom velocity mismatch would cause them to roll (figure 23 (2-4)). Whether they do or not, the result is a tendency for each air molecule to want to dive into the layer below. This is rather like running alongside a wall, dragging your arm against it. If the resultant 'shear' created by friction becomes strong enough, you are suddenly swivelled round and crash into the wall.

Providing the *velocity gradient* isn't too steep, or, to look at it in a slightly different way, providing the shear between the individual energy layers isn't too great, and the pressure isn't starting to rise, the air flow will tend to follow the aerofoil's surface and remain laminar. However, what effectively pinned the accelerating flow stream to the aerofoil at the leading edge, was a dynamic pressure force created by the flood of new air molecules arriving in the vicinity (figure 24 (A and B)). As the upper flowstream continues 'round the corner', this dynamic force helps to keep it attached, but eventually the flowstream ends up running parallel to the relative airflow and the dynamic pressure falls to zero. Only the static pressure of the free stream, acting towards the aerofoil's surface, holds the flow stream in place, but now the pressure difference between the two is starting to decrease and other forces prevail.

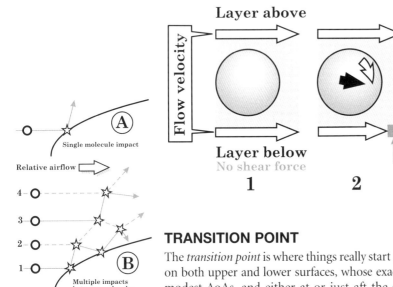

FIGURE 24 Dynamic pressure

FIGURE 23 Shear strain

TRANSITION POINT

The *transition point* is where things really start going awry. Aerofoils have transition points on both upper and lower surfaces, whose exact locations depend largely on the AoA. At modest AoAs, and either at or just aft the section's point of maximum *camber* (see figure 53, page 86) the flow stream begins decelerating and the pressure to return to atmospheric (figure 25). This *adverse pressure gradient* (in energy terms its 'uphill') results in surface friction becoming the dominant force, and the lowest layer of air molecules stop. It is as if someone running along, leaning forward, has suddenly had their feet pulled from underneath them, and over they go. Once this process has started, that's it. More and more, and in every sense higher and higher, energy layers are tripped over and dive down into a cascade of increasing disorder. From the transition point backwards, the boundary layer depth increases markedly[6]. Once *turbulent flow* has shredded the pages of this 'energy book', they're unreadable i.e. laminar flow can't be re-established. A point worth noting is that the smooth velocity lines in figure 22, under 'Turbulent flow', are 1) **average** velocities, 2) a lot of energy is being wasted by large parts of the flow effectively going in the wrong direction, and 3) the underlying velocity fluctuations are three dimensional.

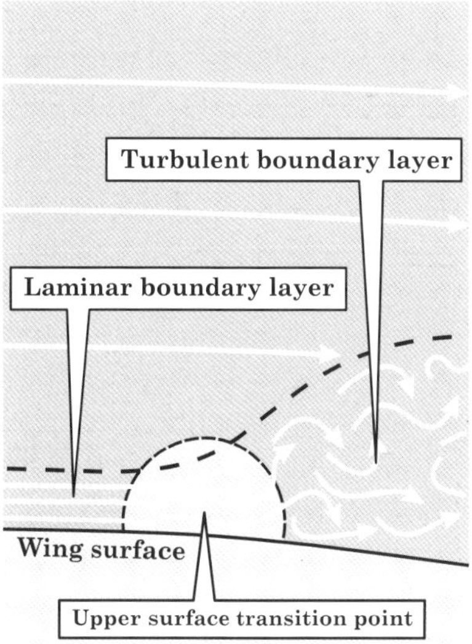

FIGURE 25 Transition point

Drag

As you might expect, most of the section on lift dealt with the wing. The same emphasis continues in this section because the wing is also one of the major producers of drag.

A simple *drag tree* (figure 26) illustrates the relationships between the main types and causes of drag. It starts by dividing the total drag into two major components, *induced drag* and *profile drag*. The latter is then subdivided into *form drag* and *skin friction*, which is the most important subdivision, and *interference drag*, *leakage drag* and *parasite drag*. When the speed and/or the AoA change, so too does the total drag and the relative proportions of profile and induced drag. The relationship between these two has important consequences for glider performance (see chapter 8, p. 229 and Appendix C, Water ballast).

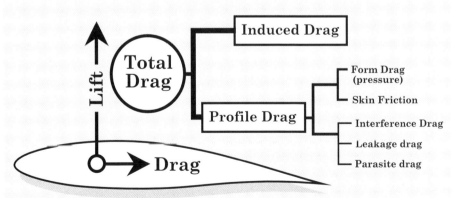

FIGURE 26 Drag tree

[6]Laminar flow breakdown often begins with tiny vibration-like ripples in the flow stream, marking where the layers are starting to mix their momentums and mutate into the whirls and swirls of the turbulent flow which finally replace it.

PROFILE DRAG

Since every aerodynamic component of an aircraft has a volume and surface area, profile drag affects every part of the airframe exposed to the airflow. For convenience, this book makes the assumption that profile drag is every type of drag except induced drag.

Profile drag is a combination of form drag and skin friction, but parasite and interference drag can be treated as combinations of form and friction drag, even of induced drag, depending on your viewpoint. No component of the total drag is wholly independent, but the link between form drag and skin friction is so close that you can't have one without being landed with the other. Deciding which contributes most to the total is not easy, but as far as pilots need to be concerned the division is entirely academic.

FORM (PRESSURE) DRAG

Any object whose surface forces the air flowing over it to change direction, and creates changes in pressure, creates form drag. Different shapes produce differing amounts of form drag, depending on how they effect a previously undisturbed airflow.

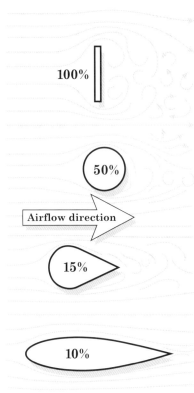

FIGURE 27 Form drag

If the flat plate with which we experimented earlier is placed vertically into an airflow, it produces 100% form drag (figure 27). When airflow strikes the 'upwind' side it is diverted away to an edge; in energy terms this is much the same as bringing the air to a dead stop in one direction, and then accelerating it off again in another. The result is an overall increase in pressure on the plate's forward side. There is also a rather messy low pressure area that develops on the plate's downwind side. The total form drag in this case is the difference between the pressures on each side. The resultant force never acts 'upwind' because overall the flow loses energy via surface friction, the effects of viscosity, and *vortex shedding*. As we found out earlier, significantly less drag is produced if the plate is parallel to the airstream.

A spherical object, or one of circular cross section, is half as draggy as the flat plate at right angles to the airflow. But, while the flow over the object's forward half is relatively smooth, as with the flat plate, whirls and swirls (*vortices*) keep forming and breaking away from the downwind side, and create most of the drag. Again, the total drag is the difference between the front and rear pressures.

Vortex effects can be seen on some tall thin chimneys, particularly those with very smooth surfaces. Given the right wind conditions, smoke can emerge from the top of the stack and then, caught by the vortices forming on the downwind edge, swirl a considerable distance down the outside of the stack before dispersing – totally defeating the chimney's original purpose. Vortices can have far more serious effects. Metal chimneys often have a spiral flange around them which helps break up the vortices and allow the smoke to escape upwards, but its more important function is to strengthen the tube. Minute variations in the flow speed cause what might otherwise be standing (stationary) vortices, to be shed alternately left and right from the rear surface. The stresses created by each individual event may not be very great, but when they all occur in phase with the chimney's *natural frequency of oscillation*, they can set it swinging from side to side with such violence that it buckles eventually and is wrecked (figure 28). *Vortex shedding* and *resonance* of this kind can be a highly significant factor in the onset and continuation of *flutter* (see chapter 5)[7].

Streamlining an object into a roughly teardrop shape helps reduce form drag even more, but the best results occur when the shape bears a strong resemblance to an aerofoil. One might imagine then, that the best way to reduce form drag to a minimum would be to make any aerodynamic object as long and thin as possible, but there are limits to this. For any given frontal area, when an object's length exceeds four times its width, reductions in form drag start to be offset by increasing skin friction.

SKIN FRICTION (VISCOUS DRAG)

This was described earlier, on page 68. Apart from keeping a glider clean, free of dust, and giving it the occasional polish, not much can be done about skin friction.

INTERFERENCE DRAG

Diagrams don't always make it very clear that flow is a truly three-dimensional phenomena. Interference drag is related to how the planes of airflow over components like the fuselage and wing, or the tailplane and the fin, interfere with each other where they combine, as they inevitably must (figure 29). Any great disparities in speed and/or pressure or direction between the root flow over the wing and the adjacent fuselage, say, result in vortices, turbulent flow and increased drag. What's slightly unexpected, perhaps, is that at high AoAs these effects can sometimes be heard by the pilot as a low frequency rumbling.

Flow breakdown is most likely to occur where two airframe components join to form a V-shaped pocket of any angle less than 90° (arrowed areas in figure 30, see over). One solution is to add carefully shaped *fillets* to smooth away awkward angles between components, and the more acute the angle the larger the fillet needs to be. For the mid-wing position, fillets are often dispensed with altogether. The wing/fuselage junction is particularly tricky because of its size, and unfortunately the best solution for one air speed may be the wrong one at another. Though the main purpose of taping the gap between the wing and fuselage, and the fin and tailplane, is to cut down on leakage drag (see later), the tape can act as a very small radius fillet.

[7]You can sometimes hear kites shedding vortices.

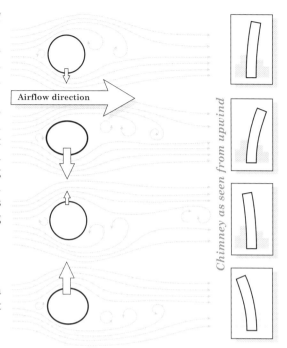

Airflow direction

Chimney as seen from upwind

FIGURE 28 Vortex shedding and resonance

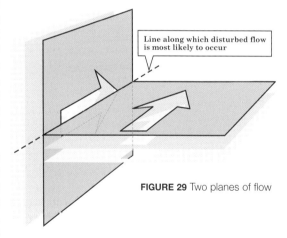

Line along which disturbed flow is most likely to occur

FIGURE 29 Two planes of flow

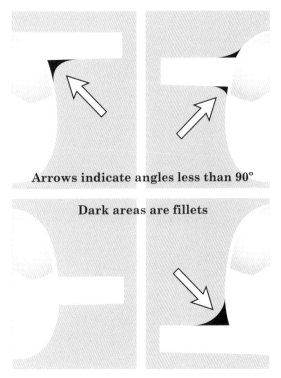

Arrows indicate angles less than 90°

Dark areas are fillets

FIGURE 30 Interference drag

Another solution to the problem of interference drag is to mount the wing above and well clear of the fuselage. This is not a new idea. Some early sailplanes had this feature, though whether it was incorporated to lessen interference drag, or had a more structural function, or both, I have no idea. Placing the wing above the fuselage avoids the need for a large smooth 'join' between components, though there is still the pylon, and it removes, or at least lessens the lift distribution 'blip' (chapter 4, figure 8) which can occur over the fuselage. It also partially sidesteps the awkward question of 'for which speed shall we fillet the wing?'

PARASITE DRAG

Parasite drag is defined as an unwanted effect created by components which makes no useful contribution to lift or aerodynamic efficiency, but which may be needed nonetheless. By this definition a non-retractable wheel, a Total Energy tube, an external radio aerial or a wingtip skid, would be parasitic.

LEAKAGE DRAG

Leakage drag's root cause is differences in pressure, suggesting a link with lift and induced drag, but it can also be seen as a type of interference drag. If the wing/fuselage junction is not properly sealed with tape or foam, then the high(er) pressure air below the wing will flood through the gap into the lower pressure area above, creating turbulence and/or vortices. These increase drag and reduce the lifting efficiency of the wing's inboard section. For gliders, particularly modern ones, leakage drag can be a significant and unwelcome extra. It affects powered aircraft as well, but is a very small percentage of their total drag.

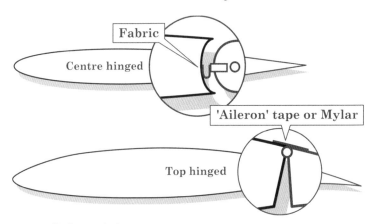

FIGURE 31 Sealing control surface gaps

Leaks will occur anywhere there is a pressure differential and a route available to equalise it. Control hinges, airbrake boxes, the canopy frame, the rear of the fuselage, the undercarriage doors – air will try to squeak past them all. The ailerons are especially likely to suffer this problem and work less well as a result, so they are almost always sealed. How, depends on the type of hinge (figure 31).

All of a modern glider's control surfaces may be sealed, but it would be crazy to tape the canopy to the fuselage or the airbrakes into the wing. An inflatable seal along the canopy's bottom

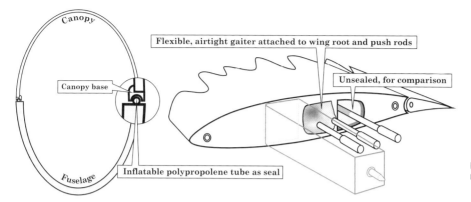

FIGURE 32 Canopy and push-rod sealing

edge can reduce leaks there. Airbrake leaks can be dealt with by having upper surface airbrakes only, and/or airtight gaiters where the actuating rods pass through the root end of the wing into the fuselage (figure 32). Opening the ventilator can create drag by altering the cockpit pressure and either intensifying existing leaks, or providing air with an excuse to find new ones. Despite that, if it comes to a choice between heat stroke or a tiny reduction in the glider's performance, open the ventilator! Besides, the ventilation systems of most modern gliders are designed to have as little effect as possible on the performance.

Profile drag increases as the square of the speed; i.e. by sixteen times if the airspeed is quadrupled (figure 33). Skin friction increases because in a given time a greater volume of air flows over the surface, and form drag increases because of the larger volume of air involved in the pressure and velocity changes. Interference drag may or may not increase, depending on the speed for which the appropriate aerodynamic fix was designed. Leakage drag will certainly increase if the area where the leaks are occurring is subjected to an increasing pressure differential with speed, as is often the case.

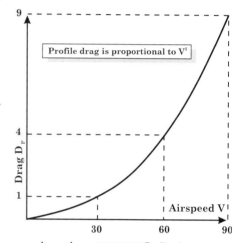

FIGURE 33 Profile drag curve

INDUCED DRAG

At low speeds and high C_Ls (see page 88 for C_L) *induced drag* (also referred to as *vortex drag*) is the major component of the total drag, and produced almost exclusively by the wing. It is a direct result of the wing creating lift, and one cause is the unavoidable difference in pressure between the upper and lower surfaces. Normally, the only place where an equalising flow can occur unhindered is at the tips. The resulting spill affects the chordwise direction of the airflow over the wing's entire span, bending the upper-surface flow in towards the wing root and the under-surface flow out towards the wingtips. This divergence between the two flows becomes more marked the nearer the airflow is to the tips.

What's actually happening is far more complex than the illustrations can show. The flow layers of the upper and lower surfaces are going in slightly different directions relative both to the surface of the wing, and to each other. They are in shear (highly

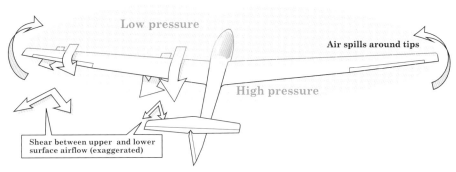

FIGURE 34 Creation of induced drag

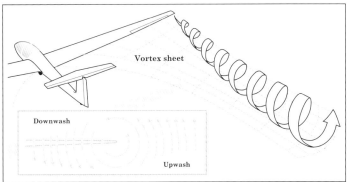

FIGURE 35 Downwash, upwash and the tip vortex

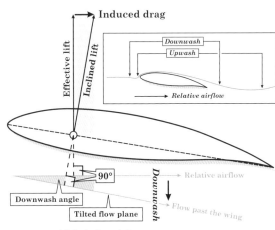

FIGURE 36 High AoA and the effects of downwash

exaggerated in <u>figure 34</u>), and where they meet at the trailing edge they have a tendency – very strong if the shear is marked – to twist round each other; an effect known as *vorticity*.

Though vortices can form anywhere where the upper and lower surface flows meet at an angle, we are not talking about the formation of hundreds of individual *vortices*, so much as a stack of multiple 'sheets' of airflow, each with differing degrees of vorticity, and all of them attempting to roll one into the other. The end result is a pair of trailing vortices where all the vorticity shed across the entire wingspan is finally wrapped up (<u>figure 35</u> – compare with <u>figure 40</u>). A short way behind the glider, only two large counter-rotating swirls of air remain. The tip vortices help pull down the local direction of the airflow in the *downwash* aft of the wing, and there is also some initial downward deflection of the air approaching the wing – see inset <u>figure 36</u>. This alters the direction of the local airflow in such a way that it is as if the entire flow plane (normally parallel to the relative airflow) has been tilted backwards slightly.

As described earlier, the measured or geometric AoA is the angle between the aerofoil chord line and the direction of the relative airflow, but the aerofoil can only ever respond to what it sees as the real flow direction, and in this particular case 'real' means the tilted flow plane. To create a given amount of lift, therefore, the aerofoil has to be more nose up than it would be if the flow plane weren't tilted, so the lift vector acts backwards, adding to the drag (<u>figure 36</u>). The effect is tiny at high speeds and low AoAs, but becomes stronger with increasing AoA until just beyond the stall.

<u>Figure 37</u> illustrates how induced drag alters with airspeed. Unlike profile drag, induced drag follows an inverse square law ($1/V^2$), so that if the speed increases by three times, say, induced drag will reduce by nine times ($1/(3\times3)$).

Circulation Theory

It's tempting to avoid describing circulation theory because, as you no doubt realised many pages back, almost anything to do with how fluid's behave (fluid dynamics) seems to equal 'incredibly complicated'. However, as well as offering one description of how an aerofoil works, circulation theory also provides another take on induced drag, so here goes. (If you're already feeling a bit faint, take it as read that aerofoils work, and skip to 'More about vortices' on page 79).

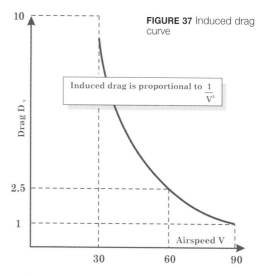

FIGURE 37 Induced drag curve

Induced drag is proportional to $\frac{1}{V^2}$

THE MAGNUS EFFECT

When an airstream flows across a rotating cylinder it produces a force at right angles to the cylinder's rotational axis (figure 38 ②). The circulation induced by its rotation (clockwise from our point of view) bends, or rather pulls the flow stream up at the front and pushes it down at the back. At the same time the flow velocity over the upper section increases and the pressure falls, while that below decreases and the pressure rises i.e. standard BP. The resulting nett force – which can also be explained in NL terms – is the one that causes a ball hit with spin, for example, to swerve in flight. Newton noted the phenomenon in 1672, but it is now known by the name of the German professor, Magnus, who studied it in 1853.

CIRCULATION THEORY AND THE BOUND VORTEX

In 1892 one of the earliest aerodynamic theorists, Frederick Lanchester, realised that aerofoils must generate a circulation similar to the Magnus effect, and that insight forms the basis of aerofoil theory to this day. For reasons already mentioned, the *perfect fluid flow* theory of Lanchester's time couldn't explain the Magnus effect. Figure 38 ① shows a perfect fluid flow around a cylinder where there is neither skin friction nor viscosity. Fatally for the theory, even if the cylinder were rotating the fluid flow pattern in ① wouldn't alter one whit, and there would be no nett force. All the physical evidence says there is. ② shows the same cylinder rotating with skin friction and viscosity added, which gives exactly the results described in the previous paragraph, i.e. a nett up force.

The degree to which the flow stream is influenced depends on the cylinder's speed of rotation; more equals more! While aerofoils don't rotate, it can be shown that there is an equivalent circular flow pattern around them (figure 38 ②) whose rate of 'rotation' relates to the airspeed. 'Circular flow pattern' does not mean, as the circle in ② seems to suggest, that individual air molecules travel all the way round the aerofoil to end up where they started and then presumably begin the whole cycle all over again, which sounds like perpetual motion. Instead, the velocity and pressure vectors – or energics, if you prefer – at a multitude of points around the aerofoil and in relation to the free stream velocity and pressure, trace out a notionally circular pattern, which is usually referred to as the *bound vortex;* 'bound' as in closed, and

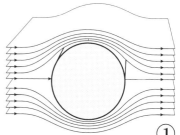

Perfect fluid flow with no circulation ①

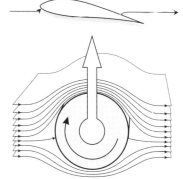

Perfect fluid flow with circulation added ②

FIGURE 38 The Magnus Effect

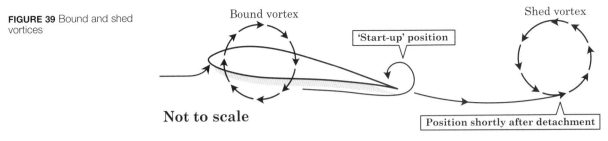

FIGURE 39 Bound and shed vortices

Bound vortex

Shed vortex

'Start-up' position

Not to scale

Position shortly after detachment

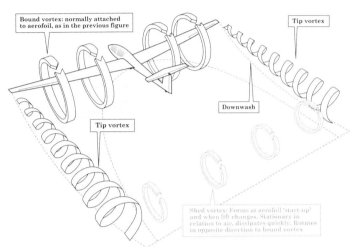

Bound vortex: normally attached to aerofoil, as in the previous figure

Tip vortex

Downwash

Tip vortex

Shed vortex: Forms at aerofoil 'start-up' and when lift changes. Stationary in relation to air, dissipates quickly. Rotates in opposite direction to bound vortex

FIGURE 40 Various vortices

created by and acting on the same aerofoil. You can think of the bound vortex as an elastic band which is wound up by differences in velocity and pressure, or momentum, between the upper and lower flow streams, and whose resulting lopsided energy distribution is what creates the nett up force, or lift (see *Vector sums*, Appendix A).

Prandtl also discovered the existence of the *shed vortex* which forms briefly when airflow begins moving over an aerofoil, or when there is any change in lift which recreates the start-up conditions; i.e where the undersurface flow is able to curl up round the trailing edge (figure 39). Even in a wind tunnel equipped with smoke streamers you can't really see the bound vortex, although you could infer its existence from the velocity differences between upper and lower surface flows. By contrast, the shed vortex can be seen, and if you're quick you can wave goodbye to it too. When the tunnel starts up this vortex forms at the trailing edge and is then carried away by the airflow. In the outside world this means that an aircraft leaves it behind, stationary in the airmass.

If we think of an aerofoil as being inside an 'energy box' rather like the earlier K parcel with its P and V, and where every plus had a balancing minus, then the shed vortex can be seen as the place where the bound vortex 'unwinds'. Mathematically speaking, the shed vortex could be a thousand miles from the aircraft that created it and still be balancing things out, but more realistically the aircraft has to continually wind up the bound vortex elastic to create lift, and so there's always a related energy 'unwind' somewhere. What initially went into the shed vortex is actually spilt outwards along the bound vortex

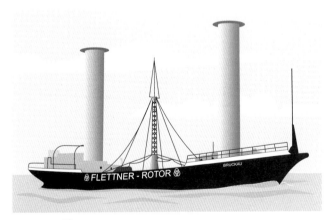

FIGURE 41 Flettner Rotorship

and round the wingtips to become, in this explanation at least, the tip vortices. The resultant shape (figure 40) is sometimes called the horseshoe vortex model.

An early example of an unusual utilisation of the Magnus Effect was the Flettner Rotorship (figure 41), the Bruckau, later renamed and better known as the Baden

Baden. Sails were replaced by two cylinders 50ft high and 9ft in diameter, and spun by 45hp electric motors. The ship crossed the Atlantic in 1926, and survived until 1931, when it sank during a tropical storm in the Caribbean. The rotorship idea never really caught on because the propulsive force generated was less than it would have been had the motors been used to drive a standard ship's propeller and, though probably more efficient area for area than sail, it had a fraction of full sail's area. You do occasionally see other direct applications of it, and some several years ago an 'aeroplane' kite with rotating wings, similar to the one in figure 42, was exactly what every boy wanted for Christmas. Even though the wings had an 'S' shaped profile rather than a cylindrical one, and needed 'flip-starting', they rotated in the airflow and utilised the Magnus Effect to provide lift.

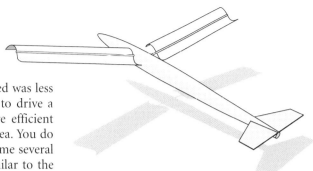

FIGURE 42 Rotating wing kite – circa 1955

SO TELL ME AGAIN, HOW DO AEROFOILS WORK?

The exact relationship between BP and NL is best demonstrated by a simple experiment often used to support BP. Since it can also be used to demonstrate NL, all it really tells us is that something slightly odd happens. See for yourself. Cut a piece of paper in two, and bend each piece as in figure 43. Holding the two fairly close together, as illustrated, blow through the gap. Instead of flying apart they move together. Three of the most likely explanations are: 1) the pressure between the pieces of paper drops and it is the higher atmospheric pressure on the outside of each which pushes them together; 2) the airflow is diverted and the reaction to this pulls (as opposed to pushes) the two together; 3) it's both!

So there's a problem? Not really. In terms of aerofoils the air mass is diverted, the pressure and velocity changes occur, weird stuff happens and the result is a nett up force. There is nothing static about the processes involved; they're not like the tension in a wire. Lift generation is entirely time/mass flow (momentum) dependent. That is to say – picking a figure at random – it involves displacing and replacing one cubic hundredweight (ton, kilogram etc) of air around the aerofoil by another, and another, because if you stop effectively replacing this mass by simply moving through it, you lose every force that's keeping you airborne. For conventional aircraft at least, airspeed is lift. For their pilots it is life.

MORE ABOUT VORTICES (WAKE TURBULENCE)

Glider vortices are normally neither intense nor, as a result, very persistent, unlike those trailing behind aircraft which are large, heavy, 'clean' (all lift enhancing devices retracted), and slow. The rotational velocity in the cores of their trailing vortices can easily exceed 100kt, and because they literally wrap up very large amounts of energy, they can take a while to disperse, particularly if the air is still or the wind light. They can be dangerous, flipping smaller

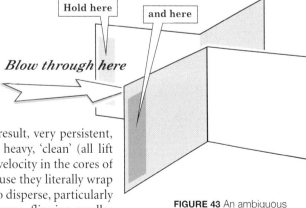

Hold here

and here

Blow through here

FIGURE 43 An ambiguous demonstration

Forecaster Lewis Richardson
writing in 1922 about the
weather:
Big whirls have little whirls
that feed on their velocity,
And little whirls have lesser
whirls and so on to viscosity –
in the molecular sense.

aircraft, gliders included, upside down, or otherwise flinging them about and causing loss of control. Slightly less energetic vortices form when large aircraft are in the landing configuration, and if you're standing in the right place and conditions are suitable, you may hear the sharp whooshing noise (like sand being tipped out of a lorry) that they make as the aircraft flares to land. On a day with light or no wind, these vortices can roll past you on the ground – they hiss! Clear of the ground, the energy within a vortex is gradually diluted out over a larger and larger area by viscosity, until it is indistinguishable from its surroundings.

In still air a looping glider can fly through its own feeble version of wake turbulence. As it pulls out at the bottom there may be a brief bump and an often sharply audible thump[8]. You are more likely to hit this wake if you pulled rather a lot of G (i.e. high induced drag = strong vortices, relatively speaking) during the entry, and the loop should be as close to the vertical plane as possible, otherwise you miss.

ENERGY LOSSES IN THE DOWNWASH

The energy lost in a glider's downwash is not large in absolute terms, particularly if the glider is in unaccelerated flight (G=1) and the AoA is also small. Any manoeuvre which increases the AoA will also increase the induced drag, and additional energy is then spilt into the tip vortices. Given that the total drag for a high performance glider flying at best L/D (see chapter 8, p. 229) can be as little as 15lb or so (about 1.5% of the AUW), an extra pound or three can make a perceptible dent in its performance[9].

Reducing induced drag

Induced drag is a direct result of creating lift and probably unavoidable, but there are teasing hints that we can rid ourselves of substantial amounts. If a test wing section butts up against the walls of a wind tunnel so that there are effectively no wingtips, the induced drag is zero, though vortex shedding from the trailing edge of a section can still create lift related drag. To lessen induced drag, we could:

(1)   make a wing with infinite span

(2)   put an end-plate on the tip to simulate the wind tunnel wall

(3)   create an annular or hooped wing, which doesn't have any tips.

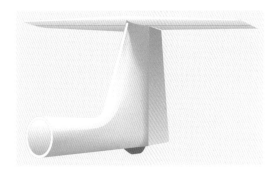

FIGURE 44 T tail

[8]ASK13s are good here because the taut fabric is like a drum, and the fuselage and wings act as gramophone horns, magnifying the sound.
[9]The minimum drag level of a glider with an AUW of 700lbs and a best L/D of 45:1 is 15.5lbs. Adding 1lb of drag reduces the L/D to 42.4:1, and 3lbs reduces it by 16% to 37.8:1. At normal flying speeds 3lbs is the equivalent of putting your hand out of the DV panel to divert air to cool yourself.

① is physically impossible, but alternative ② seems to offer a cheap and easily engineered solution. Unfortunately, early research into endplates showed that to have a significant effect they needed to be very large, and any consequent reduction in induced drag was then more than made up for by increases in other forms of drag. All the flying surfaces create induced drag, and though you won't see endplates as such on wingtips, the T tail (figure 44) acts as one for the fin and rudder, which create induced drag when counteracting the effects of adverse yaw. However, the chief reason for a T tail is to keep the tailplane out of the wing downwash, allowing its area to be reduced – less form drag – without compromising its effect on stability (see chapter 6). A helpful non-aerodynamic benefit is that if you land out in long grass or a crop, the tailplane doesn't get smashed to pieces, as often happens to low set tailplanes. It doesn't stop you from ground-looping in the same field, of course, but the repair bill *might* be slightly less.

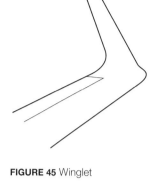

FIGURE 45 Winglet

Nowadays just about every new glider sprouts angled tips in the form of *winglets* (figure 45). Winglets are not endplates and do not block circulation round the tip. They aren't designed to produce extra lift, but to reduce the intensity of the tip vortices. The result can be a 4% reduction in induced drag, plus beneficial effects on handling and low speed performance. At mid to high speeds they create additional profile drag, and the performance of a glider with winglets will be slightly worse at speed than a similar glider without them. Winglets increase the wing bending loads, and can make flutter more likely.

There would be no point in the annular wing option (figure 46) because, complicated construction aside, the span may be theoretically infinite but the effective span is small, and a significant percentage of the wing is either doing very little or nothing in the way of generating lift.

ASPECT RATIO

The ratio of span to chord is termed the *Aspect Ratio*. If the wing area remains constant then the greater the span, the narrower the chord, and the higher the aspect ratio. For a simple rectangular planform wing the aspect ratio is calculated by dividing the span by the chord. Since the planform of the majority of glider wings is more complex than a rectangle, aspect ratio is calculated instead by dividing span squared by the wing area. Common aspect ratios are 23:1 for a 15m glider with a wing area of 10m², and 32:1 for an Open Class

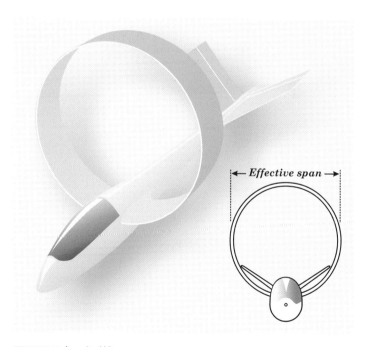

FIGURE 46 Annular Wing

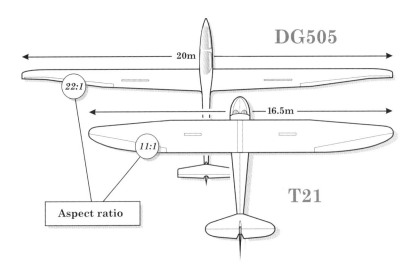

FIGURE 47 Aspect Ratio

glider with a wing area of 18m². <u>Figure 47</u> compares a T21 (circa 1950) with a DG505 (circa 1996). High aspect ratio wings are nothing new. Gliders from the 1920s and 30s such as the Meise (built under licence in the UK as the Olympia 2) and the one-off and gigantic Austria (span 30m), had high aspect ratio wings.

High aspect ratio helps us go some way towards making the impossible alternative ①. Using long span narrow chord wings (high aspect ratio) reduces the strength of the trailing vortices and the resultant downwash is reduced, as is the induced drag.

If the wing area is kept constant, doubling the span reduces the chord and cuts the *induced drag coefficient* (see chapter summary) by three quarters. In plain English, long narrow wings are more efficient than short fat ones!

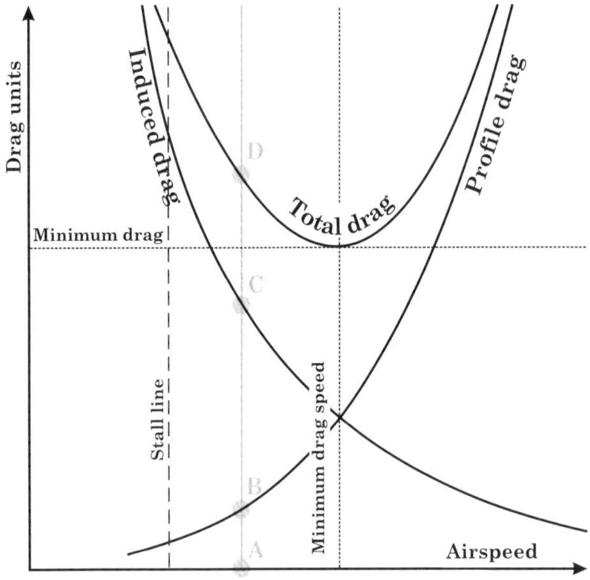

TOTAL DRAG

The *total drag* is the sum of induced and profile drag (<u>figure 48</u>). Placing both on a graph and then adding together the amount of drag from A to B (profile) on the grey line, and A to C (induced), gives a total drag point at D. By adding up the induced and profile drag values at various points on the airspeed axis it can be seen from the resulting curve that the total drag is least where the induced and profile drag curves cross. The associated speed is known, straightforwardly enough, as the *minimum drag speed*, and this is the speed at which the glider must be flown for best L/D through the airmass – mentioned earlier, but described in more detail in chapter 8. It is assumed

FIGURE 48 Total drag (profile + induced)

that the individual graphs for induced and profile drag represent values for the entire airframe, and not just for the wings.

Figure 49 breaks down the total drag of an ASW27 into the relative contribution made by each major airframe component. Note how much the wing makes throughout the entire speed range.

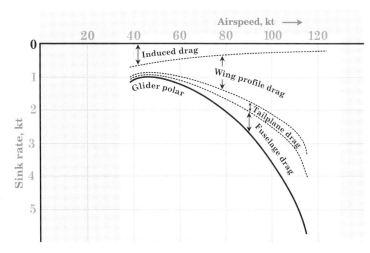

FIGURE 49 Component drag

Bubble trouble

By careful design, laminar flow aerofoils delay the transition to turbulent flow for much longer than non-laminar aerofoils, but it seems impossible to maintain laminar flow right up to the trailing edge. Low drag levels are highly desirable, but laminar flow aerofoils have an unexpected and energy sapping drawback; even on a super smooth and clean wing, the flow stream can kick completely free of the section (*laminar flow separation*), and will do so far more readily than a layer of turbulence (figure 50)[10]. This has to do with the shear stresses in the boundary layer, but instead of the various flow layers nose-diving into each other, as they do at the transition point, a huge rip occurs along the flow line, effectively destroying the energy transfer mechanism.

Despite that, detached laminar flow has a trick up its sleeve which turbulent flow can't match; it's able to reattach itself to the aerofoil further downstream. The reason why has something to do with the two flows' relative degrees of disorder. To take a slightly bizarre analogy, turbulent flow is like squabbling cats, and any forces trying to herd them back to the surface simply don't work. Laminar flow has a more coherent, indeed a more sheeplike organisation, so 'herding' is more likely to be successful.

The area skipped over by a separated laminar flow is known as a *separation bubble*. These bubbles can form almost anywhere on an aerofoil, but modern ones seem particularly prone to having them form at the point where the under-surface curvature of the aerofoil reverses. The air within such a bubble may be stagnant, or have an

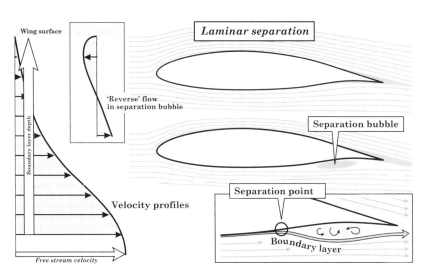

FIGURE 50 Separation bubble, lower surface

[10]There is a suspicion that a surface that is too smooth may make laminar separation more likely.

internal flow pattern circulating independently of the main airflow, rather like a river backwater. At the aerofoil surface the local airflow within a bubble can travel towards the wing's leading edge. In terms of lift creation, the affected part of the wing might as well have vanished, but drag increases. Additionally, reverse flow helps create a self-perpetuating jump-off point for the laminar flow stream. Because control surfaces work best if the air flow is (a) smooth, (b) moving at a suitable speed towards the trailing edge, parallel to the surface, and (c) crossing the hinge-line at right angles, separation bubbles that form on or near them can interfere with their effectiveness. Usually the ailerons are worst affected.

In normal conditions and at modest AoAs, an aerofoil such as the DU89-134/14 (see figure 61 (10)), can maintain lower surface laminar flow to 95% of the chord, and to about 65% on the upper surface. The drag levels of these aerofoils tend to be so low that even a numerically small increase can have a significant effect, and laminar separation does just that. There is always some point on an aerofoil where smooth flow becomes turbulent, and at about the same point laminar flow is also most likely to 'tear off'. A separated laminar flow stream can continue on above a turbulent one with little or no effect on the airstream below, but the important thing to avoid is a bubble whose internal flow is either stagnant or going against the general airflow direction, and which sits on the aerofoil's surface.

DEALING WITH SEPARATION

Turbulent flow may not be ⓐ that desirable, but it creates far less drag than a separation bubble, ⓑ it can separate at very high AoAs, but usually clings to the aerofoil surface with more tenacity than laminar flow and, unlike laminar flow, can actually make it to the trailing edge, ⓒ beyond the transition point it is unavoidable. To prevent an associated laminar separation bubble forming at about the same point, turbulent flow is often deliberately induced by discretely roughing up, or *turbulating*, the boundary layer just upstream of it. The process is referred to as *re-energising* the boundary layer, though 'making sure it's still there' would be another way of putting it.

There are a number of ingenious ways to either trigger turbulent flow or delay its appearance. *Turbulator tape* (usually the zigzag sort), can be stuck spanwise onto the wing just prior to the transition point (figure 51 (C)). On modern gliders the turbulator tape is often added upstream of most, if not all the control surfaces, rudder included. Alternatively, high pressure air may be blown through a spanwise line of small holes just prior to the transition point (A) to kick a bit more energy into the lower levels of the boundary layer. These same holes may be linked instead to a

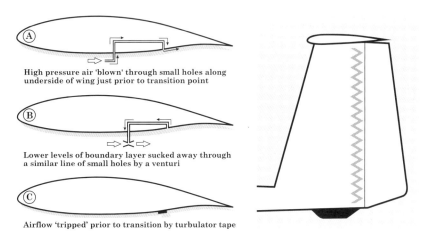

High pressure air 'blown' through small holes along underside of wing just prior to transition point

Lower levels of boundary layer sucked away through a similar line of small holes by a venturi

Airflow 'tripped' prior to transition by turbulator tape

FIGURE 51 Ways to delay separation

small venturi (another use for this apparently useless bit of equipment) which acts as a suction pump (B) to remove the sluggish lower levels of the boundary layer and help shift the transition point a bit further downstream. As with all subtle aerodynamic devices, put them in the wrong place and the glider's performance can get worse.

Looking at where lift acts

Where lift acts is crucial to aircraft stability and is discussed more fully in chapter 6. Here we'll look in detail at two ways in which the behaviour of the main forces on a wing can be described; (1) by means of the Centre of Pressure, and (2) by the Aerodynamic Centre (AC) concepts. Both are derived from the same data, and despite initial appearances, they do not contradict each other. One might well ask whether either is correct, but a better question would be 'how do they compare for usefulness?' What is their practical value? We'll look at the CP concept first because it is by far the older of the two and was originally applied to sailing ships.

THE CENTRE OF PRESSURE (CP)

When the airflow speed and/or the AoA change, so too does the pressure distribution and the relative proportions of lift provided by the upper and lower surfaces (figure 52). For the majority of aerofoils the point through which the pressure forces can be said to act (their resolution into the CP vector) moves towards the aerofoil's leading edge as the AoA increases, and towards the trailing edge as it decreases.

CP PROBLEMS

Because aircraft stability relies on the relationship between aerodynamic forces and those of weight and mass (see chapter 6), it is very helpful to aeronautical engineers (and indirectly to you) if the relevant calculations are as straightforward as possible. The main objections to the CP concept are practical ones. Chief among these is that because forces and loads alter continually during flight, calculating whether what then happens is safe or not would be a lot simpler if they acted through fixed points. Unfortunately, when the AoA or the speed alters, the CP of the majority of sections responds by shifting its position and changing in strength. It is possible to work out pitch stability parameters using the CP, but the process is needlessly complicated. CP movement also involves some physical

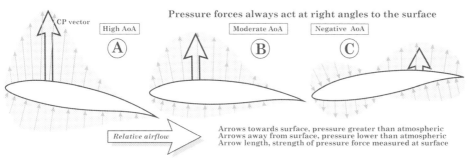

FIGURE 52 Pressure changes and CP position

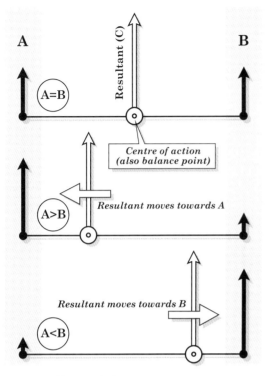

FIGURE 53 Movement of a resultant

anomalies. It would appear, for example, that in a vertical dive (not likely to bother most glider pilots) or during a transient passage through zero lift, such as a push-over to negative G, that the CP whistles off to infinity behind the wing and then reappears instantly at infinity ahead of it. You'll be happy to hear that while mathematically correct, this physically impossible trick has no effect whatsoever on flight behaviour.

Handy though the CP concept is, by 1920 it was very clear that it lacked something. Before discussing what superceded it, have a think about the following; we have a long bar, at each end of which are upward acting forces, A and B (figure 53). These two forces are equal initially, so their resultant – which is also their balance point – will be located midway between them, and be of strength A+B. If either A or B increase, the resultant will move towards the stronger force. Something very similar explains why the CP moves around.

The aerodynamic centre (AC)

SYMMETRICAL AEROFOILS

Early theorists had predicted that the position of the CP on a symmetrical aerofoil would, in normal circumstances (i.e. when not close to the stall), remain fixed, or nearly so. It was also realised that since a symmetrical aerofoil had no *camber* (see figure 54), the creation of useful lift (taking 'useful' to mean a nett upward component) would have to be due almost entirely to AoA changes.

The first thing to say about a symmetrical aerofoil is that at a zero AoA it produces no useful lift, which isn't the same thing as saying that its not working (figure 55). It is working perfectly well, but the top and bottom surfaces are producing identical amounts of 'lift' in opposite directions and neatly cancelling each other out – another example of a vector sum, but a very simple one.

At a small positive AoA the symmetrical aerofoil starts to generate useful lift. In this instance the lower vector isn't quite as strong as the upper one, so there is a very modest nett up component. At some stage, if the AoA continues to increase, the lower surface lift vector, previously acting downwards, becomes, first zero, and then upward, now adding to the upper surface lift vector, rather than not being strong enough to cancel it out!

Significantly, and providing the symmetrical aerofoil is not at or near the stall, the lift's centre of action stays within one to two percent of the total chord from the quarter chord 25 per cent point. For a wing with an average chord of 3ft, the variation is less than an inch. Within an 'everyday'

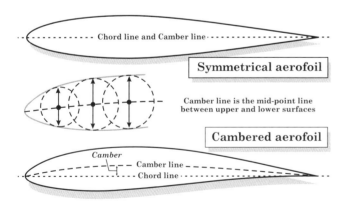

FIGURE 54 Symmetrical and cambered aerofoils

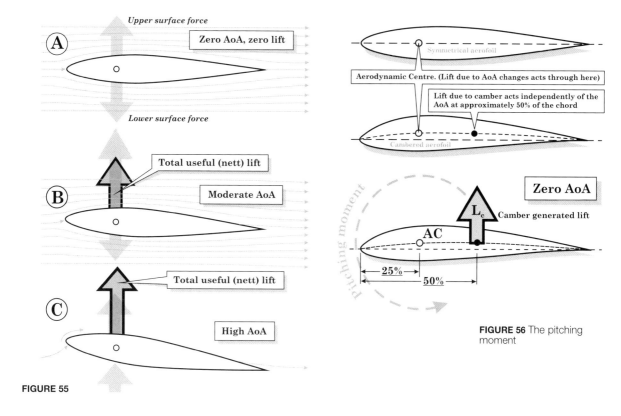

FIGURE 55

FIGURE 56 The pitching moment

CAMBER AND LIFT. NON SYMMETRICAL AEROFOILS

working range of AoAs this point, known as the *aerodynamic centre* (or AC), is treated as if it were fixed. This makes stability and balance calculations for aircraft with symmetrical aerofoils much simpler, but the overwhelming majority of gliders have cambered aerofoils, and for them the situation is slightly less straightforward.

CAMBER AND LIFT. NON SYMMETRICAL AEROFOILS

Symmetrical aerofoils work equally well either way up and are ideal for aerobatic aircraft, but is an aerofoil which appears to spend a great deal of time working against itself really that efficient, and what's the point in having an aerofoil work well upside down if the aircraft, a sailplane designed for cross-country flying, will be spending 99.99% to 100% of its life the other way up? Are there any advantages to be gained from having a non-symmetrical aerofoil?

Answers are respectively, none and yes! If we place a symmetrical aerofoil into an airflow at zero geometric AoA, keep that constant, and add camber by gradually pulling the aerofoil out of shape, upwards – see the cambered aerofoil in <u>figure 54</u> – it will begin generating useful lift, and tend to pitch nose down, an effect referred to as the *pitching moment* (<u>figure 56</u>). Up to a point, lift and the pitching moment increase along with the *camber*. This suggests strongly that the pitching moment is due to the camber generated component of lift acting somewhere aft of the AC. Its point of action is related to the maximum camber point, which varies from section to section, but for many glider

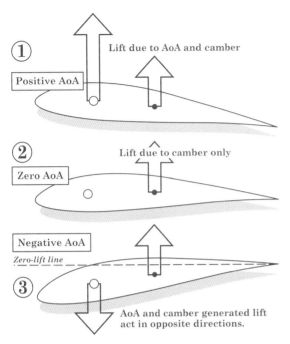

① Positive AoA

Lift due to AoA and camber

② Zero AoA

Lift due to camber only

Negative AoA

Zero-lift line

③

AoA and camber generated lift act in opposite directions.

FIGURE 57 Zero lift case for cambered aerofoil

aerofoils is near 50% of the chord. Like the AC this point can be treated as fixed. One result is that for normally cambered aerofoils the nose-down pitching moment varies with speed and not AoA. The problem with using the CP concept here is that because the CP is a resultant – the sum of AoA and camber generated lift components (see figure 53), any changes to either start it off on its nomadic wanderings.

ZERO LIFT LINE AND ZERO LIFT PITCHING MOMENT

Cambered or not, every aerofoil has one specific AoA at which it produces no useful lift – in effect, no lift. The *zero lift line* – also known as the *aerodynamic chord line* – is the horizontal line drawn from the trailing edge forwards, of an aerofoil developing no nett lift. For a symmetrical aerofoil the 'no lift' AoA is 0°, so the zero lift line is also the chord line. The equivalent AoA for a cambered aerofoil is negative.

To see why, take a cambered aerofoil and assume that the airspeed is constant and the aerofoil nowhere near the stall. At a positive AoA, both AoA and camber generate useful lift (figure 57 ①). At 0° AoA ②, AoA generated lift is also zero, but the camber generated component is still there. At a negative AoA ③, AoA generated lift acts downwards, but the camber generated component continues to act upwards. The moment at the AC is the same in all these cases, but at one AoA specific to the section, the two components will act with equal force in opposite directions and cancel each other out i.e. zero lift overall. They aren't acting through the same point, so the pitching moment is still there – hence the phrase, the *zero lift pitching moment*.

TOTAL LIFT

As a matter of convenience the camber and AoA generated components of lift are both thought of as acting through the AC. This bit of housework doesn't get rid of the pitching moment, which still acts about the AC, is proportional to the speed squared, and is always a force of considerable aerodynamic and structural significance.

Lift coefficients

One very useful extension of Euler's BP based formula is $L = C_L \frac{1}{2} \rho V^2 S$. The added terms are S, for the wing area, and C_L, which is the *lift coefficient*. Chambers Twentieth Century Dictionary defines a *coefficient* as, among other things, *that which acts together with another thing*. A number of factors have to be taken into account when judging how effectively a component like the wing is creating lift. For an aerofoil, C_L is a convenient 'chuck it all in the same basket' measurement of the relationship between camber and AoA generated lift.

Without mentioning speed (or velocity), figure 58 compares the C_Ls of a cambered and a symmetrical aerofoil over a range of AoAs. Of note is the parallel relationship between the two, particularly the negative AoA of the cambered aerofoil at $C_L=0.0$. Given the previous discussion of the zero lift line, this is exactly what you'd expect. The higher C_L of the cambered aerofoil at all AoAs shows its greater efficiency in terms of creating useful lift.

LESS OF ONE, MORE OF THE OTHER

The formula is revealing. Let's say a powered aircraft is in steady level flight (genuine steady and level flight isn't possible in a glider – see chapter 4). One basic requirement is that L stays constant. For non-mathematicians (which is most of us), changing any term in the $C_L\frac{1}{2}_pV^2S$ group will also change L. For example, if L=12 and we alter V, then L might become 10, or 23, or anything. To change V and at the same time keep L=12, we have to change another term in the group. The practical result is that if the pilot maintains the aircraft's attitude and simply opens the throttle, V increases and so, inevitably, does L, and the aircraft begins to climb. To fly faster, maintain height and keep the same value of L as the aircraft accelerates, the pilot has to progressively lower the nose to reduce the C_L – in this case the AoA component. Equally, if flaps were down and the pilot retracted them, the C_L's AoA component would increase as the aircraft started to sink, and to maintain height the pilot would have to increase either V, or at least the AoA, which might not be possible. For example, V is at its lowest and C_L at its highest at the unaccelerated stall (see chapter 7) and just prior to touchdown in a fully held off landing (figure 59); retracting the flaps during the hold-off would result in an 'arrival'. The C_L can't be increased because the aircraft's already on the point of stalling, and there's no time to speed up. For a glider, there's also no height available in which to increase the speed. Not much can be done about this except not retract the flaps in the first place.

Time isn't something which the formula really takes into account, except implicitly through V. Say that the aircraft is sinking a bit too quickly just prior to touchdown. For the pilot of a propeller aircraft, a burst of power to sluice extra slipstream over the wing creates some additional lift, but there's no instant response from either the engine or the wing. A glider pilot would close the airbrakes, but even here there would be a short delay before the sink rate reduced. Because V is a squared term in the formula, altering it makes a big difference. Even so, accelerating takes time, or huge amounts of energy if it is to be rapid. By comparison AoA changes are almost instantaneous. Altering the AoA (C_L) gets quicker results than altering the speed (V), but swift and even quite small positive AoA changes at low values of V and high C_Ls can stall the aircraft, whereas swift negative changes can

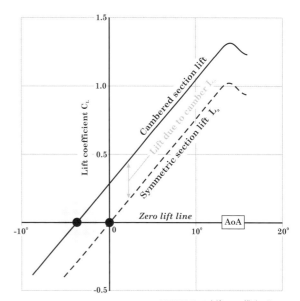

FIGURE 58 Lift coefficients

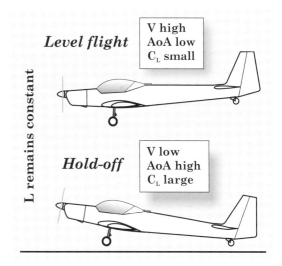

FIGURE 59 V, C_L and AoA

FIGURE 60 Pressure coefficient profile comparison

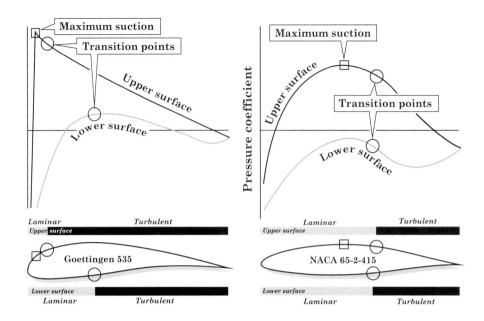

leave everything else lagging far behind[11]. For example, if you lower the nose of a glider fairly abruptly and then maintain a constant attitude, the AoA will change almost immediately and will continue doing so, only settling to a constant value when V catches up, as it were, to match the attitude (see chapter 4 p. 106 [flight sag]).

Changes in air density (ρ) can have slightly strange consequences, and one of the less benign is described in chapter 5, pp. 161–3.

Other things

NON-LAMINAR AEROFOILS

This chapter has probably given the impression that there are only laminar aerofoils but the very earliest aerofoils, and all those used by gliders until the early 1950's, or thereabouts, were non-laminar. Non-laminar doesn't mean no laminar flow, only that the chord depth over which it can be maintained is a great deal less than for a section specifically designed to be laminar. The transition points for earlier aerofoils were much further forward and the turbulent flow more extensive, so the overall drag levels were higher.

The Goettingen 535 section in figure 60, for example, was developed to produce high lift and low drag at low speeds, suiting it admirably to slope soaring and duration flights. The NACA section with which it is compared was designed to produce less drag and provide

---

[11]'Slow' acceleration is sometimes attributed to so-called ASI lag. In pressure instruments, unlike those where through-flow is required – such as variometers – pressure changes propagate at the local speed of sound. The narrow bore of the connecting tubes, as well as the response of the ASI diaphragm, may create some lag but the rate of almost every other change, including 1G acceleration, is glacial by comparison. 'Slow' acceleration really is slow!

better high speed performance. As the figure shows, at similar AoAs there are some dramatic differences between them, both in the proportions of laminar and turbulent flow and the chord-wise position of maximum flow velocity; likewise the transition points.

THE CHANGING SCENE

Aerofoils have gradually evolved as aerodynamicists and designers have laboured to improve L/D ratios, and usually their creations have worked as they were supposed to, but occasionally not. Whole families of aerofoils have been developed to meet specific requirements because, convenient though it would be, we can't yet create a fixed shape aerofoil which works optimally across the entire range of performance of which aircraft are now capable. Sections (7), (9) and (10) (figure 61), were designed specifically for gliders. The flapped DU89-134/14 (10) was optimised for the wider speed range needed to make both the best use of lift at low speeds when thermalling, say, and better glide ratios at higher speeds – two requirements which aren't exactly compatible. What is most noticeable about the newer aerofoils is how far back the point of maximum camber has moved.

Design and theoretical advances are all very well, but not a lot of use if you can't build to a standard accurate enough to take advantage of them. Without new and better materials and constructional techniques we wouldn't be enjoying the benefits of the latest sections and their greater degree of laminar flow. It was, and remains difficult to make wood and fabric structures smooth enough and with sufficient long-term stability – in terms of any lumps and bumps that might develop over time – to take full advantage of laminar sections, though many wooden gliders do have them. Unfortunately, as wood dries out the underlying structure starts to become visible – the so-called 'starved horse' look. The aerodynamic shape isn't now quite as svelte as the designer envisaged, and the almost invariable result is poorer performance, though not always by much. Metal isn't that ideal either. Corrosion roughens the surface, and any dents change the section and, in that area at least, undo the advantages of having a laminar flow aerofoil. This is not to say that metal aircraft with laminar sections are either that rare or new. The North American Mustang fighter of 1942 was one of the first (figure 62, see over)[12].

The new material which allowed further improvements in glider performance (something which at one time seemed doubtful) is Glass Reinforced Plastic or GRP. Unlike wood, GRP keeps its shape extremely well and is very easy to keep smooth and clean. The use of moulds which effectively build gliders from the outside inwards, rather than the more traditional inside outwards approach, make it possible to manufacture very accurately profiled shapes; important, because very small changes to the section

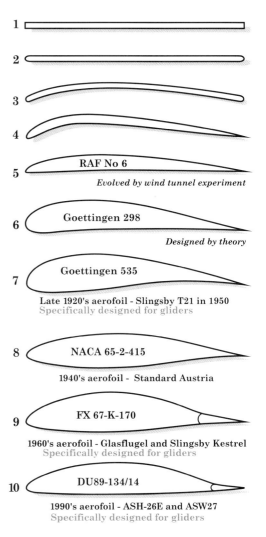

1

2

3

4

5 **RAF No 6**
Evolved by wind tunnel experiment

6 **Goettingen 298**
Designed by theory

7 **Goettingen 535**
Late 1920's aerofoil - Slingsby T21 in 1950
Specifically designed for gliders

8 **NACA 65-2-415**
1940's aerofoil - Standard Austria

9 **FX 67-K-170**
1960's aerofoil - Glasflugel and Slingsby Kestrel
Specifically designed for gliders

10 **DU89-134/14**
1990's aerofoil - ASH-26E and ASW27
Specifically designed for gliders

FIGURE 61 Aerofoil evolution

---

[12]It's arguable whether the laminar flow aerofoil or the ram-jet-like heat exchanger in the cooling duct under the fuselage did most to give the Mustang its performance edge. Smart money's not on the aerofoil.

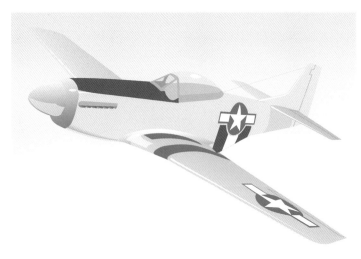

FIGURE 62 North American
P51D

coordinates of a laminar flow aerofoil can have disproportionately large and usually deleterious effects on its efficiency. Shapes once difficult to construct to the required degree of accuracy in wood or metal, are relatively easy in GRP, but if in practice laminar aerofoils made with the earlier materials had their problems, some of their GRP relatives have been the victims of their own excellence.

BUGS AND OTHER BOTHERS

Anything which is optimised is exactly that. It will work well within a defined set of conditions, and not very well (maybe not at all) anywhere else. All aerofoils are affected to some degree by biological bugs, dirt, dust or rain on their surfaces – particularly anything on or near the leading edge – but a few of the earliest GRP laminar flow sections responded to such foreign objects by becoming absurdly over-priced imitations of flat-plates. Aerofoil designers have woken up to the reality of nature's general non-optimisation (in terms of human definitions of 'optimisation' anyhow) and now create aerofoils that are relatively bug/nasty tolerant.

At its outset the boundary layer is very thin, and it doesn't take much to disrupt it. Normally, no matter how messy the flow becomes, you can't see it, but if condensation forms on a wing, premature transition and boundary layer disturbances can become visible. Bugs squashed on or near to the leading edge can be seen acting as trigger points for a series of V shaped wakes that spread back over the wing (figure 63). Rather surprisingly, model aircraft can sometimes gain considerable advantage from airflow disturbed at the leading edge in this way, but not their full size cousins. That's not to suggest that turbulent flow can't be useful, if only, as we've seen, to prevent something worse.

As part of the experimental environment, wind-tunnel airflow is usually smoothed before it reaches a test aerofoil. This has the same kind of tidying effect on the results as putting a bib on a small child to stop it splattering itself with food. Real air, so to speak, is often awash with small scale turbulence, particularly when conditions are thermic, and the effect on an aerofoil's efficiency can be similar to that of bugs – though to a less disruptive and far more random degree – simply because some of the air arriving at the wing is already turbulent and aerofoils don't smooth it out. Given such conditions, some sections work less well than others.

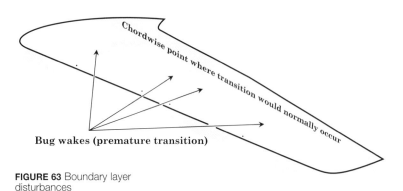

Chordwise point where transition would normally occur

Bug wakes (premature transition)

FIGURE 63 Boundary layer disturbances

Summary of chapter three

Page	Subject	
71	**Adverse pressure gradient**	where pressure is rising and returning to atmospheric. A trigger for turbulent flow.
86	**Aerodynamic Centre (AC)**	located at approximately the quarter chord. Point through which AoA-generated lift (and drag) are assumed to act. Excepting extreme AoAs, can be regarded as fixed.
88	**Aerodynamic chord line**	*see zero lift line.*
62–4	**Aerofoil**	cross sectional shape of lifting surface (e.g wing). Critical to lift creation. Sometimes referred to as a section.
–	**Ambient pressure**	atmospheric pressure near to but not affected by aircraft's presence.
63	**Angle of Attack (AoA)**	angle between *relative airflow* and aerofoil's *geometric chord line*, some times measured between relative airflow and *aerodynamic chord line*.
81	**Aspect ratio**	ratio of span to chord of a component, or span squared to area if the component is non-rectangular in plan.
64	**Attitude**	relation of glider to horizontal plane. Usually refers to pitch angle in relation to horizontal.
65	**Bernoulli's Principle**	the energy due to pressure plus energy due to velocity = constant; $p + \frac{1}{2}\rho V^2 = K$. (p = air pressure, ρ = air density, V = air's velocity. Other terms, such as temperature, are usually ignored). The formula was actually the work of L. Euler.
77	**Bound vortex**	vector sum of airflow velocities and pressure changes around an aerofoil. Notionally circular.
69	**Boundary Layer**	critical area between any object and a fluid when either is moving (energy transfer layer).

Page	Subject	
87	**Camber-generated lift**	lift due to camber; acts at approximately 50% chord; proportional to speed squared; unaffected by AoA; usually resolved to act through the aerodynamic centre (AC).
86	**Camber line**	mid-point line between upper and lower surfaces of an aerofoil. Amount of camber is difference between this line and the chord line.
85	**Centre of pressure (CP)**	point where resultant of aerofoil's pressure forces appears to act.
77–9	**Circulation Theory**	theory describing how an aerofoil creates lift as being analogous to flow around a rotating cylinder (see Magnus Effect).
76, 80	**Down wash**	descending airflow behind aerofoil (there is related upwash ahead).
–	**Drag coefficient (C_D)**	abstract describing the general 'dragginess' or air resistance of an object.
71	**Drag 'tree'**	diagram showing the familial relationship between types of drag.
68, 71	**Drag, types of**	(72) **form drag:** pressure changes in flow caused by object's shape
		(68) **skin friction:** resistance between the airflow and airframe
		(74) **leakage drag:** air at a higher pressure leaking into a lower pressure area, causing flow breakaway (not induced drag)
		(74) **parasite drag:** drag produced by any component not vital to flight, e.g. radio aerial, undercarriage, etc.
		(72) **profile drag:** combination of form and interference drag. Increases as the square of the speed. Can be taken to be all drag except induced
		(73) **interference drag:** result of flow along one surface interfering with the flow along another, i.e. wing/fuselage junction
		(75) **induced drag:** *see* facing page.
64	**Flight path**	direction of flight, not necessarily related to attitude.
–	**Fluid dynamics**	the study of fluids and flow. Complicated!
73	**Flutter**	*see* chapter 5 summary (p. 167).
69	**Free stream velocity**	airflow velocity just beyond airframe influence.
63	**Geometric chord line**	straight line joining aerofoil's extreme leading and trailing edges.
58, 59	**Impact theory**	Early theory of lift based on the transfer of momentum between air molecules and a wing. Newton's explanation of how birds could fly, and

Page	Subject	
		the reason behind many claims that heavier than air flight was impossible. Blamed for delaying the advent of the aeroplane by several hundred years. A bit harsh, given that it was an hypothesis (suggestion). This doesn't mean that molecular impacts don't occur.
75	**Induced drag**	by-product of differential pressure between upper and lower surfaces of wing (for example). Increases with AoA. Inversely proportional to speed squared ($1/V^2$).
82	**Induced drag coefficient (C_{Di})**	$C_{Di} = k \times (C_L^2/3.1416 \times A)$, where k is a correction factor related to wing shape and A is the aspect ratio.
61, 83–4	**Laminar flow**	smooth, 'layered' flow; ordered.
–	**Laws of motion**	Newton's three laws – *see* chapter 2 summary (p. 53), also ch 4
62, 85	**Lift**	force required to support weight.
88	**Lift coefficient (C_L)**	lifting efficiency in relation to AoA- and camber-generated lift.
–	**Local velocity**	speed of airflow close to top of boundary layer but not moving at free stream speed.
77	**Magnus Effect**	resultant nett force created by airflow over a rotating cylinder.
67	**Manometer**	device for measuring gas pressure, using liquid in a tube – like a barometer.
77	**Perfect Fluid Theory**	early theory of fluid flow which took no account of friction, viscosity or the boundary layer. Still used for modelling airflow outside the boundary layer.
87	**Pitching moment**	nose-down pitching moment created by camber-generated lift.
67	**Pressure profile/distribution curve**	graphical representation of changing air pressures over aerodynamic surface.
63	**Relative airflow**	general airflow direction in relation to an aircraft, but just far enough away to be unaffected by aircraft's presence.
73	**Resonance**	link between applied force and natural frequency of oscillation of a component, which encourages further oscillation.
60	**Second law of Thermodynamics**	*see* chapter 1 summary (p. 25).
83	**Separation bubble**	area beneath a separated laminar flow which has reattached itself to the surface further downstream.

Page	Subject	
83	**Separation point**	where a laminar or turbulent flow separates from aerodynamic surface (before reaching downwind edge).
78	**Shed vortex**	vortex formed initially at wing trailing edge when airflow starts moving over aerofoil.
–	**Shear**	**aerodynamic:** change of speed or direction within a flow stream
		meteorological: change of wind speed and direction with height
		structural: forces acting in different directions and/or with different magnitudes through a material.
67	**Stagnation point**	where central streamline meets aerofoil at right angles, and stops.
68	**Stalling**	*see* also chapter 7 (pp. 205).
59	**Streamline**	path of a train of air molecules, say, travelling over a surface.
67	**Streamline, central**	marks division between air flowing over and air flowing under something like an aerofoil.
70	**Transition point**	point on the upper and/or lower surface of an aerofoil where a previously laminar flow becomes turbulent. On a clean aerofoil it is either at or just aft of where the airflow starts to decelerate and the pressure to rise.
84	**Turbulator tape**	zig-zag tape added to the aerofoil to change laminar flow to turbulent flow. Helps prevent separation bubbles.
61	**Turbulent flow**	airflow layers which are intermixing; disordered flow.
–	**Useful lift**	term used in this book to describe a nett 'up' lifting force.
78	**Vector sum**	the adding together of vectors like airflow velocity and pressure at various points on an aerofoil, to ascertain the nett force. See *bound vortex*.
70	**Velocity gradient**	change of velocity in relation to distance from a surface (*see* boundary layer).
66	**Venturi**	tapered tube which creates velocity and pressure changes to the airflow passing through it. Used as a suction pump to drive T/S, for example, and as part of boundary layer control devices.
68	**Viscosity**	internal friction in a fluid.
68	**Viscous drag**	skin friction (*see* also *viscosity*).
73	**Vortex shedding**	process of alternating creation and release of vortices from an object in an airflow.

CHAPTER 4

FORCES IN FLIGHT

CHAPTER CONTENTS ★ should know ☆ useful

NEWTON'S LAW OF MOTION
1) a particle not subjected to external forces remains at rest or moves with constant speed in a straight line
2) the acceleration of a particle is directly proportional to the external forces acting upon the particle and inversely proportional to the particle's mass
3) for every action there is an equal and opposite reaction

4 FORCES IN FLIGHT

Equilibrium, acceleration and reaction

Our tribal ancestors understood the idea of balance between competing forces, even if they did choose to dress it up in mythic terms. It took the grumpy and antisocial Sir Isaac Newton to turn supernatural soap opera into something less riveting, but far easier to put to practical use. Considering the almost entirely negative effect impact theory had on the development of early aviation, it is ironic that his Three Laws of Motion describe just about everything you need to know about the forces to which aircraft and their pilots are subjected. Physicists seeking the holy grail of a theory of everything must look longingly at these tightly scripted little gems, and hope for something similar; just the sort of cool stuff to slap onto a T-shirt and set people dancing joyously in the streets. Well, maybe not.

The laws of motion, in particular the first, hint at an absolute and universal frame of reference against which everything can be measured, but that idea – like older notions of 'heavenly perfection' – seems to be fraying at the edges, and the universe is beginning to look even weirder than it probably did to our ancestors. Nonetheless, on the parochial scale at which biological things like ourselves and our world operate, the three laws are excellent predictors – viz the celestial navigation of spacecraft – and, as you might expect from the accuracy required on such ballistic voyages, precise way beyond the needs of a normal life. In that respect it is probably OK to say that anything which appears to violate them should be viewed with the deepest suspicion.

The first law describes equilibrium, which, as chapter 1 mentioned, is a state of balance, though it doesn't follow that there is anything static about it, at least, not in the usual sense of the word; an object can be motionless or tumbling crazily end over end, and in both cases be in equilibrium. All that's required is that any forces acting upon it balance out and, if they don't, changes occur which almost always involve accelerations. A tumbling object in the depths of outer space, say, could continue to tumble, potentially forever. One can be very certain that the same object, tumbling wildly in the draggy atmosphere of a planet, wouldn't do so for anything like as long.

The second law deals with what happens when equilibrium is disturbed, either by the intrusion of an external force into a stable set-up (relatives at Christmas), or a change in the balance between the original forces (family row). For example, if either of two equal and opposite forces acting on an object becomes stronger or weaker, the object will accelerate in the direction in which the dominant force is acting, and the greater the difference, the greater the rate of acceleration. Think of a tug of war.

The third law was described in the previous chapter, page 65. To recap; if you pick up something heavy, for example, and then throw it, you have to take up a stance which, in

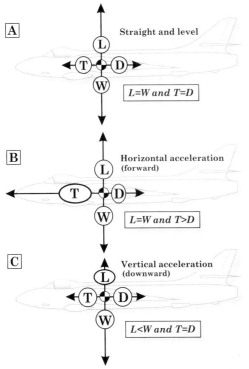

A Straight and level

L=W and T=D

B Horizontal acceleration (forward)

L=W and T>D

C Vertical acceleration (downward)

L<W and T=D

FIGURE 1 Disposition of Forces

effect, prevents you from throwing yourself over backwards. The recoil of a gun would be another example of action and reaction, as would be standing still. Even if nothing appears to be happening, your weight (action) has to be supported by the ground (reaction) otherwise you'd sink out of sight.

As the previous chapter stated, for conventional aircraft to be able to fly at all, weight (W) must be supported. There's no way round this. Gravity just keeps on working, and were it to stop, lack of weight would be the least of our problems. For steady level flight the first requirement is that lift, L, acts in the opposite direction to and exactly equals weight, W (figure 1 (A)). Balloons create L by passively displacing air, as described in chapter 2 (pp. 38–9), but aircraft must actively create it. If L is even fractionally less than W (C), and if no other forces are involved, both aircraft and balloons will start to descend and the rate will inexorably increase. The opposite is true if L is fractionally greater than W. In the horizontal plane a steady speed can only be maintained if there is a similarly exact balance (A) between the Thrust, T, component provided by the engine, and airframe's drag component, D. If there is any difference at all, then the speed will change. In order to accelerate a powered aircraft in level flight the pilot has to create a deliberate imbalance by opening the throttle and increasing T (B). Whether accelerating or decelerating, the bigger the difference between T and D, the faster the rate of change. So for take-off, let's say, T needs to be greater than D, preferably by a large margin. Being on the ground involves other forms of D than the aerodynamic sort, and both life and runways are of finite length.

A conventional aircraft will never take off, let alone start to move, unless T is greater than D simply because it won't ever reach a speed where the minimum requirement for sustained flight, L=W, is met. Deceleration is easier because D is an integral part of that universal 'can't be bothered' weak cold grey cup of tea thing, and when you are moving it can be regarded as more or less the default state. Once you've stopped moving, of course, D stops working against you, so you don't end up going backwards if you're on level ground. In any event, closing the throttle, having an engine failure, lowering the flaps or opening the airbrakes, all of these will slow an aircraft at a rate entirely dependent on the size of the instantaneous difference between T and D. Of course, if you are far too impatient to wait for normal decelerations to slow you down, you can hit something solid like the ground and stop immediately.

Motive power

Heavier-than-air machines have a volume and displace air, which gives them residual buoyancy, but nowhere near enough to make them behave like balloons, or to provide useful lift. For a wing to generate useful lift, air must flow over it, and regardless of whether the aircraft is stationary in relation to the ground or not (a glider in wave, say), energy must be expended to do this. Whatever it can sometimes look like, that energy doesn't come out of nowhere.

As far as powered aircraft are concerned, the engine is there to do two jobs:

(1)   help create the forces which make flight possible, and

(2)   overcome various anti-flight forces, the majority of which are, perversely, the direct result of managing to do ①.

Aerodynamically there are no fundamental differences between powered aircraft and gliders, easy as it is to think that once a glider has been launched it then wafts around, dancing free and engineless upon the breeze. This annoying misconception is part of a general belief that machine 'things' which don't appear to have an engine (i.e. something that thrashes the air noisily and has smoke curling out of its rear) really don't have one. Besides, goes the argument, only 'real' aeroplanes have engines, so it follows that since a glider isn't a toy – arguable! – it must be a sort of balloon, and equally uncontrollable. As it happens, gliders are as real as any aeroplane and need an engine just as much. We'll look at their controllability in a later chapter.

GLIDING BY CYCLE

Gravity is one of the most reliable engines in the world, not to say the universe, but exactly how does it power a glider? Take a cyclist (<u>figure 2</u> ①) pedalling at a steady speed along a completely flat road. All the acting forces balance out. W is supported by the ground's reaction, which for convenience we'll call L. The cycle's speed is constant, so T and D must also be in equilibrium. Let's say, however, that at the start of one trip, the chain breaks ②. Drat! Now there's no T.

Assuming the cycle never got moving in the first place, both T and D remain resolutely zero. L and W haven't gone away, but they're no help because neither has a horizontal 'along the ground' T component. The options open to the rider are;

(a)   abandon the bike (can't do that. Cost thousands of pounds)

(b)   get off and walk it along (slow. Bad for image)

(c)   use it like a scooter (kid stuff)

(d)   make good use of gravity by finding a suitable hill down which to freewheel. Freewheeling is what a glider does, and it's a case of finding, or rather making, a suitable hill.

A hill is just an inclined plane. Under the influence of 'normal' gravity (1G), W always acts vertically downwards. The ground's reaction, L, is always at right angles to the local surface, but in this case the surface's tilt means that L and W don't line up any more (<u>figure 2</u> ③). The *parallelogram of forces* that results (see chapter 1, p. 18) shows that the vital component of motive power, T, is not provided by L, but by a component of W, acting downhill and parallel to the surface slope. We'll come to TR, the *total reaction*, in a moment.

The steeper the slope the smaller the value of L and the larger the along the slope component of W, T (<u>figure 3</u>, see over). It may not be clear why T increases, and the ground's reaction, L, decreases. Take the extreme case where the hill is a cliff (i.e. vertical). In this instance T=W and L=0 (no need for L when you're going straight down). It is

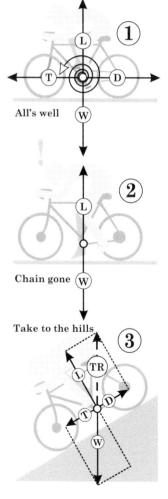

All's well

Chain gone

Take to the hills

FIGURE 2 Forces acting on a cyclist

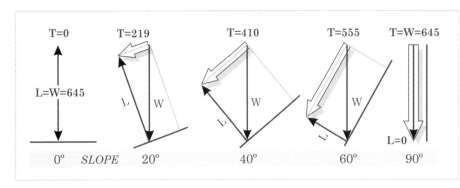

FIGURE 3 Changes in T as slope steepens

highly unlikely that T suddenly flips from zero when you're stationary on level ground, to W when you're pointing vertically downwards. More likely that T increases progressively as the hill steepens. Equally, on level ground L=W, but as the hill steepens less and less L is needed until finally, when the hill is vertical, it becomes zero. Alternatively, you can think of W as striking the steepening slope ever more glancing blows (in physical terms, less hurtful ones) until it eventually runs parallel to the ground and fails to hit it at all i.e. no reaction. Figure 3 shows how the value of T changes with the slope, given a value for W in lbs of a generic unballasted 15m glider. The parallelogram of forces in the figure has been slightly re-arranged to keep it compact, and not all the forces are shown.

The pilot controls the slope of the 'hill' – the flight path – by altering the glider's pitch attitude with the elevator. More nose down equals faster. Crucially, this can't work unless there is an at least notionally solid surface, a 'ground', against which the necessary reactions can occur, and the equivalent of the 'ground' is the lift produced by the glider's wings. There is always a catch, as you might have guessed. To maintain controllable free flight the glider has to go downhill fast enough for the wings to work so that it can go downhill and **be** controlled, all of which is exactly what puts it back on the ground again. The upshot is that genuine steady level flight is not possible in a glider. There are no exceptions to this, and anything that looks as if it might be one is hiding something.

ACCELERATING AND DECELERATING

We've talked about D's unavoidable influence in largely negative terms, but it has positive aspects. For example, without D accurate speed control would require impossible precision. The tiniest deviation from exactly horizontal flight – assuming we maintained the new attitude against all the trim forces – would cause the glider to accelerate or decelerate until it either stalled, or people started complaining about supersonic bangs. Besides, there are times when we want to create D deliberately, often in large amounts. One example is the use of airbrakes to control the rate of descent on the approach. Without D, airbrakes wouldn't work and we could stay airborne forever. By the same token landings would be tricky! In reality, airbrakes do work and we can't stay airborne forever, so D is not a force we can ignore.

Surprisingly, the 'always downhill' complication which gliders introduce into the neat L=W, T=D setup of powered aircraft, results in a component of D becoming one of the forces that helps support a glider. Downhill means a tilted reaction plane i.e. the 'ground' slopes. L is a reaction at right angles to the ground, and on a slope it neither lines up with nor fully supports W. The glider ought to start sinking vertically and forever at a greater and greater rate, but it doesn't. Using the parallelogram of forces again, we find that W's real counterbalance is a combination of L and D, referred to as the total reaction, or TR (figure 4 ③).

With that in mind, and out of interest, let's look in detail at what happens to the various forces when the glider's pilot lowers the nose (figure 4). T increases by an amount directly related to the change in attitude. Steeper equals more T. Immediately after the attitude change T will be greater than D ① to ②, and the subsequent rate of acceleration will depend on how big that difference is, but it is largest immediately after the attitude change. Assuming the attitude stays constant during the period of acceleration, T won't change, but D will inevitably increase. As the difference between the two gets smaller and smaller, so the rate of acceleration reduces. It ceases eventually when T=D, and equilibrium returns ③. (Note that unbalanced forces lead to the upper and lower parallelograms – the grey boxes – having different areas, whereas for equilibrium states they are identical. A larger box can be thought of as containing more dynamic energy than a smaller box.) The pilot now raises the nose and returns the glider to the original attitude ④. T becomes smaller than D and the glider starts to decelerate. Equilibrium is again restored when T=D ⑤.

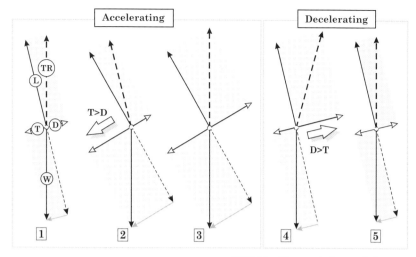

FIGURE 4 Changes in forces during acceleration and deceleration

For small changes in attitude the difference between T and D is also small, as are the resultant changes. But what happens if the pilot lowers the nose to, say, 55° below the horizontal? The slope of the notional hill (figure 5 ①) is now very steep and the initial difference between T and D very large, so it's a fair bet that the T=D equilibrium speed is going to be high. Providing the dive didn't begin with an extremely abrupt change in attitude, the glider can never accelerate faster than 1G (32ft/sec^2). Even so, it will still accelerate at about 26ft/sec^2, won't take many seconds to go from 45kt to VNE, the never exceed speed, and probably won't stop there.

Figure 6, see over, is essentially a more elaborate figure 3, illustrating the way the rate of acceleration alters with the flight path angle, and giving T as a percentage of W; a measure of 'gravity engine' power available. For example, if an ASK13 with an all up weight (AUW) of 1000lbs dives at 45°, the value for T will be approximately 70% of W, or 700lb. This glider will only stop accelerating when D=700lbs. Given that D for an ASK13 at best L/D can be 40lbs or less, and despite the fact that increases in D follow a square law, 700lbs (318kg, 6.25cwt) is very big bucks in terms of force, and it still doesn't tell you the likely equilibrium speed.

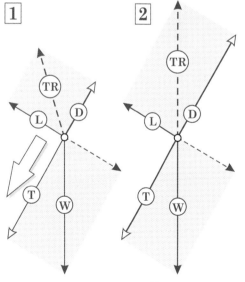

FIGURE 5 About to overspeed?

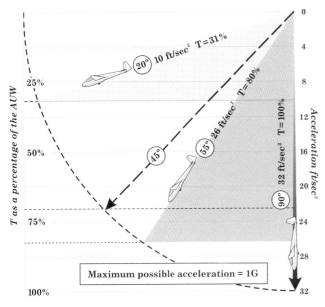

FIGURE 6 Changes in T with dive angle

Let's go further and take the extreme case where an overenthusiastic pilot does the equivalent of the cyclist going over a cliff, and dives the glider vertically. The only force able to support the glider – now dropping like a stone – is D, and until D=W the glider will continue to accelerate. In practice, and for all but the most aerodynamically inefficient gliders, once the dive angle goes beyond a value specific to the machine (30° with airbrakes fully out for some modern gliders), D will only equal T when the glider has exceeded all its design limit speeds, so it is quite likely to have broken up before reaching what will, in this case, turn out to be an entirely theoretical state of equilibrium.[1]

FLIGHT PATH SAG

When you lower a glider's nose, particularly if the initial speed is low and the attitude change relatively large, the flight path at the outset has a distinct sag to it (figure 7). The reasons for this are that immediately after the attitude change the AoA and L decrease, but D doesn't, or initially at least, not by much. The result is that TR goes out of line with W (figure 5, ①) and the glider's sink rate increases. Subsequently, the speed builds, the AoA decreases, L and D increase, and TR starts to swing back to line up with W. The sink rate then begins decreasing from its previous higher value at Y, towards a lower value at Z where TR=W, T=D, and equilibrium has been restored. Until then the glider will continue to accelerate along a gradually changing flight path.

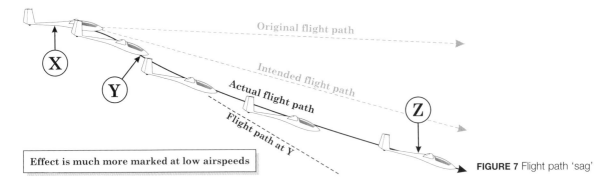

FIGURE 7 Flight path 'sag'

[1]Surprisingly, acceleration is independent of weight. Practical demonstrations don't tend to bear this out because air resistance and other forms of D have a disproportionate effect on less dense and/or more draggy objects. In a frictionless and dragless environment, a ping pong ball, a tennis ball, and a bowling ball placed on the same inclined plane and released at the same instant, would accelerate in parallel for as long as the slope continued. Intuitively this seems nonsense, but it is correct! What really counts is the slope, which governs the rate of acceleration.

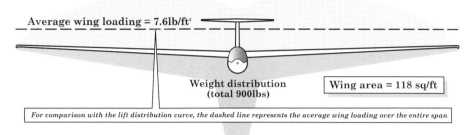

Lift/wing loading distribution

Average wing loading = 7.6lb/ft²

**Weight distribution
(total 900lbs)**

Wing area = 118 sq/ft

For comparison with the lift distribution curve, the dashed line represents the average wing loading over the entire span

FIGURE 8 Wing loading

Assuming the new attitude was maintained throughout, the sink rate at Z won't ever reach the value it had at Y, but it will be greater than it was at X. Despite the initial sag being very tiny at moderate and high speeds, it does have an effect on a variometer's total energy (chapter 9, p. 251).

Wing loading

Before discussing the forces involved in turning we need to look at wing loading. Wing loading is important because it is a measure of how hard the wing has to work.

In order to sustain normal unaccelerated (1G) flight, each square foot of the wing must support a proportion of the glider's weight. That figure, whatever it is, is the *wing loading*. Because the wings tip portions create less lift per square foot than the mid and inner portions – as illustrated by the lift/load distribution curves in figure 8 – any quoted value for the wing loading is an average. The numbers can be surprisingly high. A 15m glider with an all up weight (AUW) of 900lb and a wing area of 118sq ft, has a wing loading of 7.6lb sq/ft. This is the equivalent of four (and a splash) pint bottles of milk sat on an area about the size of an A4 sheet. By comparison, the wing loading of a military jet could easily be 100lb/sq ft or more; about the same as an A4 area supporting a smallish adult.

G and load factor

So far any attitude changes we've talked about have been implicitly gentle, and changes in effective weight (W_E) have been ignored. This isn't very realistic because changes in velocity, which mean alterations in speed and/or direction, produce inertial effects which alter the *effective weight* of both the glider and the pilot, and these affect the wing loading and the amount of work the wing must do. They also give rise to a variety of sensations, not all of them pleasant, including feeling heavier, lighter, or weighing nothing at all, or even, on occasion, with gravity seeming to act in the wrong direction.

Partly because pilots use 'G' to describe something based entirely on the physical sensations they experience, and because these sensations are not 100% reliable, sometimes a rather fine distinction is made between G (subjective) and load (objective). Strictly speaking loads can be in any direction, but those affecting the airframe in the

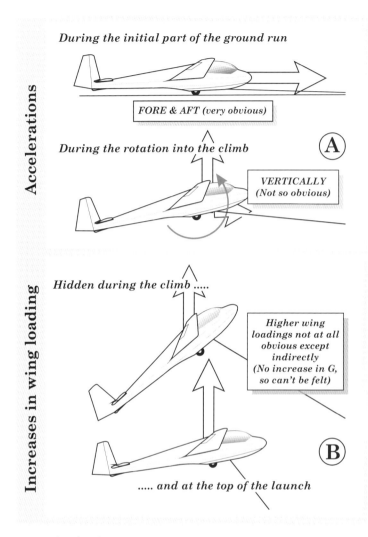

Accelerations

During the initial part of the ground run

FORE & AFT (very obvious)

During the rotation into the climb

(A)

VERTICALLY
(Not so obvious)

Increases in wing loading

Hidden during the climb .....

Higher wing
loadings not at all
obvious except
indirectly
(No increase in G,
so can't be felt)

(B)

..... and at the top of the launch

FIGURE 9 Load and
acceleration direction

vertical plane are referred to in terms of a *load factor*, normally abbreviated to 'n'. G and 'n' are usually exactly the same thing, and when talking about G pilots generally don't become too confused about it: "Managed 6.5G on that last loop!". "Hey! Cool! I bet the glider's next pilot would like to hear about that!", and so on. Unfortunately, this entirely 'sensational' (I can feel it) view of the forces to which the pilot and, by implication, the airframe are being subjected, has a catch.

Not all the loads to which a glider is subjected are caused by G changes. In some cases, say during rolling manoeuvres, the major loads can't be felt and G meters don't register them. There are also occasions when the AoA can be high and there is or has been no corresponding increase in G, so the instinctive connection we make between changing weight and changing load, which is part of balance and orientation, and almost impossible to avoid, isn't always correct.

For example, during most of a winch launch the glider doesn't accelerate, and at these times the pilot's weight will be normal (1G), and he or she won't be physically aware of any extra loads (figure 9). Yet, in what is, in effect, a tethered flight situation – rather like that of a kite – the wing can be doing more than 1G's worth of work, with a consequent increase in the stalling speed and the AoA. Stick forces and stick position, as well as wing flexing, give clues to what's happening, but none of them may be that obvious, or even particularly accurate. For example, if the glider has been mis-trimmed, the stick loads could easily be higher or lower than the pilot considered were normal, and hence open to misinterpretation. An example of a very high AoA and normal 1G would be a mushing stall; see chapter 7.

Further sensational revelations

Strictly speaking they aren't forces in flight, but it's worth looking in more detail at some of the G related sensations we experience. Positive G is very familiar to pilots even if they've never blacked out as result of getting rather too much of it. Reduced G is fairly common, but zero G, which is the unpleasant sensation associated with falling over, far less so. Genuine negative G is quite rare in gliders and there is little need to subject yourself to it unless you're an aerobatics pilot.

In order to produce true negative G from level flight, we either have to fly upside down and hang in the straps or, from upright flight, push the stick forward far and hard enough to tuck the glider's flight path inside the curve of the free-fall parabola (figure 10) (see chapter 1, p. 12). The only way the latter can happen is if the glider accelerates vertically downwards faster than 1G (32ft/sec²). Given that a glider is weight powered, like some kind of grandfather clock, the trick would seem impossible, but it can be done, albeit briefly. With a sufficient initial speed, pushing the stick forward far enough and swiftly enough will cause the wing to reach a high negative AoA and produce enough negative lift to accelerate the glider downwards faster than 32ft/sec². One of the very few occasions when you might experience genuine negative G, is pushing over hard after a cable break.

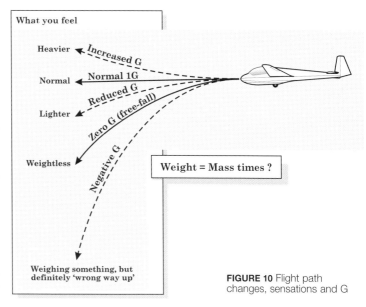

FIGURE 10 Flight path changes, sensations and G

In aviation's early days pilots were not provided with straps, or only a lap strap, and didn't have parachutes either, and occasionally they got thrown out. Parachutes are a good idea but being properly strapped in is an even better one. In a negative G scenario, for example, we leave the seat as our body tries to take the free fall path. At our command the glider is following a tighter curve and diving away from under us. This first 'throws' us up against the straps, and then the glider hauls us down along the tighter curve it is following. We feel as if G is operating upwards, towards our head. At the subsequent pull-out the glider is on the opposite side of the free-fall curve and pushes up from underneath. We interpret this interference with our apparent desire for endless free-fall as an increase in weight, and feel pushed down into the seat by the increasing G.

Figure 10 gives a general idea of changes in effective weight produced by moving the stick fore or aft from horizontal flight, and the related sensations. While the glider has no need of the 'what the hell's going on?' reactions required by biological systems, the pilot can feel and respond, possibly vocally, to any of these G related effects with the glider in any attitude, even upside down.

OTHER EFFECTS

A novel sight during a really vigorous push-over is dirt rising off the floor, and things occasionally flying out of the side pockets. Such effects are largely due to negative G. The dust and the logbook have gone into free-fall because, unlike us, they're not strapped in. At the same time as the glider tucks inside the free-fall parabola, it is also pitching swiftly about the CG. For a short while the front pilot can be accelerating downwards faster than the rear

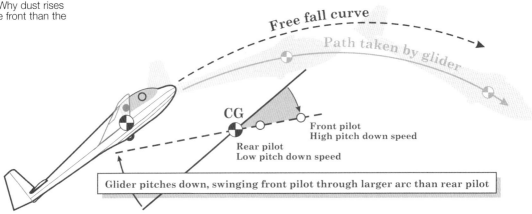

FIGURE 11 Why dust rises higher in the front than the back

Free fall curve

Path taken by glider

CG

Front pilot
High pitch down speed

Rear pilot
Low pitch down speed

Glider pitches down, swinging front pilot through larger arc than rear pilot

pilot, who is sat nearer the centre of rotation, if not always exactly on it (figure 11), and is subjected mainly to the negative G created by the flight path. Because there is, briefly, a difference in the speed of the pitch change between front and rear seats, the dust in the front may rise higher than that in the back. This is something which you will only see if you happen to be in the back seat of a tandem two-seater.

LOAD FACTOR AND STALLING SPEED

The stalling speed is related to the load factor and, inevitably, to the wing loading, but the relationship between the two is non-linear; that is to say, if you plot the stalling speed for various values of 'n' on a graph, you get a curve. A similar plot assuming a linear relationship between them would be a straight line (figure 12). Doubling 'n' (2G) would then double an unaccelerated stalling speed of, say, 38kt, to 76kt, and 4G would increase it to 152kt! Manoeuvring would be a tiptoe affair; turns would have to be far wider and flatter than they are under the current laws of physics, and you wouldn't dream of attempting a loop. It's a good thing that the relationship is the non-linear $\sqrt{n} \times V_S$, where V_S is the normal (unaccelerated) stalling speed. The table in figure 13 gives the stalling speeds for various values of 'n' for a glider with a V_S of 38kt.

Forces in a turn

As described by Newton's first Law, things won't go round corners unless you literally force them to do so. To go to the left, for example, a left acting force (an acceleration) is needed, and without it the glider would just keep going straight on. Aircraft provide this component by rolling left or right and tilting the lift vector (L_2) in the required direction.

The moment the glider rolls there is less L to support W. For a balanced turn, however steep, the lift vector L_2 must be large enough to provide the vertical component, L_1 (figure 13), which is the one actually supporting W, regardless of how heavy the pilot may feel at the time. When L_2 is sufficient,

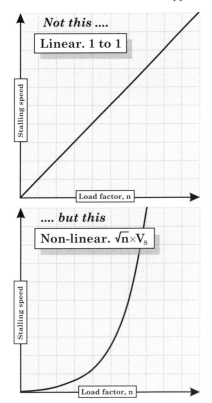

Not this ....

Linear. 1 to 1

Stalling speed

Load factor, n

.... but this

Non-linear. $\sqrt{n} \times V_s$

Stalling speed

Load factor, n

FIGURE 12 Stalling speed against n

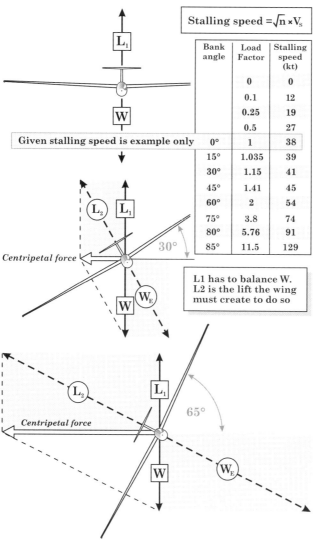

$$\text{Stalling speed} = \sqrt{n} \times V_s$$

Bank angle	Load Factor	Stalling speed (kt)
	0	0
	0.1	12
	0.25	19
	0.5	27
0°	1	38
15°	1.035	39
30°	1.15	41
45°	1.41	45
60°	2	54
75°	3.8	74
80°	5.76	91
85°	11.5	129

Given stalling speed is example only

FIGURE 13 Forces in a balanced turn

L1 has to balance W. L2 is the lift the wing must create to do so

a simple parallelogram of forces shows that the *centripetal force* – the into turn component – will also be sufficient. If L_2 isn't strong enough to provide L_1 (viz the 'lift shortfall' in figure 14), then the glider will slip into the turn. One reason why you can't do a balanced turn using rudder alone – and shouldn't ever try to do so – is that there's no L_2 component (the into turn one) until the yaw induces roll, and even when such a 'turn' is stable the glider will continue to skid sideways and outwards. This is a recipe for spinning (see chapter 7).

Simply roll into a turn without easing the stick back and the glider will start to sink, the nose will drop and the speed increase. If

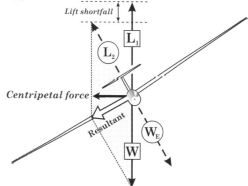

FIGURE 14 Forces in an unbalanced turn

the speed during a turn is to stay constant and the wing create sufficient L_2, then the AoA has to be increased by an appropriate back pressure on the stick. This is chicken and egg stuff because the same action also prevents the speed from increasing. In practice the pilot applies the bank and the required back pressure at about the same time because he knows from experience not to wait until the nose has dropped.

In a well-balanced turn the increase in load experienced by the glider and pilot is related to the glider's pitch rate, so the steeper the bank and the faster the rate of turn, the higher the G. The line marked W_E in the figures again represents the glider's effective weight (W x $\sqrt{n}$), which includes the pilot – who will be well aware that his/her effective weight is increasing. The vertical component W is still there and still needs L_1's support. For a gentle bank, the necessary pitch-up and related aft stick movement will be very small. As the angle of bank is increased, a correspondingly greater aft movement of the stick is needed to provide the required pitch up, and the G increases. In a sense, the glider is more and more reluctant to go round the corner and greater effort is required to make it do so. The extra load increases the stalling speed by the amounts shown in <u>figure 13</u>.

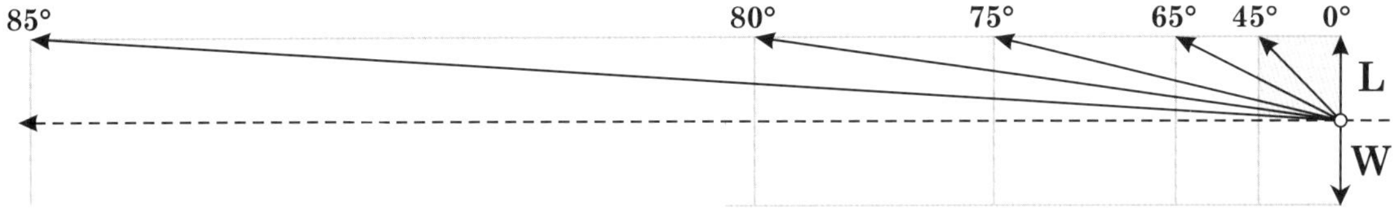

FIGURE 15 Changes in the magnitude of L2 with increasing bank angles

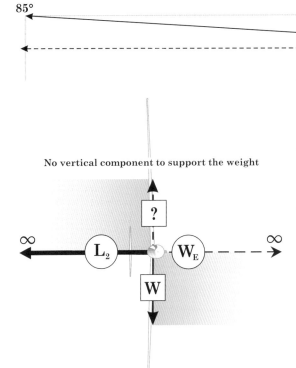

FIGURE 16 Forces in a vertical bank

<u>Figure 15</u> illustrates how L_2 increases rapidly (non-linearly) from about 50° of bank onwards. At 90° of bank (<u>figure 16</u>) the turn is all pitch, and assuming nothing else has happened in the meantime, the stick will be on the back stop and the stalling speed will be infinite! No matter how large L_2 now becomes, it is acting horizontally, as a counterbalance to W_E only. Powered aerobatic aircraft can sustain this knife-edge flight by using a combination of fuselage lift, drag and engine thrust to provide the L_1 component. In the same situation a glider's fuselage creates nowhere near enough lift, and the 'engine' is in any case acting in the wrong direction. The resulting sideslip which quickly develops can be so strong that despite the pilot's best efforts the glider can end up yawing into a near vertical dive. However confident you may be of controlling all of this, don't try it. There are limits to the side-loads the fin can take before it breaks off, and if you try using rudder to raise the nose above the horizon in an understandable but misguided attempt to slow down, you will hugely increase these loads – and add new ones.

As bank steepens, a turn changes from a largely yaw-based manoeuvre into a pitch based one (figure 17). So, if we start from wings level and roll fairly slowly into a turn with a bank angle of, say, 55°, remaining in balanced flight throughout may require constant rudder adjustments. There is some argument about where the string should be 'pegged' during a turn, particularly when trying to optimise climb rates in thermals. The glider's CG follows the real turning circle, with nose and tail both scribing out slightly different arcs, and at those extremities there is, in effect, yaw[2]. Should the string be in the middle, or out to one side because of the way the nose meets the relative airflow? Depends on the bank angle! If it is large, then the turn is mostly pitch based, and less rudder is needed than at a bank angle of, say, 20°.

Whether having the string in the middle all the time or carefully adjusting it to allow for apparent yaw is worth bothering about, I can't say, but in general flying accurately is the most energy efficient option – and usually the safest.

For the most efficient turns, minimum drag is the aim. The minimum drag speed also happens to be best L/D (see chapter 8), but during a turn we are not talking about normal best glide speed, rather best glide speed at a higher load factor and wing loading (higher 'n'); in other words, not only is the entire glider heavier, but all the benchmark speeds, like stalling, minimum sink and best glide have increased as well. The effect is identical to adding water ballast (Appendix C).

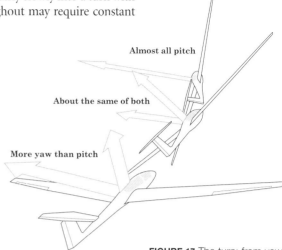

Almost all pitch

About the same of both

More yaw than pitch

FIGURE 17 The turn; from yaw to pitch based manoeuvre

TURNS AND LOOPS, A COMPARISON

The major difference between loops and turns is the plane of the manoeuvre: one horizontal, the other vertical. It may strike you as a first class example of full-frontal nerdity, plus stating the blindingly obvious, but even though gravity affects both manoeuvres, the results are quite different. A constant and steady turn is possible (figure 18) largely because the glider's relationship to the normal direction of gravity doesn't change, but there's no such thing as a steady loop (figure 19)! Here the gravitational engine is continually operating in different directions in relation to the glider which, as a result, is always either accelerating or decelerating along the line of flight. If we try to keep a constant pitch rate during a loop, as we would during a turn – where it is easy – we end up with constant changes in speed. The result is the usual and perfectly acceptable non-competition aerobatic pilot's bodged ovoid (inset, figure 19). To execute a completely

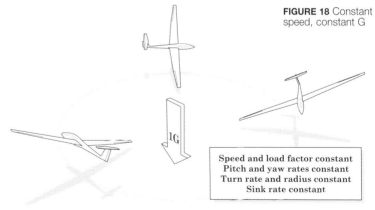

FIGURE 18 Constant speed, constant G

1G

Speed and load factor constant
Pitch and yaw rates constant
Turn rate and radius constant
Sink rate constant

[2]Confusingly, the 'yaw' at the front is in the opposite direction to the 'yaw' at the back, so it's arguable which end is creating the most drag!

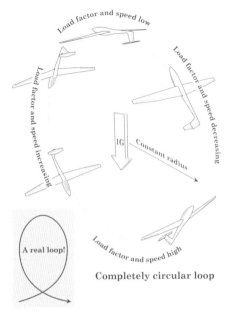

Load factor and speed low

Load factor and speed decreasing

Load factor and speed increasing

1G Constant radius

Load factor and speed high

A real loop!

Completely circular loop

FIGURE 19 Circular loop and 'normal' loop

circular loop we must maintain a constant speed and pitch rate, which can't be done in a glider, or pull large amounts of G when going fast at the bottom of the manoeuvre, and zero or less when we are upside down at the top and going very slowly. We also have to alter the pitch rate continually. The ovoid may be aesthetically ho-hum, but it's far easier to do.

DIVE RECOVERY AND AIRCRAFT ATTITUDE

Being less stressful to both pilot and glider, constant G is the preferable way of recovering from a dive or completing a loop. On the basis of what's been said previously, you might think that maintaining a constant load during a recovery where you are also accelerating – as in the recovery from a loop – would be difficult because, as the speed increases, you will have to increase the radius of the circle whose circumference you are following. But that's the complicated version. All you need do is **maintain the G at a constant and appropriate value** by gradually easing off on the back pressure as the speed builds. The radius of the pullout curve then adjusts itself, taking a shape similar to that of the last part of the non-aerobatic pilot's loop (figure 19).

Releasing the back pressure might seem an invitation to overspeed, but if the initial speed isn't too high, and the G is kept at a reasonable level throughout (above 2.5 and less than 5), you're very unlikely to go too fast. Pull less than 2.5G and you might, but this depends on your initial speed. In any case, it isn't as if the glider continues to accelerate until it is in level flight.

The speed of any glider in steady free-flight is directly related to its attitude. For example, when flying at a steady 90kt in still air, glider type X will always be in attitude A (figure 20), and attitude B when flying at a steady 50kt. Let's say that this glider exits a manoeuvre at 105kt and takes up and maintains attitude B. What next? First, the drag level at 105kt is far higher than 'normal' for attitude B, and second, the T value usually linked with attitude B is much lower than the value needed to maintain 105kt. True, glider X has arrived at B with far more energy than it needs to stay there, but in the form of a T/D imbalance very much in favour of D, so the glider inevitably decelerates, and quite rapidly initially.

All this helps you slow down (using the airbrakes when pulling lots of G isn't a great

FIGURE 20 Dive recovery

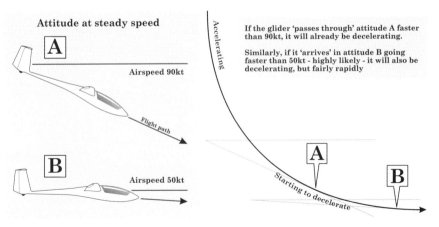

Attitude at steady speed

A

Airspeed 90kt

Flight path

B

Airspeed 50kt

Accelerating

If the glider 'passes through' attitude A faster than 90kt, it will already be decelerating.

Similarly, if it 'arrives' in attitude B going faster than 50kt - highly likely - it will also be decelerating, but fairly rapidly

Starting to decelerate

A

B

idea – see chapter 5, p. 164), but one could argue that increasing the induced drag by pulling fairly hard would also help. It would, and by default it usually does, but there are two riders; (1) induced drag increases with the AoA and there is a real danger of a high speed stall if you pull too much G at lowish airspeeds – perhaps finishing off with a flick followed by a plain old fashioned spin (see chapter 7) – and (2), if you deliberately try to create useful 'slow me down' amounts of induced drag at a high speed (where the initial AoA and induced drag are very low), you'll have to pull so much G that you'll overstress the glider, if not have a major structural failure. One reason, among others, why some modern gliders aren't cleared for aerobatics is not that they accelerate quicker than anything else, but that at high speeds their C_D (drag coefficient) is still low, so they are able to continue accelerating for longer. Put a Duo Discus and an ASK13 side by side at 80kt, and it is quickly apparent which has the most D. For the really slippery modern gliders there is a very small margin between the pilot correctly executing an aerobatic manoeuvre and not overspeeding, and getting it wrong and exceeding the airframe limits.

Flying uphill

Since a glider can't even sustain genuine level flight, attempting to fly uphill can hardly be described as a long-term project. The gravitational engine now works back to front, with T and D operating together as a relentlessly effective brake. A common cause of gliding accidents is pilots' unwitting attempts, one way or another, to try and keep on going uphill, come what may. Can't be done! What <u>figure 21</u> is saying should be indelibly imprinted on your mind – that when you're trying to fly uphill just about everything in the physical world is working against you. Powered aircraft are able to go uphill because they can use T to do so. To see how that works, swap T and D in <u>figure 21</u> ① and imagine the aircraft travelling in the opposite direction to the glider.

For gliders there are two sorts of uphill flying, if you don't count launching. One where the pilot raises the nose and literally tries to fly uphill, and a more subtle one where kinetic (speed) and potential (height) energies start to run out and there's no way of topping them up. Both are dangerous because they can result in the pilot attempting to use energy that isn't really there.

Gliding is all ups and downs, with height and speed varying continuously throughout a flight. Juggling the two is part of the skill and the enjoyment. However, potential energy starts to leak away irretrievably when you're on a cross-country, miles from anywhere, and the day suddenly dies on you. The rest of the flight is an inevitable downhill slide to a field landing. 'Uphill' in this case would be doing something that squandered the energy you had, i.e. flying far too slowly to 'stay up longer'. In a psychological sense, 'uphill' would be thinking that you weren't going to land out (something will save me) – better rewrite the laws of physics first then! – and failing to choose a field soon enough as a result. Here's a few other examples of uphill flying in its various guises.

Racing finishes are popular at competitions . . . and it's a good finish for that one, hurrah, and, oops, the pilot seems to have run out of height,

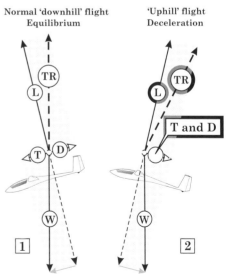

FIGURE 21 A very effective brake

FIGURE 22 Pull-up profiles

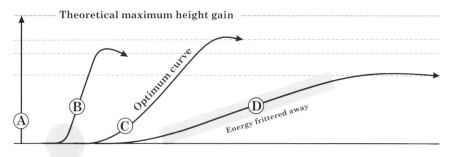

Theoretical maximum height gain

Optimum curve

Energy frittered away

High induced drag
Energy thrown away

speed and ideas simultaneously! Pilots sometimes come unstuck, not by hitting the ground at high speed – an unexpectedly rare occurrence – but by miscalculating the energy equation during the last minutes of the flight. Long and low finishes involve deliberate 'uphill' flying in the sense that whatever the height and speed at, say, five kilometres out, the 'oomph' is definitely dribbling out of the dynamics and the chances of a top up are zero. If you make it, no sweat. Besides, don't competition pilots sometimes squeak onto the airfield and land downwind at considerable ground velocity, but with marginal airspeed, simply because there wasn't enough energy left to do anything else? The trouble with the downwind bit, apart from early loss of control on the ground run, is that it can look to the pilot as if there's more airspeed and hence more energy than there really is.

Frustrating though it is to be on final glide and have some higher power shift the airfield further away, any attempt to reach the receding goal by gradually raising the nose (stretching the glide) counts as uphill flying. The major problem with any form of 'low and slow', which is the inevitable result of attempting to stretch the glide, is that you can be left with insufficient energy to manoeuvre safely. If you have to turn through 90° at the last minute to avoid dicing yourself through a hedge or hitting an inconsiderately placed tree, you may not be able to do so without spinning in. It is difficult to pick out which is the most attractive option.

As for that final triumphant pull-up, well . . . in theory the maximum gain of height possible from a zoom climb would translate the initial horizontal velocity directly into a vertical one (<u>figure 22</u> (A)). In other words, if the glider went instantly into a vertical

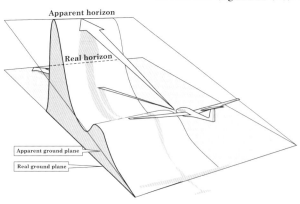

Apparent horizon

Real horizon

Apparent ground plane

Real ground plane

FIGURE 23 Real and apparent

climb without any initial loss of energy (or falling to bits), it would behave exactly like a ball thrown straight up into the air. Clearly, a gain of height which at its peak leaves you with useful flying speed, a sensible flying attitude, and some control over what happens next, has to be significantly less than the simplistic assumption that you just go straight up until you stop! There is also an optimum curve that balances the energy you chuck away by pulling up too quickly and increasing the induced drag, as against pulling up too slowly and frittering the energy away via the other forms of drag – compare examples (B) through (D) in figure 22.

A further 'uphill' scenario which can be a problem in mountainous areas, is confusing the position of the real horizon with the apparent one (<u>figure 23</u>). A similar situation, in terms of what you think you're seeing, can be trying to fly uphill during an approach to land in a field which slopes towards you – see the 'apparent ground plane' in figure 23. Frequent cross checks between attitude and ASI help avoid disaster in such scenarios.

On the face of it, gliders climbing in thermals would seem to be indulging in a form of uphill flying. However, unlike the previous examples – many of which seem tailor made to end in disaster – the glider is still flying downhill in a normal attitude even as it climbs. All that's needed is for the air mass to rise faster than the glider is descending through it. Imagine someone trying to walk down an up escalator. As long as the escalator carries them upwards faster than they are walking down, then up they will go (figure 24). The same applies to a glider flying on a working ridge and able to stay airborne, more or less exactly level, for hour after hour. In both the thermal and ridge cases the potential (height) energy being used up to maintain the kinetic (speed) energy required for controllable flight is constantly replenished, even increased, by the air's upward flow. Once again you're not getting something for nothing, nor are you flying uphill.

Many completely avoidable accidents follow winch launch failures, and it doesn't help that the most critical are those which, rather obviously, occur close to the ground. Some result from a delayed response ('Instructor failed to take over in time', for example), others have the pilot attempting to carry on 'uphill' long after the gravity engine, T, has gone into reverse, even if ever so slightly. With most winch launch failures there's easily sufficient time to do the right things, but some scenarios play out in negative time, so to speak, where even if you react instantly you're still too late! Or, to put it another way, whatever needed doing ought to have been done before the failure.

Figure 25 shows three cable break/launch failure scenarios. To avoid taking up inordinate amounts of space the illustration has been vertically compressed, so that the first glider of each sequence – representing where the cable breaks – appears in a far steeper attitude than would be wise at such an early stage in the launch. That apart, in (A) the pilot responds quickly and lowers the nose a sufficient amount, and the glider subsequently has speed and height enough to round-out and land safely. In (B) the pilot responds less quickly and then fails to lower the nose as much. At best the outcome is a round-out and no float i.e perilously close to not being able to round out at all. (C) represents a substantial delay, relatively speaking, in lowering the nose, resulting in the glider stalling. There's only a few seconds difference in the pilot's response times between (A) and (C), but they are critical. The chief problem with (C) is that when the glider stalls at the top of the arc, the elevator has little effect, the glider starts to sink vertically at an extremely high rate and initially in a relatively flat attitude, and even when it does begin to pitch down, whether pilot assisted or automatically, it

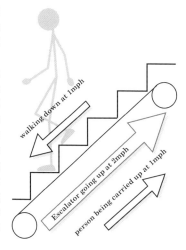

FIGURE 24 Ascending while descending

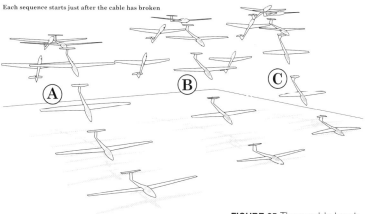

Each sequence starts just after the cable has broken

FIGURE 25 Three cable break scenarios

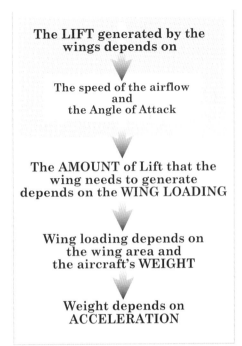

The LIFT generated by the wings depends on

▼

The speed of the airflow and the Angle of Attack

▼

The AMOUNT of Lift that the wing needs to generate depends on the WING LOADING

▼

Wing loading depends on the wing area and the aircraft's WEIGHT

▼

Weight depends on ACCELERATION

FIGURE 26 Summary of lift/load

may be very close to the ground and either still stalled, or only just unstalling. Round-out is **impossible** and the glider crashes.

Wind gradients can create bleak scenarios if they aren't taken into account, and if strong could make even (A) difficult, and (B) a very heavy arrival at best. (C) would be what it was always going to be, a crash, but this time much more violent. Overall, none of the scenarios might seem to involve anything uphill, except temporarily, because, having pitched nose-down, the glider ought to get back all the energy it lost just after the break on the way up. In the case of (C), not quite getting the speed back is the same as never, unfortunately. Into wind wind-gradients make things worse because as you descend through them they subtract the wind speed from your airspeed, and if they are very steep – not unusual at hill sites – the gradient can subtract from your airspeed far faster than any sensible attitude can accelerate the glider to make up the difference. So, when glider (C) comes to the round-out, it can't because almost all the potential and kinetic energy required for the manoeuvre has been wasted somewhere else. One can hardly blame the glider for that. For better or worse, a safe winch launch is very much up to the pilot, but winching's far from alone among launch methods in being able to produce unpleasant surprises for the unwary.

BASIC RELATIONSHIP OF THE FORCES

Before looking at the forces involved in winch launching, figure 26 summarises the relationship between lift and load (L and 'n'), or work and G, if you prefer, which we've already discussed. I have been told that from an engineering point of view the sequence is dreadfully imprecise, a comment which seems to miss the point. It is important that the relationships outlined are understood, but if you're not a mathematician the numbers won't mean much. Even if they do, in real life nobody is going to take five seconds making a calculation which the situation only allows them two seconds to complete.

Forces in a winch launch

THE GROUND RUN

The main component of the initial forces acting on a glider being winched or auto-towed is the cable pull, C_T (figure 27). The launch begins by accelerating the glider from standstill to take-off speed, and because the cable does little more here than overcome the glider's inertia, this phase is one of quite literally straightforward acceleration. The tension in the cable (C_T) will be approximately half the glider's all up weight, plus whatever is required to overcome the surface-dependent *rolling resistance*; on soft ground the wheel would dig out a rut and the rolling resistance would be much higher than on a hard surface like a runway. During this early phase the cable loads can be increased dramatically if the winch driver is particularly heavy handed, but the weak link can usually cope.

In a more or less level attitude the glider will take off once the wing is generating sufficient lift. What the pilot does during the next few seconds is crucial to how high the

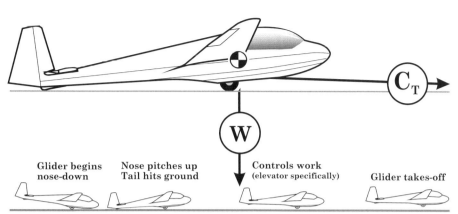

FIGURE 27 Forces during initial ground run

Glider begins nose-down | Nose pitches up Tail hits ground | Controls work (elevator specifically) | Glider takes-off

launch is likely to be, whether the cable breaks or not (assuming everything was in good condition to start with), and whether the glider is likely to perform any unusual and inappropriate stunts, most of which relate to high AoAs and stalling, and are dealt with in chapter 7. The only thing to say here is that they are usually the pilot's fault.

THE INITIAL PITCH-UP

When correctly trimmed most gliders will take off by themselves and rotate at the correct rate into the appropriate climb attitude for their speed. In the right glider, take-off and rotation ought to be perfect hands-off – theoretically! However, if the glider takes off while still accelerating fiercely, the cable-induced pitching moment may be strong enough to prevent the nose being lowered, even with the stick fully forward, though this is type dependent.[3] Very fierce initial accelerations can also slam down the tail of a glider that normally starts with a front skid or nosewheel on the ground (e.g. ASK13 and ASK21). This 'tip-up' is almost impossible to avoid at any rate of acceleration, but if it's really violent the walloping received by the airframe can cause serious damage or worsen any already done, not to mention jangling the pilot's nerves at a crucial moment. The remedy lies almost entirely in the hands of the winch driver.

Assuming the trim is set correctly and the pilot holds the elevator neutral throughout, the major component of the initial pitch-up is the result of a couple between the cable pull, the winch hook and the CG; partly offset by the wing pitching moment. Any dynamic set-up (figure 28 ①) where a force's line of action fails to pass through the CG of the object being acted upon – in this case the glider – is out of balance, and the 'system' attempts to straighten things up, literally.

[3]The K8 is bad in this respect, and even under very modest accelerations – trim and stick well forward – can pitch up quite strongly. The Olympia 460 (1960) was far worse. Most modern gliders are OK, but the often very light stick forces – and occasionally bad geometry between hand and stick which can result in the stick being pulled back under vertical accelerations – can lead to inadvertent over-rotation, particularly with a powerful winch.

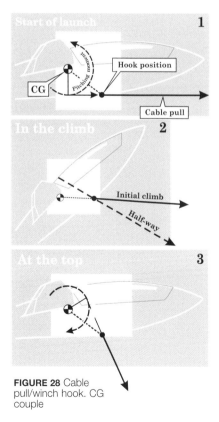

FIGURE 28 Cable pull/winch hook. CG couple

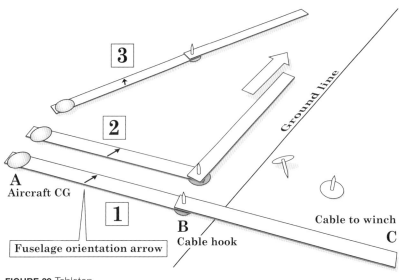

FIGURE 29 Tabletop demonstration of the couple

At some point later in the launch, the glider's attitude will be such that the cable pull, the hook and the CG are all in a direct line. Other causes excepted, the pitch-up ceases (figure 28 ②). Towards the top of the launch ③ the couple changes direction and the system's attempts to straighten out now have the effect of pitching the nose down.

To simulate the initial pitch-up, cut out two strips of card (AB and BC in figure 29 ①), put a drawing pin to act as a fixed pivot at A, and an inverted drawing pin at B to act as a hinge between them. AB represents the fixed distance between the CG and the hook; in the real world it is fixed, like a solid rod, into the glider. Mark AB with a small arrow to represent the orientation of the glider's fuselage. BC is the cable pull. Draw a 'ground line' or arrange the edge of a table to act as one. Arrange the strips as in figure 29 ②, which is approximately the relationship between the CG, the hook and the cable pull at the start of the launch, then pull C in the direction of the arrow. The whole system straightens out as in ③, and AB (glider attached!), swings nose up. This simple experiment is worth doing. Compare figures 28 and 29.

VERTICAL ACCELERATION

When a glider takes off on a winch or autotow launch and rotates into the climb, the balance between L and W has to change for the glider to start climbing at all. During the ground run the glider's vertical component of velocity is zero (figure 30). At the rotation into the climb, this zero has to be accelerated to a climb rate of, say 30kt (3,000ft/min), independent of any horizontal acceleration. It's easiest to think of this in terms of picking up a heavy object. Doing this quickly takes far more effort than doing it slowly. Quick or slow, the same amount of energy is expended overall, but quickly means having to pack it all into a shorter time (see chapter 1, p. 9; inertia), and in terms of rotating into the climb, that energy burst, so to speak, must be provided by the wing. The vertical rate of acceleration is dependent on the speed of the rotation, and the latter affects the wing loading and the AoA. If the rotation occurs too quickly for the airspeed at that instant, the wing can be 'overloaded' and stall. More likely, the loads become sufficiently high to break the weak link or a weakened cable. It is conceivable that the cable or weak link could break and the glider stall at the same instant. Normally, rotation takes place with the airspeed increasing, but even then more lift is required than usual. Once established in the climb, there is no further vertical acceleration even though the wing may still be having to do more work than in steady straight flight – it depends on the tension in the cable.

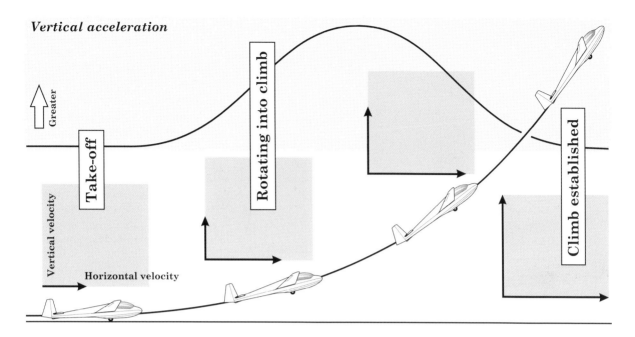

Vertical acceleration

Greater

Take-off

Rotating into climb

Climb established

Vertical velocity

Horizontal velocity

FIGURE 30 Vertical acceleration during rotation

FORCES IN THE CLIMB

The basic forces involved in a winch launch are not that complicated, even if they don't have quite the easy symmetry of figure 1. Taking each of the elements in figure 31 (see over) in turn, they are:

(1)   the lift generated by the wings. This is a function of speed and AoA, and will change, depending on the load factor

(2)   the wing pitching moment. This is an aerodynamic effect which remains more or less constant

(3)   the pull of the cable

(4)   the influence of the cable, hook and CG couple

(5)   the weight of the glider

(6)   the drag forces. Aerodynamic again, and very large if the glider is operating at a high AoA

(7)   the tailplane loads, which aren't necessarily downwards.

Almost regardless of where the glider is in the launch sequence, and assuming the cable is being pulled in at a constant speed throughout, note the following;

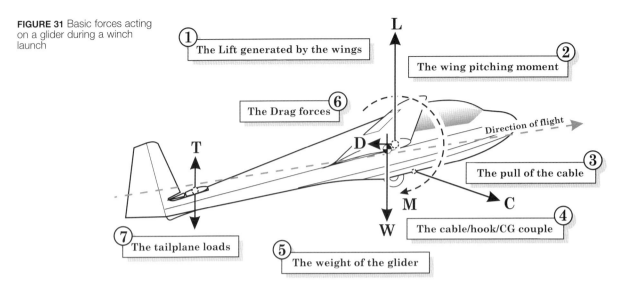

FIGURE 31 Basic forces acting on a glider during a winch launch

① The Lift generated by the wings
② The wing pitching moment
⑥ The Drag forces
③ The pull of the cable
④ The cable/hook/CG couple
⑤ The weight of the glider
⑦ The tailplane loads

- when the glider rotates into the climb there is a vertical acceleration – you are going from a zero vertical velocity to whatever the climb rate happens to be after you've stopped rotating

- in a steady climb, rotating to a steeper one increases the cable/glider loads. If the initial steady climb was shallow, the increases are low. If the climb was already steep, then the increases will be correspondingly larger

- the steeper the climb, the higher the load and the larger the pull on the cable, and vice versa. (Pulling back hard on the stick will, apart from anything else, break the weak link, or the cable, whichever is weakest)

- if the cable speed remains steady, a steeper climb will give a higher airspeed (this is not true for constant torque or underpowered winches because the cable speeds fluctuate)

- the highest airframe loads, but not necessarily the highest AoAs, are at the top of the launch.

The load calculations assume a weak link of a specified strength. **It is very important to use the correct one**. If the glider you normally fly was designed to use a white weak link (breaking strain 1,100lb) and you try to launch using a black one (breaking strain 2,200lb), you can double the loads on the glider, and not know a thing about it, until .... !

Summary of chapter four

Page	Subject	
110	**Centripetal force**	into turn force; also 'into' any manoeuvre, such as a loop.
–	**Centrifugal force**	apparent force acting in exactly the opposite direction to centripetal force.
102	**Drag producing devices**	*see* also chapter 5, section 2, pp. 164–5; chapter 6, pp. 197–9.
104	**Deceleration**	decrease in rate of change of velocity.
102	**Drag (D)**	assumed to act parallel to and against the direction of flight, at right angles to lift.
107	**Effective weight**	increase or decrease in weight as a result of acceleration.
106	**Flight path sag**	a non-technical term describing what happens during the first few seconds after a glider pitches nose down.
119–20	**Initial pitch-up**	couple between CG, hook position and cable pull during a winch launch (*Couple, see* chapter 1, p. 18).
119	**Level flight**	not really possible in gliders (*see* 'flying uphill', p. 114–8).
107, 110	**Load factor, 'n'**	measure of the number of G units to which a glider is being subjected.
110	**Stalling speed**	increases with the overall load factor (n) $V_s = \sqrt{n} \times$ *unaccelerated stalling speed. See* table on p. 111 for V against n. Loadings applicable to turns and pullouts, etc (*see* also chapter 7).
102, 103	**Thrust (T)**	for gliders – an 'engine like' force producing forward motion.
103	**Total Reaction (TR)**	usually refers to the resultant of lift and drag, but can be the resultant of any forces.
106	**Wing loading**	wing area (S) divided by all up weight (W); an average over the whole wing.

CHAPTER 5

THE PLACARD, STRUCTURE AND FLIGHT LIMITATIONS

CHAPTER CONTENTS ★ should know ☆ useful

CHAPTER CONTENTS   ★ should know   ☆ useful

5 THE PLACARD, STRUCTURE AND FLIGHT LIMITATIONS

Section one: structure

```
┌─────────────────────────────────────────────┐
│ LIMITATIONS PLACARD              BGA/267/P    │
│                                               │
│ B.G.A. No   4198        TYPE   K21            │
│                                               │
│ CATEGORY:  NON AEROBATIC/AEROBATIC            │
│            SEMI AEROBATIC/CLOUD FLYING        │
│                                               │
│ SPEED LIMITATIONS (Knots)                     │
│                                               │
│ Auto/Winch    81         Rough Air    108     │
│                                               │
│ Aero Tow      97         VNE          151     │
│                                               │
│ Flaps         N/A        Gear Down    151     │
│                                               │
│ WEIGHT AND C.G LIMITATIONS                    │
│                                               │
│ Max. Wt. (dry) 1320    Max. Wt. (water) N/A   │
│                                               │
│ Empty Wt.  792         Min. Solo. Wt.  154    │
│                                               │
│ Max. Solo Wt. 242      Date Weighed  12 Feb 96│
│                                               │
│ Note: Refer to Flight Manual for full limitations │
│                                               │
│ Issued by .............    Dated .............│
└─────────────────────────────────────────────┘
```

FIGURE 1 The flight limitations placard

The placard

The flight limitations placard (figure 1) is familiar to glider pilots, who will know something about the limits specified, even if it is only 'thou shalt not exceed', rather than the reason behind it. The first part of this chapter describes how the glider's structure copes with the loads to which it is subjected, while the second part describes how and why the limiting speeds are defined. The placard weights and CG limitations are dealt with in Chapter 6, p. 174.

Joint Airworthiness Requirements (JAR)

In different countries over the years there have been various sets of airworthiness standards relating to glider design. These include OSTIV (Organisation Scientifique et Technique Internationale de Vol a Voile); BCAR (British Civil Airworthiness Requirements); and JAR (Joint Airworthiness Requirements). Between 1945 and about 1965 all UK gliders were designed and built to BCAR, now superseded by

JAR. All the design criteria examples in this chapter are taken from JAR22: 'Sailplanes and Powered Sailplanes'. Bear in mind that you will fly gliders – particularly older ones – which have been designed to meet different standards.

The JAR is published by the Civil Aviation Authority (CAA) and is the UK version of several European countries' 'wish to cooperate in agreeing common comprehensive airworthiness requirements'. JAR22 covers every aspect of glider design in some detail, from the loading requirements to the minimum acceptable handling characteristics, crash worthiness and – in the case of a dual control glider – control cables/rods to allow for the pilots 'acting in opposition'. JAR22 details what should be in the maintenance manual, on the flight limitations placard, how the instruments are to be marked, what the icons on the smaller placards shall look like, and so on. Every known loading condition is catered for in one way or another, and where appropriate, there is a formula for working out what is or isn't acceptable.

Bureaucratic though it may seem, JAR22 represents the design and theoretical savvy of many people over many years. Minimum design criteria are defined, and how the various elements are supposed to interact with each other, giving designers an agreed standard from which to work. This is important, but there is nothing to prevent them from working to a higher standard if they wish. Even though JAR22 does make a number of assumptions about how the average pilot behaves, these are based on years of experience and rightly make little allowance, if any, for the individual who feels duty bound to prance off into a clearly marked minefield to demonstrate exactly where at least one mine is located.

Gliders not built to JAR22 or something very similar, are unlikely to be granted Certificates of Airworthiness (Cs of A), or an equivalent in countries which either don't use or don't recognise the standard. Even so, a national test group charged with the task of assessing aircraft for certification could suggest the issuing of a restricted rating if, in their opinion, the glider in question met the majority of the criteria, though this would obviously depend on which requirements were not being met. In this country at least, any surprises that the average pilot might get when evaluating his newly purchased state-of-the-art glider will probably be his or her own fault.

STRAIGHT FLIGHT

If correctly trimmed and left undisturbed, a glider will coast along by itself, neither accelerating nor decelerating. Even without manoeuvring, the structure of the glider is being subjected to loads of various kinds, most of them in the vertical plane. During any manoeuvre the glider's effective weight will change, subjecting the airframe to additional loads, not all of them directly G-related. More complicated manoeuvres subject the airframe to more complicated and often much more savage loads.

Types of load

Figure 2 (see over) illustrates the types of load to which any structure can be subjected:

- *torsional* loads involve twisting, an action similar to wringing a towel

- *compression* loads involve a material being pushed in on itself; squashing-type loads

- *tension* loads result when a material is being pulled apart

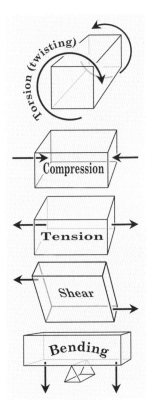

FIGURE 2 Types of load

- *shear* loads are created when the top part of an object, say, is being pulled one way and the bottom part another. Two separated but unequal forces acting in the same direction on an object also create shear.

- *bending* loads are snapping loads of the kind you would apply to a pencil if you were trying to break it – they combine most of the above loads.

Structural components of a glider can be subjected to any or all of these loads at any time.

SOME GENERAL POINTS

Loads and forces are as invisible as the air and all that we see of them is their effects. In the very early days of engineering, long before aviation came along with its own special set of requirements, when anything broke you replaced it with something bigger. This might then break under its own weight, but somewhere between 'too weak' and 'too heavy' there would be a nice balance, usually arrived at by trial and error.

All engineering techniques, including architecture and aeroplane construction, undergo a process of gradual refinement. Once built and shown to work, cost-effective considerations gradually pare components down – make this thinner, remove that (it doesn't seem to do much anyway!) – until just sufficient for the job remains. The last stage can be overdone, and the result is a wreck.

Computer-aided design can now help us see the previously invisible, loads included, and one might imagine that this would reduce levels of likely error to zero. Imagine is the word; for all their sophistication, these newer tools are still model-making. They have some of the limitations of more conventional models, and add a few of their own, some of which we haven't seen before, so things still tend to go snap.

DESIGN CONSIDERATIONS

Less guesswork is involved in design these days, and for aircraft there should be as little as possible. Listed below, not necessarily in order of importance, are some of the items that need to be taken into account in the design of almost any structure:

- its purpose (bridge, garden shed, ocean liner)

- what is the most stressful combination of loads to which it is ever likely to be subjected, and how often are they likely to occur (marching soldiers, tornadoes, meteorite impact, children)?

- how long does it need to last (temporary, permanent, disintegrate two seconds after the guarantee expires so that the customer has to buy another one)?

- what are the most suitable materials to use (paper, metal, glass-reinforced plastic, stone)?

- the operating environment (under the sea, out in space, inside a handbag)

- who is going to be using it?

Cost can also be a significant and sometimes detrimental factor in the design process.

BASIC PRINCIPLES OF DESIGN

The first and most basic principle of engineering is: 'this is a load, resist it'. The second is: 'do as much as you can with as little (effort and/or money) as possible'. Most engineering textbooks, belying this principle of economy of means, seem about six feet thick, so 30 pages or so is hardly enough to cover the subject in full.

In one sense every structure is *load bearing*, even if all it does is hold itself up. A structure can be reasonably straightforward from a design point of view if the loads it has to withstand remain either relatively constant or never exceed well defined and well understood limits. A glider's structure, on the other hand, has to cope with a wide range of different types of load, very few of which have constant values or maintain the same relationship to each other. A major load-bearing component like the wing must resist the vertical bending loads produced by the weight of the fuselage and gusts in the air, as well as fore and aft and torsional loads, whatever their causes; very often all of them at once.

As well as the more obvious design requirements are others which are more subtle. Contrary to what we might expect, a flexible structure can be as strong as a more rigid one which is otherwise comparable in every respect. A flexible structure may actually appear to be the stronger precisely because it 'gives'. Equally, individual components don't have to respond in the same way to loads along different axes, though this does depend on the component's exact function. For example, the wing must have high *torsional rigidity* (resistance to twisting), and without it can end up twisting itself to pieces. On the other hand, there are advantages to some flexibility along the wings' main load-bearing vertical axis, including the comparatively trivial one of a more comfortable ride in rough conditions. However, there are types and frequencies of structural springiness which could easily make the ride a great deal worse.

Just because floppy wings help with a 'comfy glide' it does not follow that the glider was designed with that in mind. A glider cleared for looping manoeuvres may be enjoying a by-product of a design aimed at meeting more mundane manoeuvring requirements, rather than having been designed 'to do loops'. The same goes for floppy wings. One component that must be as rigid as possible along every axis is the rear fuselage. If this exhibited the same kind of whip-like strength and flexibility as, say, a fishing rod, the results would be lethal.

Some glider components bear no significant loads, but are necessary nonetheless. Fairings smooth the flow of the air and reduce drag; the cockpit canopy keeps the pilot out of the airflow, prevents him or her becoming a drag, and provides an opportunity to enjoy the view every once in a while. Whatever its function, there is very little on a glider which can be called cosmetic.

TESTING TO DESTRUCTION

As indisputably trite as it may sound, a common feature of the materials used in load-bearing objects like chairs, tables, aeroplanes and so on, is that they don't break easily. There are, however, some apparent exceptions to this observation. For example, the fibres in glass cloth are neither particularly strong nor rigid by themselves, and would seem to be entirely unsuitable for use in a life-critical structure.

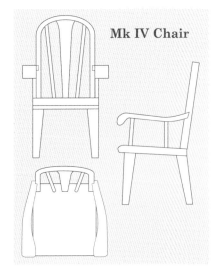

FIGURE 3 A 'standard' chair

Regardless of the individual characteristics of a material, a distinction needs to be drawn between the material and the structure of which it forms such a crucial part. It is perfectly possible to create a weak structure out of strong materials, and vice versa.

All load-bearing materials also have something else in common. Each will pass through a series of critical and measurable points on their way to complete failure.

A single seat chair (figure 3) is designed to support a standard person who can weigh anything between a few pounds and, say, 18 stone. The chair fits its specification if it does the job for which it was designed without endangering the occupant. If 12 people all sat on a normal chair simultaneously it would certainly be operating outside its *design envelope*, and probably collapse. If not, then it was far too strong for its intended job, and both material and money were wasted – the structure was over-engineered.

The various critical points can be located if you can persuade enough volunteers to take part in a dodgy experiment which involves squeezing them all on to the chair, one at a time. As the load increases, put on a white coat, stand back and make notes. The starting point is the unloaded chair, made of wood, let's say, properly designed, and not trendily bendy. With one occupant, the chair will deform very slightly, usually unnoticeably. When the occupant stands up and the load is removed, the chair returns to its original shape and has lost none of its original strength.

As you begin loading the chair with more and more people, it will begin to deform noticeably. Initially, if all the sitters stand up, it will spring back to its original shape and be as strong as ever. Technically, the material's *elastic limits* have not been exceeded. The material may have bent, but it sprang back into shape without anything inside having been ripped, torn, fractured, split or otherwise overstressed.

The second, and more critical point occurs when enough people are sat on the chair for it to deform noticeably, but not return to its original shape when they all stand up again. The material has now been stressed beyond its elastic limit and the chair as a whole has exceeded its *limit load* and been weakened. The permanent deformation that results from this kind of damage is known as *set*. Wood reaches this critical point, but unlike most metals, the distance to the next point may be almost non-existent.

The third critical, and in this case terminal, point occurs when the already weakened chair is only just able to support, let us say, six people. Put a straw on the top of this human stack and the chair immediately collapses, throwing everyone onto the floor. You are now aware of the *ultimate load* and are the proud owner of useful scientific knowledge, half a dozen writs, and a small stack of firewood.

THE PILOT AND LOADS

Airframes need to be as light and strong *as is practical*, not as strong as possible. There's a big difference. A virtually indestructible glider could be milled out of a solid block of metal, like the wings of many military aircraft, but huge expense and weight apart, the exercise would be pointless. Without the benefit of a G-suit even the fittest pilot would black out way before such a sturdy airframe had even flexed. JAR22 uses human biology to define some of the design limits, and assumes that the average pilot will begin to black out just beyond four G.[1] This will cause them to either relax back pressure on the stick or just let go, and thus limit the loads on the airframe, saving it from ruin. One could interpret this to mean that it is acceptable for the glider to break up if the pilot is unconscious at the time, but all it says is that an airframe need only be sufficiently rather than excessively strong. It's a point worth remembering.

In any event, aerodynamic forces increase as the square of the speed, and there are very definite limits to the loads a glider can withstand, although the result may not be a catastrophic structural failure. The glider can become uncontrollable instead.

What the foregoing boils down to is these two points:

(1) the design of any load-bearing structure is often a juggling act to find the least exciting balance between the wastefully silly and the downright dangerous

(2) aircraft are designed to operate within the constraints of a manoeuvring envelope (*see* p. 152) whose boundaries are defined by speed and loading limitations.

Materials

In the same way that every design requires a set of operating parameters of the 'what is it supposed to be doing?' kind listed earlier, so too is there a sub-list relating to the choice of materials. For example, not in order of importance, is a material:

• easy to rip or tear?

• stronger in one direction than another (does it have a grain)?

• easy to cut and shape, and are specialised tools required?

• simple to join to itself or to other materials and. . .

• . . . what's the best way to do this?

• easily fatigued? Does repeated bending, however caused, gradually (or suddenly) weaken and/or break it?

• subject to *creep*, i.e. deforms gradually and permanently even under very small loads?

• uniform, or does it vary in strength and/or density, i.e. knotholes in wood?

• durable in the sense of being resistant to rot, rust or other forms of corrosion?

• flexible or brittle (does it shatter?)?

• affected by temperature, and in what ways?

• chemically inert, or does it react with other materials?

---

[1]The black out point is partly dependent on a pilot's general health and blood pressure. High blood pressure means higher G before black out. A semi-reclining pilot is more resistant to blacking out than one sitting upright, because the heart doesn't have to pump blood so far uphill.

JAR22.613 MATERIAL
STRENGTH PROPERTIES
AND DESIGN VALUES
(a) Material strength
properties must be based on
enough tests to establish
design values on a statistical
basis
(b) The design values must
be chosen so that the
probability of any structure
being under-strength,
because of material variation,
is extremely remote

The last item is probably the least obvious. When two dissimilar types of metal are brought into contact they can act like a battery, and current will flow between them. You can give yourself a very unpleasant shock by touching a fork or a piece of silver paper to the mercury amalgam of a tooth filling. The voltage involved wouldn't light a torch bulb, but that's not what the nerves in your tooth tell you. For you, the effect lasts as long as the split second it takes you to break the contact. Two dissimilar metals in contact have no nerves and do not spring apart, so any current that flows between them will do so continuously, and one of them will corrode.

Two further items that could be added to the list are the persistent 'is it cheap?' and the more contemporary 'is it poisonous?' A number of the modern materials, or some of their associated chemicals, are not very good for your health.

THE STRUCTURE OF MATERIALS
Wood
We tend to think of wood as a single thing which comes to us ready made, courtesy of nature. In fact, the structure of wood is a sophisticated and complicated composite made up of a number of elements which have evolved together over time, not merely to prevent the tree from being flattened by the wind, but to fulfil several other functions one of which includes the transport of water from the roots to the leaves. Not only does the tree support itself, but it is, among other things, also a pump.

Much of a tree's strength is down to a very specific arrangement of several not always very obviously distinct parts. To oversimplify the case, the internal structure of trunk and branches is a series of bundled tubes of various lengths, each stiffened with a helical pattern of cellulose threads, called fibrils (figure 4). The tree's flexibility depends on its type and age, and the thickness of the trunk, but the overall structure is resilient and damage-resistant. A drawback of the alignment and grouping of the major cells is that it gives wood a *grain*, which results in a weak and a strong direction (figure 5) – very obvious if you split a log for firewood. An additional 'feature' of cut and seasoned wood is that its moisture content changes with the climate.

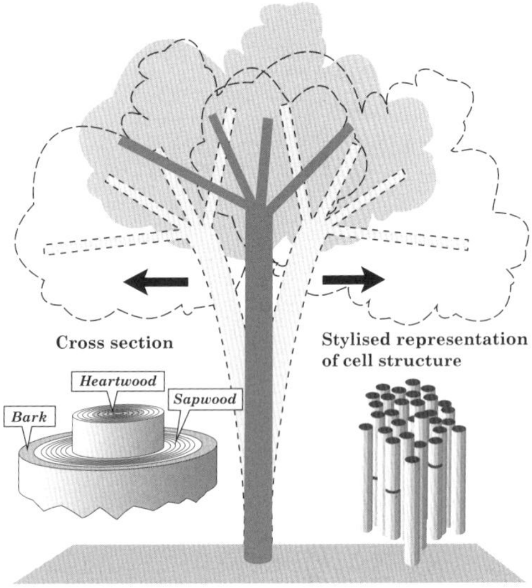

Materials which split or crack easily, even if in one direction only, aren't ideal. Were aerodynamic loads always in the same direction to within predictable and quite narrow limits, then the material's best and strongest direction could be arranged to always lie at right angles to these loads. This principle is both the most logical and the one that actually works, but sometimes, organising the loads to conform to the grain isn't entirely straightforward.

To set strength against weakness, thin sheets of wood are layered together so that the grain of each runs in a different direction (figure 6), forming plywood. The ply illustrated is only two layers thick (two-ply) with the grains at right angles, but

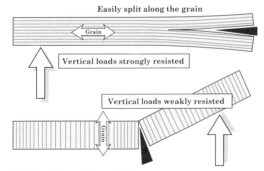

Cross section

Heartwood

Bark | *Sapwood*

Stylised representation of cell structure

FIGURE 4 Tubular tree

Easily split along the grain

Grain

Vertical loads strongly resisted

Vertical loads weakly resisted

Grain

FIGURE 5 The effects of grain

there is no reason why there shouldn't be many more layers, as there usually are. Such layering also helps to prevent buckling (*see* p. 140), and thin, multilayer ply is both flexible and strong enough to be moulded around simple curves without splitting.

Many woods are not much use in aviation, for the following reasons:

- crooked grain

- easily split

- too many knotholes

- too heavy, though they may well be very strong. Aircraft spars are not made of oak, even though it was once the major material for oceangoing ships

- they don't come in long or straight enough lengths, and are either too flexible or not flexible enough

- too soft.

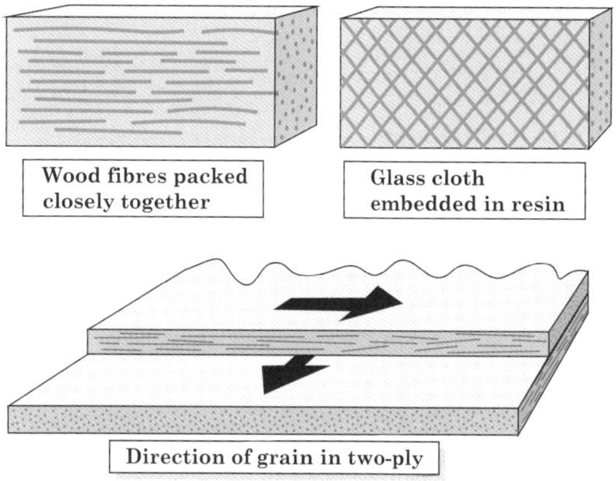

Wood fibres packed closely together

Glass cloth embedded in resin

Direction of grain in two-ply

FIGURE 6 Comparisons of wood and GRP

High quality spruce, Baltic pine or ash are the main woods used for glider construction. They are fairly flexible, with a long, even grain and few knotholes. They have good strength to weight ratios. Birch is also frequently used for plywood.

Fibreglass (GRP)

There would seem to be no connection whatsoever between wood and glass reinforced plastic (GRP), but there are, in fact, some interesting similarities. For a start, the long fibres and cells in wood are analogous to the strands in glass cloth (figure 7). And even though the cloth is woven and wood is not, plywood can be seen as a form of woven wood – the principle is very similar.

By themselves the glass strands are thin and somewhat brittle; far too frangible for a load-bearing structure. They are, however, highly resistant in tension. Nevertheless, pick up glass cloth and it usually sags wearily (figure 7, (A)). The frictional resistance between individual strands is low, so they slide past each other fairly readily; if the ends of a bundle were straight to start with, they remain so (B), but no longer form a right angle. Each fixed length strand is being bent round a curve of a different radius, and for them to be able to bend at all, each must slide past its neighbours.

Encasing the strands in a resin – not particularly strong by itself – sticks them together and creates a locking mechanism which prevents sliding (figure 7, (C)). The result is a big increase in rigidity and shear

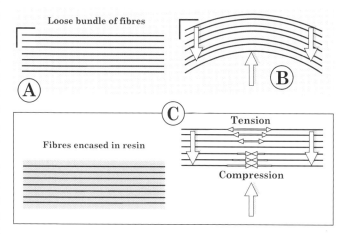

Loose bundle of fibres

Fibres encased in resin

Tension

Compression

FIGURE 7 How fibreglass gets its strength

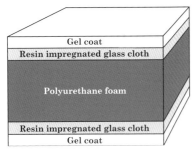

FIGURE 8 Basic GRP structure

strength, partly offset by the fact that the resin – the P (plastic) in GRP – needs to retain some small degree of flexibility to prevent it cracking if the structure bends. The polyurethane foam layer lying between many GRP gliders' layers of fibreglass (figure 8), which helps maintain the smooth shape, is another example of two items, neither of them particularly strong or rigid, combining for greater strength. Balsawood was the sandwich material for early generation GRP.

Some of the advantages of fibreglass over wood are:

- easy moulding into *compound curves* (simultaneous curvature in more than one plane). The wing's leading edge is a single plane or *simple curve*, like the tube in figure 9. The fuselage nose is a compound curve, like the ball

- structural stability (keeps its shape well)

- a more seamless structure, internally and externally, than is possible with metal or wood

- metal fittings can be embedded rather than bolted on (although awkward to replace)

- relatively *low maintenance*

- repair work ought to be quicker and easier.

As for the disadvantages, cheaper gliders was one of GRP's original selling points, and whatever happened to that? In addition, some resins weaken in high temperatures and, for that reason, the overwhelming majority of GRP gliders are white, to reflect heat. Depending on the chemical formulation, steep temperature gradients through the *gel coat* are bad news. When a glider spends long enough at altitude for the entire airframe to cool to below freezing, the stresses caused by descending rapidly into warmer air can crack the gel coat into crazy paving.

Metal

The internal structure of metal is basically a crystalline lattice, the simplest form of which is shown in figure 10. Unlike wood, metal in its pure form is composed of exactly the same stuff throughout, and the regularity of the atoms' arrangement helps to make the metal equally strong in all directions, or, as in the case of graphite (figure 10), equally weak. Graphite, or pencil lead, has little resistance to shear stress, and as you run the pencil over a page successive layers shear off and transfer to the paper – not ideal for a structural material.

Melting metals together produces *alloys*, whose combined characteristics are different from, and very often more useful than, those of the pure metals. The commonest alloys are iron-based. Adding small quantities of carbon to iron produces steel. Other 'flavourings' might be manganese or molybdenum, for example, or almost any combination of any of them. *High tensile steel* as used in a roller bearing for a wheel, or for a glider wing-root

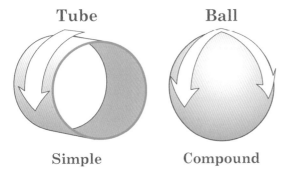

FIGURE 9 Types of curvature

fitting, would contain somewhere between 0.7% and 0.25% of carbon, and probably trace amounts of other metals. Phosphor bronze – a very hard material used for bearings – is, as the name suggests, based on tin and copper (bronze), and phosphorous. In all alloys the percentage amount of each ingredient can be critical, and the 'cooking' process has to be tightly controlled. Aluminium-based alloys have better strength to weight ratios than iron-based ones, and so are used a great deal in aviation.

Whether the metal is an alloy or not, forging, casting or rolling, as well as sudden heating or cooling, can affect the material's hardness, brittleness, *ductility* (stretchability), and so on. In any case, aircraft metals are either chosen for, or tailored to, their specific function. When the addition of some 'flavourings' can raise the melting point of a pure metal, and the addition of others lower it, something fundamental must be happening at the atomic level. It is probably fair to say that we know what *alloying* does, but not exactly how it works, so it is difficult to come up with an analogy which suits! One view is to imagine the lattice of the added ingredient interlocking with the lattice of the base material, with their combined properties being determined by how tangled the interlock is.

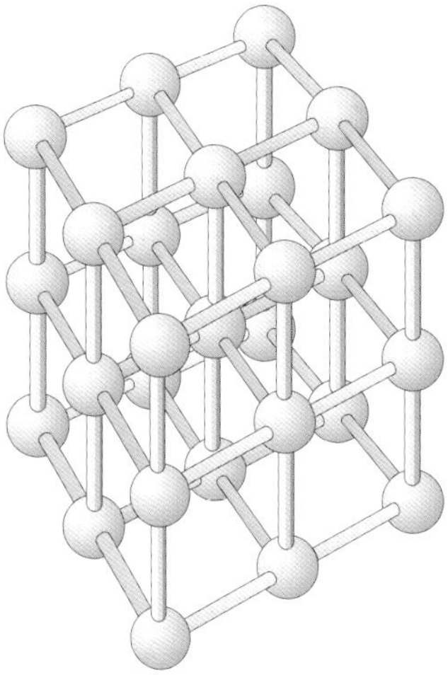

FIGURE 10 A simple lattice (graphite)

CRACKS, FRACTURES AND FATIGUE

A weakness of crystalline lattices is that once the bonds between the atoms have been broken in one area – whatever the cause and no matter how small and invisible the result – cracks then tend to propagate out in almost any direction throughout the rest of the material. Such *stress fractures* propagate very readily from the stress concentrations which naturally occur at sharp corners and edges, so load-bearing metal components are always rounded and smoothed off in these areas (figure 11).

Were glass cloth to crack as readily as window glass there would be a serious problem – and we wouldn't use it – but the spread of any cracks that do occur is largely contained by the physical separation of the individual strands. But because GRP structures are built up out of several layers or laminations of cloth, they are relatively weak along the plane between the layers. Certain types of load can crack or shatter the binding resin and the layers then separate, or *delaminate*. The only external clue to extensive damage may be some local cracking or crazing of the gel coat. Delamination is very serious because even though the cloth may be intact, it has lost rigidity.

Fatigue is exactly what it says: weariness within a material's structure. Materials vary greatly in their resistance to fatigue, but given continual and sufficient flexing – which can have causes ranging from normal in-flight loads to noise vibration (*acoustic fatigue*) – the internal structure of almost any material will eventually start to break down. If you are a modeller, or know somebody who is, take the polystyrene sprue to which the kit's bits were attached, and keep bending it quickly and fairly vigorously until it fails, which won't take very long. The material changes colour where it is under the greatest stress, and can become exceedingly hot. The heat is a

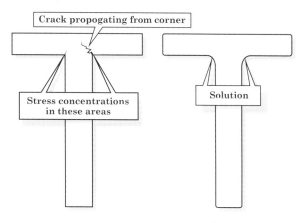

FIGURE 11 Stress fractures at sharp corners

FIGURE 12 The glider as a series of linked girders or beams

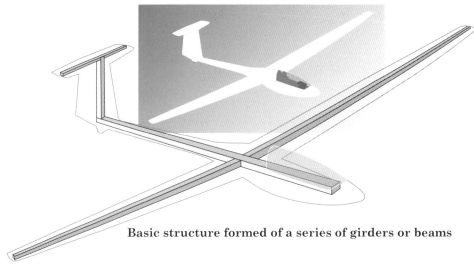

Basic structure formed of a series of girders or beams

result of molecular bonds being ripped apart, and indicates that failure is occurring, even if you can't see any obvious cracks or fractures. The material eventually snaps.

GRP's resistance to fatigue seems good, though an assessment of just how good will have to await the first failures. Wood has been in use for so long that its fatigue characteristics, which are generally excellent, are well understood. Its biological ancestry has fine-tuned it to weather years of random buffets and blows, and, in that sense, it is in its element as part of an aircraft. Metal, given its structure, is more prone to fatigue.

BRIDGES

The basic load-bearing structure of a glider can be viewed as a series of linked girders or beams (figure 12). How does a beam work, and how are loads led through a structure in such a way that no individual component is put under excessive strain?

Most bridges over country ditches are little more than planks, with no apparent connection with either aircraft or far more complex 'knitwear' structures like the Forth Rail Bridge. Yet a load is always a load, and the unassuming plank is doing much the same job as its more self-important relatives.

We'll assume that our crude plank bridge is wide enough to walk on and relatively rigid (figure 13). It is laid across a ditch and supported at each end by a few bricks. When we use it, several things immediately become clear:

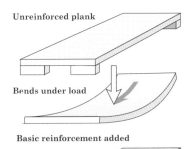

Unreinforced plank

Bends under load

Basic reinforcement added

FIGURE 13 Simple plank bridge

- the plank bends when we put any weight on it

- it bends most when we are standing over the middle and deepest part of the ditch (OK from an engineering point of view, perhaps, but psychologically dispiriting)

- it is as springy and difficult to walk on as a trampoline

- we always have to walk uphill from the centre, and.. .

- if it isn't strong enough it breaks, usually when we're nearest the middle.

Even if the plank doesn't break it will almost certainly be far too flexible. There are two ways to stiffen it. The first is to make the plank substantially thicker. This is the twelve bore shotgun solution: fire in approximately the right direction and hope that at least one of several hundred pellets will strike home. Thickening things up increases the weight, and is inappropriate for a slightly less obvious reason: plank bridges are almost invariably far too strong in directions in which loads are hardly ever applied – in this case sideways. Material is being wasted allowing for something that is either never going to happen, or so infrequently that it isn't worth taking into account. For instance, 150mph gusts of wind occur somewhere in the UK about once every 70 years. Would there be any real point in allowing for them in a bridge designed to last five? Probably not, but then the weather can't count. There might be three big gusts in 10 years, and then none for 100 years afterwards. That aside, removing 'excessive' material from the sides and adding it to top and bottom creates what is effectively a plank on its edge – which we'll need to be tightrope artists to use.

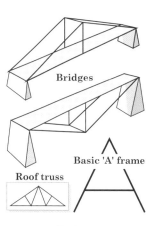

FIGURE 14 Triangular structure

The second and far more efficient way of stiffening the plank is to leave it as it is and add reinforcement only along the axis or axes requiring it, in this case the vertical one. Given that we are trying to keep the weight down, we have to do just enough to give the vertically acting load created by our weight the impression, so to speak, that the plank is far beefier than it really is. The crudest solution is to add two beams at right angles to the plank, along the lower outside edge (figure 13). It's clumsy, but effective. However, for about the same overall increase in weight, we could make something much more robust. The simplest and most open structure for the job is based on a triangle (figures 14 and 15). By itself a triangle, as outlined by *abc* (figure 14), is not enough. When there is any load the plank will bend and the structure distort. Adding the vertical strut *bd* ties the top and bottom of the triangle together. Now when we step onto the plank, *bd* transmits the major bending load to the apex of triangle *abc*, and tries to pull it downwards. The attempt is thwarted by the two side struts, *ab* and *bc*, which are pushed up along their length by their end supports and pulled down by the central load. The result is a stalemate between the various forces involved. All other things being equal, our weight is now well supported by a more rigid structure of no great extra weight, and as far as the vertical loads are aware, the plank is thicker.

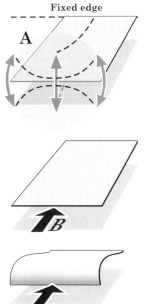

FIGURE 16 Rigidity of flat sheet

FIGURE 15 Basic triangular constructions

RESISTANCE IS USEFUL

By way of making some additional points about *reinforcement*, take a reasonably thin sheet of ply or metal which can be easily flexed from side to side (figure 16, (A)). Fixing one end of the sheet rigidly to a workbench makes

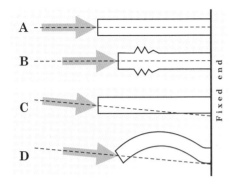

FIGURE 17 Result of applied forces 'end-on'

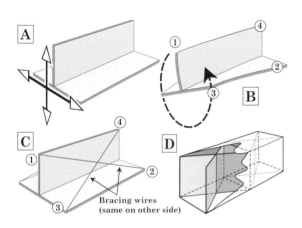

FIGURE 18 Bracing to add rigidity

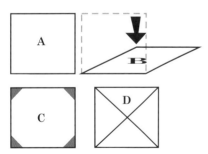

FIGURE 19 Diagonal reinforcement of box section

the various modes of flexure, particularly the lack of *torsional* (twisting) *rigidity*, more obvious.

Depending on the sheet's thickness, a considerable compression force can be applied by pushing against it in the direction indicated by the arrow in figure 16, (B). At first nothing happens, then, very suddenly, the sheet buckles (C). The resistance to compression all but disappears, leaving only the *bending resistance* which, by comparison, is far weaker. If we keep pushing, the sheet will buckle further and may break where the bending is greatest.

It is difficult to say precisely when buckling will occur – the whole process is a bit knife-edge – but it depends partly on the direction of the compression force. With the applied force acting exactly along the sheet's centre line, parallel to the top and bottom surfaces (figure 17, (A)), bending and buckling will be resisted longer than if the applied force acts slightly out of line (C). Even if bending or buckling doesn't occur, the internal structure of something like wood can be seriously damaged by crushing or crumpling (B).

Bending and buckling can be delayed, if not entirely defeated, by reinforcing an appropriate axis, so a sheet likely to buckle in a vertical direction (D) needs vertical reinforcement.

TAKING THE TWIST (TORSION)

Placing a vertical sheet on the previous horizontal one (figure 18, (A)), prevents vertical flexing in a similar manner to the bridge's triangular frame. Additionally, the vertical sheet acts as a *stiffener* in the horizontal plane, making the inverted 'T' combination far more rigid in the directions indicated by the white headed arrows (A). This has scant effect on the torsional rigidity, unfortunately, and twist applied to the inverted 'T' will deform it easily (B). This reduces the 'T's bending resistance, and a given load applied from vertically below will have far more effect on (B) than it does on (A), even though they are essentially the same structure.

Clearly reinforcement is needed, but where? When the 'T' beam is twisted anti-clockwise (B), corners ① and ② move further apart whilst corners ③ and ④ move closer together. A diagonal tie, a *bracing wire* (C), between ① and ② stops them moving apart. Wires aren't perfect because, when the one joining ① and ② tightens up, that between ③ and ④ goes slack, and vice versa. One wire is always doing nothing, which is inefficient. The wires can be replaced by sticks or rods, or by additional sheets (D), all of which brace when in tension or compression. The penalty is likely to be extra weight, but that can be set against the extra strength.

BOXES AND GIRDERS

The optimum load bearer will probably turn out to have a box section (a *box girder*) containing diagonal members for internal bracing, and/or *formers* or *frames*, to help maintain the cross-sectional shape (figure 19). Box (A) has no internal stiffening, and like a cardboard box on its side with both ends open, collapses easily (B). (C) shows triangular *fillets* in the corners, and (D) shows diagonal internal bracing to prevent this. Though both types of reinforcement do the same job, the choice of shape, internal structure, and so on, comes down to 'what's the component supposed to be doing?','how stressful is its job?', and again, 'do we want extra weight?'

In aviation's earlier days, saving a pound or two of weight could mean the difference between staggering into the air and pretending to be a racing car. The fuselages of the oldest aircraft, and some of the older gliders still around (T21), were 'outline' boxes from which absolutely everything except the barest essentials had been removed. The resulting skeleton (figure 20) is yet another variation upon the triangular frame of the bridge.

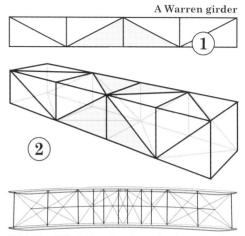

A Warren girder

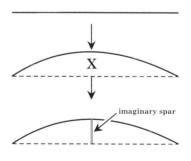

Wright Flyer 1903 - Struts and bracing on wings (approx locations)

FIGURE 20 Girder, box and bracing

SUCH A DRAG

Early airframes would have collapsed without wire bracing, but it was all out in the airflow and created most of the drag. Hiding it in a fabric-covered fuselage is easy (figure 20, ②), but the wings are a different matter. The aerofoil sections of early aircraft were not very deep, and the wing wasn't much more than a bed sheet supported and shaped by a series of very thin ribs, a leading and trailing edge spar which were not load-bearing, and a fairly minimal main spar – if there was one. When airspeeds were low, the drag created by the elaborate crisscross of largely external wires was also relatively low; luckily so, because the engine power available was anaemic.

As power output improved and speeds rose, up went the drag levels along with all the aerodynamic and structural loads. Adding more external wires would not have helped, and they mutated, as it were, into smaller numbers of streamlined struts. By what seems now to be an inevitable process, these too finally disappeared and the wing became a curved box with all the load-bearing elements inside, out of the airflow. Interestingly, aerofoil theory had quite a lot to do with speeding this process along (*see* chapter 7, pp. 207–8).

STRESSED SKIN, OR MONOCOQUE CONSTRUCTION

In the previous how-to-make-it-stronger (and lighter) discussions, every solution contained straight lines of one kind or another. Since loads act in straight lines and can't do much else, that's not surprising. Nevertheless, direct though loads are, curved sheets of material can create huge amounts of extra strength.

The key lies in what happens when a sheet of suitable material is bent into a curve (figure 21). The effect is similar to introducing an imaginary spar of the same material and approximately similar depth at point X in the figure. Crudely speaking, the curved sheet will be as strong in the vertical plane (up and down the page) as would be the imaginary spar – it can be seen as another variation of the 'T'. When a suitably flexible sheet of material is bent into a curve (figure 22, see over), it becomes very inflexible at right angles to the plane of the curve, and the more so the sharper the curvature. The results can be so strong that, used as a

X

imaginary spar

FIGURE 21 Principles of monocoque

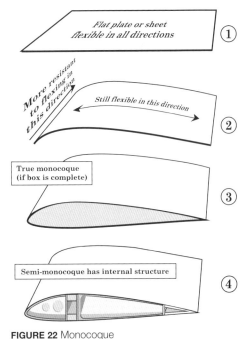

FIGURE 22 Monocoque construction

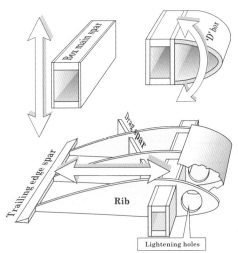

FIGURE 23 Basic construction of wing

covering, the sheet bears some if not most of the loads previously taken by a more complex unclad structure, much of which then becomes redundant and can be removed – but with care.

A structure in which the skin is either the major or the sole load-bearing element (figure 22) is known as a *monocoque*, or *stressed skin*. Roughly translated, monocoque means 'one shell', and 'stressed skin' means exactly that – the skin is load-bearing. Cars used to be manufactured with a strong, independent chassis to which the bodywork was later attached, but in modern cars you can't have one without the other.

The strength and integrity of a monocoque depends on its overall shape, but that can be weakened by any apertures. A tin can and an egg are monocoques which remain rigid as long as they aren't opened. Push rods are monocoque tubes; if they buckle it is a very bad idea to bend them straight and then carry on as if nothing had happened. Most of their bending resistance will have gone and the metal on the inside of the tube may have fractured, where it can't be seen. The weakened tube is highly likely to buckle again, and much more readily. Tubes that have buckled or been severely dented should be replaced.

Of course, a people-box for the living must have door holes allowing persons to get in and out, and window holes so they can see where they are going. The result is that the placement of curves is not just about sales and streamlining, but adding rigidity to a shell which – if you look at your own car – is more hole than solid substance, what with doors, windows, boots, bonnets, and so on. The surround of any opening in a car's body is almost always reinforced, either by bending the edges into girder-like shapes or by welding or bolting on stiffeners. The car will also be very much stronger with the doors shut. Almost every man-made monocoque is such a structural hybrid, known as a *semi-monocoque*.

Major components

THE WING

Most of the structural examples in this chapter refer to wood rather than the now universal GRP, and there's a reason for this. A GRP structure is an almost completely empty box, devoid of load-path clues. While in one sense simple, what the box actually does is quite complicated. Wood and metal structures are, by comparison, complex, but show far better how loads are transferred, if only because there are distinct structural components there to do it.

The wings of wooden gliders are rarely completely ply clad. The forward section round and ahead of the main spar is the main load-bearing box girder, and anything behind that looks to be tagged on for streamlining purposes! But whatever the material used to skin the wing, it helps to maintain the aerofoil shape which produces the lift, and must transfer the resulting loads to the wing ribs (if there are any), which pass the loads to the spar(s), and so on through to the fuselage. It is easy to think of the wing's skin, particularly if it is fabric, as either being the passive bearer of loads created elsewhere, or not really doing anything very much, particularly near the trailing edge. In fact, the skin of every wing is actively creating all the significant aerodynamic loads.

Metal wings have a similar internal structure to wooden ones, and like them are semi-monocoque. GRP, on the other hand, is probably about as close to a genuine monocoque as we can currently get. Every job previously done by wires, struts, ribs, drag spars, *Warren girders*, and so on, is now done by a main spar and the wing shell.

GRP or not, most wings have a *main spar*, usually an oblong box with its longest side vertical, to handle the major and predominantly vertical loads. The main spar does most of the vertical donkey work and provides some torsional rigidity, but most of that is provided by a 'D' shaped box added to the front of the spar (figures 23 and 24). The *D-box* may be solid, or a hollow beam, or wrap round plywood or metal over the rib's leading edges. With GRP, the D-box is part of the overall wing box.

Fore and aft loads created by the initial acceleration on a winch launch, or a rapid stop, are dealt with by the main spar and D-box, and a *drag spar* (figure 25). The drag spar may go from the wing's rear fuselage attachment point, diagonally forward to the main spar, or it may angle back to the main spar from the forward attachment point. In flight, the fore and aft loads can be surprisingly high in some circumstances. For example, when as much G as possible is being applied just before the wing stalls, the fore and aft loads can amount to nearly a quarter of the vertical loads, so they are not insignificant, particularly at speed. They would be larger if the airbrakes were out, or came out at the same time.

Other spars include the *aileron spar*, to which the aileron hinges are attached – the associated wing ribs are usually reinforced to take the extra loads – and, obviously, the *trailing edge spar*, which serves as little more than an anchor for fabric and/or a trailing spacer for wing ribs. It is not designed for, nor does it usually take, large loads.

THE FIN AND TAILPLANE

The structures of the fin and tailplane are very similar to that of the wing. For wooden and metal aircraft the most important load-bearing element in a semi-monocoque tailplane will be a main spar, like the wings. There will also be an *elevator spar* to which are attached the vital elevator hinges. In some gliders the elevator spar may be the only full span spar in the tailplane. There may also be short *stub spars*. Ribs can be few and far between, with most of the loads being taken by the skin, so any damage to that should be taken seriously.

The fin also has the equivalent of a main spar. The vertical *sternpost* (figure 26) is an important load-bearing member, serving also as anchor point for the rudder hinges. There may be additional spars, more like formers, to add extra support and rigidity for, say, a fin-mounted tailplane. A problem with the fin is that most of it lies above the longitudinal fuselage axis, so sideways loads twist the fuselage.

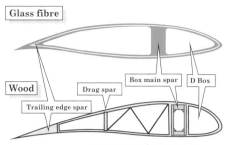
FIGURE 24 Comparison section through wood and GRP wings

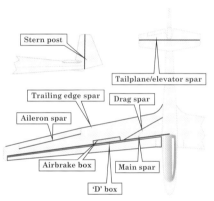
FIGURE 25 Types of spar and reinforcing boxes

FIGURE 26 Mid-mounted tailplane

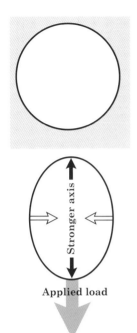

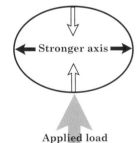

THE FUSELAGE

The structural requirement for the fuselage, particularly the aft section, is extreme rigidity along all axes. What must *not* happen when the glider is flying within its design limits is that the fuselage bends or distorts and alters the sit of the tailplane in relation to the airflow.

The fuselage of almost every high performance glider from the 1930s onwards has been a semi-monocoque tube. This tube necessarily contains a number of openings, and additional internal structural elements – such as formers or fuselage *frames* – are added to prevent the cross-section changing under load; an important requirement if the fuselage is not to buckle. Applied loads will try to deform a circular section into an elliptical or oval one (figure 27), strengthening it along the lengthening axis and weakening it along the other.

Wooden structures are often further stiffened by *longerons* or *stringers* which run the length of the component (figure 28). Greater resistance to vertical loads can be built in by deliberately making the fuselage elliptical or oval (longest axis vertical) in section rather than circular. GRP gliders dispense with longerons and stringers, but the fuselage may still be reinforced with additional layers of glass cloth in areas where the loads are likely to be large, and one such area is around the mid-fuselage. The wing is by far the heaviest part of the glider, and on the ground it sits on top of the fuselage tube, with the pilot sat at one end. The whole lot is more or less poised on a point – the main wheel. Bending (snapping) and compression (squashing) loads are high.

Similar loads are there, differently disposed, when the glider is airborne, but in the air the fuselage hangs from the wings and produces most of the wing bending loads. Even GRP gliders have additional frames of GRP, or plywood wrapped with GRP, to provide extra strength, particularly in the area around the undercarriage. Fuselage frames may also be made of cast aluminium, but like most cast materials it is prone to stress fractures.

DISTRIBUTING LOADS

Having several times emphasised what a bad idea it is to make things stronger by increasing their bulk, in some areas it is the only practical solution. Every aerofoil has a specific *thickness-to-chord* ratio which inevitably limits the depth of the main spar. The general weight and bulk of the spar box may have to be increased simply because if it is to be strong enough there is no other choice. Indeed, any component may sit in a space which is for practical reasons restricted; the dimensions of the cockpit are a compromise between least cross-sectional area (lowest form drag), smoothest shape, strength (the cockpit section is effectively a 'U'-shaped girder), and a space adjustable for large and small pilots alike.

FIGURE 27 Distortion under load

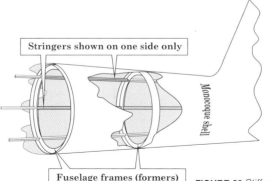

FIGURE 28 Stiffening the fuselage

For gliders on the ground the loads to which the main spar is subjected are due simply to the weight of the wing (figure 29). The bending loads are, as in flight, greater the closer you get to the wing root, but in the opposite direction. In-flight bending loads are infinitely more variable and can be far higher than the resting loads. In either case the usual way of dealing with the span-wise changes in load is to gradually increase the depth of the main spar towards the root.

In-flight and ground running loads also change so that a component, at one moment in tension, can shortly afterwards be in compression (figure 29). The most effective structure may be one where the main spar's construction changes throughout its length. A wooden spar might be solid at the root end, and turn into a hollow box further out along the span where the bending loads are smaller. With a GRP glider a solid root end may also mutate into a box further out, but then vanish as it approaches the tips, leaving the wing shell alone to deal with the loads there. Much the same kind of considerations apply to fin and tailplane spars.

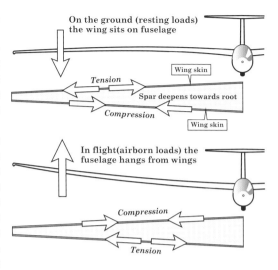

FIGURE 29 Spar load directions

Joining of parts

A so far unspoken assumption in this chapter has been that the separate parts of an airframe always join with seamless perfection. In reality, even the most perfect weld is a join, a join is a discontinuity, and a discontinuity is potentially a weak point. With most materials the perfect join is impossible (some of the newer welding techniques, like cold welding, get close to the ideal), so it is important that the *contact area* between the parts is as large as possible, or at least large enough.

Butt joints (figure 30, (A)) are inherently weak because the contact area between the components is usually small. Wood has an additional problem in that, because of the grain, the fibrous layers are relatively easy to tear away from each other. The concentration of stresses at a glued joint of almost any sort may leave the glue intact and just rip away the wood's top few layers. If a butt joint has to be used, extra contact area can be provided by triangular fillets or *gussets*. For two components which meet end-on, the joint is chamfered, or a long narrow triangle of material is inserted between them forming a *splice* (B). The more highly loaded the component, the shallower the splicing angles used. For 'cabinet maker' woodwork, contact area is increased by sliding one component inside the other using a slotted joint of some description, but these aren't always practical with aircraft structures.

GRP structures are more seamless than their wooden and metal counterparts, but, like them, not unbreakable. GRP

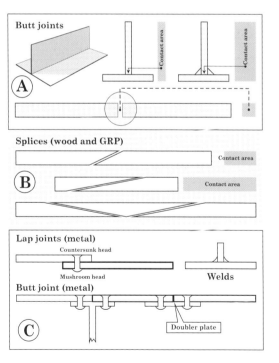

FIGURE 30 Joints

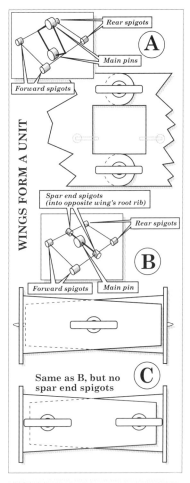

WINGS FORM A UNIT

Rear spigots

A

Main pins

Forward spigots

*Spar end spigots
(into opposite wing's root rib)*

Rear spigots

B

Forward spigots *Main pin*

Same as B, but no
spar end spigots **C**

WINGS USE FUSELAGE

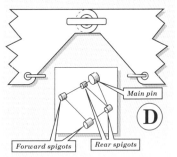

Main pin

D

Forward spigots *Rear spigots*

FIGURE 31 Wing/fuselage
attachment

repairs must be spliced like wood repairs, and for the same reasons. The metal equivalent of a splice is either an overlapping joint of some kind, or, where the surface has to be smooth, a butt joint supported by a flanged frame or a *doubler* plate, and *flush riveted* (C). Alternatively, the metal parts may be glued or bonded together.

SURFACE PREPARATION

Materials can only be glued or bonded together if the joining compound can in some way key into and get a grip on both surfaces. Plywood is manufactured by applying glue to the various layers and then using a press to squeeze them all together. This squashes the fibres of the outermost layers and they become smooth and shiny; this is made worse if a waxy release agent has been used to prevent them sticking to the press. The result is a very poor bonding surface, and for the glue to penetrate and grip onto something, the surface needs gently pre-roughening with emery paper or fine sandpaper. This simple procedure makes an enormous difference to the joint's final strength.

Oxygen reacts with many ferrous (iron-based) materials to produce rust. It also reacts with aluminium to produce a surface patina of corrosion, and sparkling new aluminium sheets quickly dull. Luckily the corrosion (aluminium oxide) forms a protective layer which slows the *oxidation* process, but that same *oxidised layer* must be removed if anything is to be strongly bonded with the aluminium, not weakly with the oxide.

When metal components are bolted together, or to wood, *zinc chromate* paste, or something similar but less toxic, may need to be applied between the surfaces to prevent (a) the penetration of moisture and/or (b) chemical reactions which create electrical currents and/or corrosion. GRP is far less critical in all these respects, but even so, you would not add resin to glass cloth that you'd just covered with oil, dust or a fine haze of paint splatterings.

RIGGING

Gliders are very likely to land out, whatever their owners say, and so should be easy to de-rig and transport. Inevitably, they will need putting back together again, and that's when damage is most often done, usually by sheer carelessness, and things are forgotten, particularly when everyone is in a great hurry. The fewer bits involved and the more foolproof the reassembly procedure, the better. Ideally it should be impossible to take off in a mis-rigged glider, or one that has been damaged by 'untrained persons'.

Self-connecting controls have led to a reduction in accidents caused by the controls being incorrectly connected, or not at all. Even so, Murphy's Law prevails; no matter how unlikely the circumstances required, if something can go wrong, it will. There are no gliders with self-inserting *main pins*, but pilots have still managed to take off with the usual DIY sort neatly stowed in the side pocket, clearly relying for survival on blind chance and the good fairy of friction. Take a winch launch without the main pin(s) inserted and you will die. Take an aerotow, and the wings may fall off as you land (it has happened); everything depends on the function of the main pin. Libelles, Kestrels, and others, have main pins whose primary job is not to take huge loads but to prevent the wings sliding apart (figure 31, (B)). With a setup like example (A)(e.g. Ka 6E, ASK13, ASW20) or (D)(e.g. Dart 17R), you wouldn't even get the glider off the rigging dolly!

The majority of the pins, main included, are inserted from the front. A few gliders (SHK) have an expandable pin which drops vertically downwards through horizontal rather than vertical flange plates on the spar ends.

Whatever the system used to link and lock components together, the smaller the number of attachment points, the higher the loads at each. Metal fittings are essential at these points of high stress, and must be of the best quality high tensile steel. In any event, mains pins are usually chunky and always made of materials which are extremely resistant to shearing loads.

TRANSFERRING LOADS BETWEEN COMPONENTS

If the two wings are linked in a way that turns them into a single unit – i.e. they wouldn't fold up if you unhooked the fuselage – the effect of the wing bending loads on the fuselage fittings may be zero. What isn't zero, and can be very large indeed, is the tailplane loads resulting from the wing pitching moment that are transmitted through the fuselage to the wing fittings. There is also the weight of the pilot to contend with, and loads created by yaw. These and fore and aft loads are taken care of by the fore and/or aft attachment points on the fuselage (figures 31 and 32). The design of some gliders can result in the wings not forming a self-supporting unit, and then some of the resultant loads may be in rather surprising directions, e.g. the wing ground loads trying to squash the fuselage in sideways.

All-moving tails are connected together by a *torque tube* through the fuselage if the tailplane is low (K6E), or the torque tube may run through the fin (ASW 15). All-moving tails at the top of the fin usually slot directly onto an actuating mechanism built into the fin, with two locating pins at the rear and a locking bolt of some description. More conventional tailplane/elevator layouts at the top of the fin have a triangular set of load-bearing and location points. The two rear attachment points prevent the tailplane rocking from side to side. The unit slots back onto the rear lugs and is locked in place by a pin (possibly springloaded) pushed through from the fin or tailplane leading edge (figure 33, see over). The locking pin may act also as the forward support. The horizontal triangle layout may be replaced by a vertical one, with two vertically separated lugs on a small 'spar' on the underside of the tailplane fitting into the sternpost.

Where the tailplane sits on top of the fuselage, as in a glider like the AS-K13, for example, the rear of the tailplane again has two rear locating bearings which slot over lugs on the

JAR 22.612

PROVISIONS FOR RIGGING AND DE-RIGGING

The design . . . must be such that during rigging and de-rigging by untrained persons, the probability of damage or permanent deformation, especially when this is not readily visible, is extremely remote. Incorrect assembly must be avoided by proper design provisions. It must be possible to inspect the sailplane easily for correct rigging.

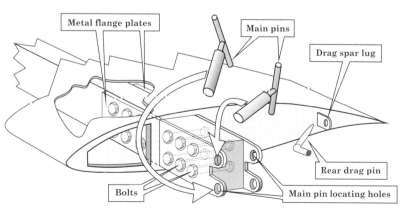

FIGURE 32 Attachment points, a closer look (wooden glider)

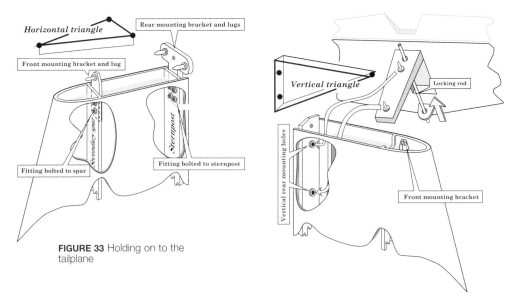

FIGURE 33 Holding on to the tailplane

fuselage frame, and a single bolt that screws downwards, and through a metal plate at the front of the tailplane, and into the fuselage frame.

Care is taken to ensure that transmitted loads are spread as widely and evenly as possible from any fittings into the underlying structure. In <u>figure 32</u>, for example, the metal flanges at the root ends are bolted to each other through the main spar. To avoid concentrating the stress these plates usually extend some way along the spar, forming a tight flush fit with the surrounding structure, but not so tight that the material underneath, if it is wood, is crushed and damaged.

Ancillary bits

THE RETRACTABLE UNDERCARRIAGE

Of all glider components the undercarriage probably gets the worst hammering, but only for a tiny percentage of each flight, and on the ground. Once the glider is airborne the undercarriage is redundant. A few early gliders had droppable wheels, but the best solution is a retractable undercarriage. The gear's extra weight has far less effect on the performance than the drag created by non-retractable gear.

The U/C loads can be extremely violent, so the whole assembly has to be very robust. The vertical legs deal with the vertical loads, which designers take to be the glider's entire weight multiplied by a suitably large number to allow for inevitable bumps and thumps (about 4G), and the occasional less than perfect landing. The vertical legs pivot and are rarely jointed, but the rearward sloping legs must have a joint so that the U/C can be retracted. Again, joints are weak points, so to help prevent the U/C folding up at inopportune moments, the 'knee' is arranged to go slightly overcentre when the under-carriage is down and locked (<u>figure 34</u>). Impact or ground running loads then act slightly out of line with the leg, bending it towards rather than away from the hinge – the equivalent of trying to bend your own knee backwards. When the U/C is retracted, the

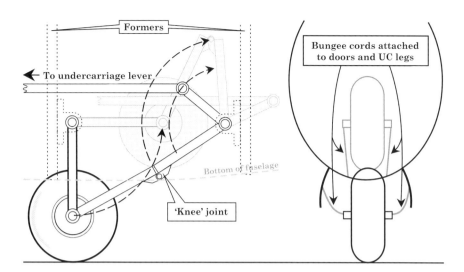

FIGURE 34 Retractable undercarriage geometry

geometry of the actuating rods may include a similar overcentre lock to stop flight loads lowering it again.

While it is very important that the U/C attaches to a strong bulkhead, the U/C itself is usually designed to collapse progressively in the event of a very heavy landing, absorbing some of the loads which might otherwise cause major structural damage.

WINCH AND AEROTOW HOOKS

For the duration of the launch the winch hook is one of the glider's most highly stressed components. All the forces that come into it via the cable are fed through four mounting brackets and their attendant bolts, into a single bulkhead. The launching hook has to be able to carry at least a limit load of $1.5Q_{NOM}$, as defined by JAR22, and the bulkhead to which the hook is attached must, in effect, be able to support the weight of the fully loaded glider 'acting at . . . 90° to the plane of symmetry', i.e. directly sideways.

Early hooks had no automatic back release. After a number of winch hang-ups, some with fatal consequences, significant changes were made. The modern winch hook is failsafe and will release the cable even if the pilot doesn't, or can't. If hang-ups do occur, it is usually because the winch strop has been dragged into the wheel-box or snagged on something else.

The release hook has two main mechanical functions which work independently of each other. The first is the basic pull-from-the-cockpit release mechanism (greyed items in <u>figure 35</u>; the black circles represent through-bolts fixed to the box casing, here represented by the dotted outline. Note that the box contains a slot beneath the lower pivot bolt).

A strong spring – anchored at one end to the case, bent around the upper pivot bolt and then over the top of the release knob actuating arm – holds the hook in the shut position. When the

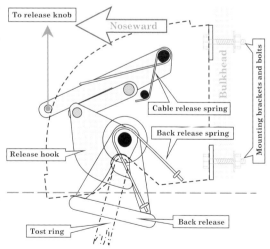

FIGURE 35 A Tost release hook

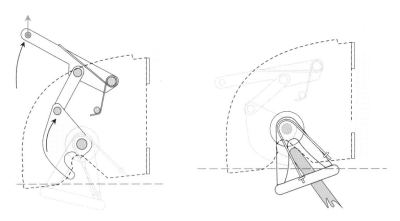

FIGURE 36 Releasing the cable   **FIGURE 37** Back release

release is pulled (figure 36), the hook swings forwards (clockwise from the reader's point of view) allowing the cable ring to slide out of the casing slot and the back release ring. When the knob is released, the spring draws the hook shut again. The *back release* is a circular ring welded to a triangular pivot arm, as shown in the figures. It too is held in the shut (inactive) position by a strong spring. Failing a normal release, for whatever reason, a sufficiently rearward pull on the cable forces the triangular pivot and ring to swing backwards (anticlockwise from the reader's point of view), allowing the cable ring to drop free (figure 37).

An important safety feature is that if either of the springs fail, the feeblest pull on the cable causes the rings to fall out. It is important that the hook has no notches that might cause the rings to hang up.

The aerotow hook is either the same unit as the winch hook, or a very similar one, located elsewhere, and with the back release facility either missing or disabled.

The glider is now complete (figure 38) and we need to look at how the limiting speeds are worked out because, no matter how strong an aircraft, there is always a limit to the loads it can take, never mind the pilot.

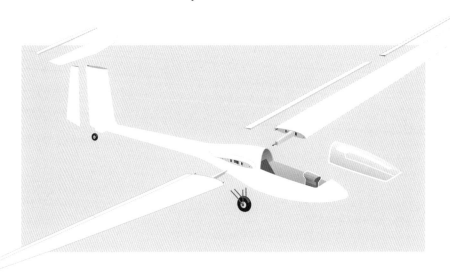

FIGURE 38 Main components of a glider

Section two:
the manoeuvring envelope

More about G and loads

JAR22 defines two categories of sailplane:

(1)   'U', or utility/semi-aerobatic and

(2)   'A', fully aerobatic.

The semi-aerobatic 'U' category allows spins, loops, tight turns, lazy eights and chandelles, but not the more advanced manoeuvres such as rolling off the top of a loop, flick rolls, outside loops or genuine and prolonged inverted flight. The designer of a 'U' category glider won't take into account the stresses produced by the advanced manoeuvres, so any margin that might seem to exist for their performance will probably be very small and entirely accidental. The overwhelming majority of gliders belong in the semi-aerobatic category. Even though some of them are theoretically strong enough for a limited range of more complicated manoeuvres, if you do them the glider will almost certainly be operating close to, or perhaps beyond limits *which the placard may only imply*.

The placard of most gliders in the 'U' category normally makes no mention of G limitations, but the flight manual almost certainly will. It pays to read it. A flapped glider, for example, may have different G and speed limitations for flaps up, neutral and down. You need to be careful about taking the G limitations too literally as you can argue yourself into a hidden trap.

Assume that the normal positive and negative G limits for your glider are +5.3 and −2.5 respectively. You might think that if you keep within these limits, all will be well. Not necessarily. Even the most skilled and sensitive pilot cannot feel many of the loads to which the airframe is being subjected. Where rolling manoeuvres are concerned, even when the accelerometer indicates that G is within the prescribed limits, most of the really damaging stresses cannot be felt directly.

Modern gliders are also relatively easy to overspeed, and the airbrakes may only hold the speed below limits if the dive is no more than 45 degrees below the horizontal, and 30 degrees for some gliders. A few aren't cleared for any aerobatic manoeuvres and are prohibited from spinning. This does not mean they won't, that you can't, that their spin characteristics are appalling, or that they are structurally weak, but that overspeeding during the recovery is highly likely. We are allowed, of course, to have a shot at recovering them from accidental spins.

Overspeeding is dangerous, but not necessarily because of the risk of structural failure and/or flutter. Not too far beyond V_{NE} (Velocity Never Exceed) a few gliders can't slow down because they can't pull up, and they can't pull up because they can't slow down –

FIGURE 39 An accelerometer

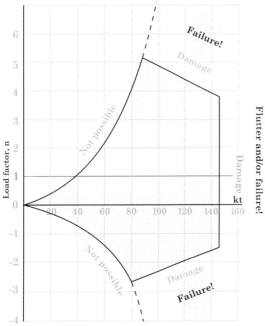

FIGURE 40 Basic manoeuvring envelope

pure catch 22. In any case, attempting to perform 'A'-type aerobatic manoeuvres in 'U' category gliders invites catastrophe, not to mention invalidating the insurance.

These examples are, admittedly, extreme. Most pilots are never going to do flick rolls or fly deliberately way outside the placarded speed limits. Comforting as it is to think that designers have allowed for everything, the guidelines to which gliders are built (pre-JAR 22 or not) do assume that the average glider pilot is both cautious and light on the controls. Pilots, the criteria imply, will never use the full deflection of all the controls simultaneously at high speed, nor, come to that, of any *single* control. In practice, because adverse yaw is so marked a feature of gliders, allowance is made for the simultaneous use of aileron and rudder at high(ish) speeds, though nothing official calls for this.

The designer must also allow for the effects of gusts, shock loadings on take-off and landing, high levels of sideslip at high speed (e.g. poor spin recovery technique), and much else. Among the occasionally conflicting design requirements, none of the limits are infinite, and all can be exceeded if the pilot is sufficiently careless and/or unlucky.

In the early stages of design, choices are made about the aerofoil, the materials, general performance parameters, and so on, all of which have their effect on some of the chosen speeds and loadings. Almost none of the limits to be discussed arise in isolation. The design process is also more a matter of making the glider strong enough to fit the chosen envelope, rather than the other way round.

The manoeuvring envelope

JAR22 defines the boundaries of the *manoeuvring envelope* and specifies the maximum loads which the glider must be able to withstand, as well as the associated speeds. Within the envelope there is an area where you can do just about what you like – short of a mid-air or striking the ground a hefty blow – and the glider won't be damaged. This 'OK area' is bounded on one side by a region which you cannot enter however hard you try – though the border here is not as sharp as the diagrams might suggest – and on the other three sides by areas where it becomes progressively easier to create problems for yourself the further you push into them. Despite the size of the envelope as a whole, for many gliders the OK area is fairly small.

Ideally, the manoeuvring envelope (figure 40) would be three-dimensional, but it deals only with pitch-based loads, taking no obvious account of those produced by rolling (into a turn), or yawing, though obviously these are allowed for.

THE STALL LINE

Plotting the stalling speed values against various positive load factors creates the envelope's upper left hand boundary, or *stall line* (figure 41). Theoretically, if we flew at

54kt, say, and suddenly applied full up elevator, the load factor couldn't exceed 2.0, because the moment we reached it the wing would stall and prevent any further increase. By contrast, full up elevator at 91kt (don't try it!) wouldn't stall the wing until the load reached +5.76. The 38kt un-accelerated stalling speed (a misnomer because normal 1G is an acceleration) in the table is a theoretical figure only, but the table as a whole might suggest that it isn't possible to operate above the stall line, even though, as detailed later, that's not quite the case.

Cambered aerofoils work poorly upside down, and the 1G stalling speed inverted is significantly higher than the 1G stalling speed (V_S) topside up. The lower left boundary is the stalling speed at various negative loadings (effectively the glider in inverted flight), and will only mirror the upper stall line if the aerofoil is symmetrical.

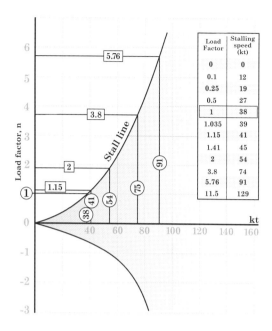

Load Factor	Stalling speed (kt)
0	0
0.1	12
0.25	19
0.5	27
1	38
1.035	39
1.15	41
1.41	45
2	54
3.8	74
5.76	91
11.5	129

FIGURE 41 Plotting the stall lines (+ and -)

Design dive speed (V_D)

With the envelope's leftward limits defined, the right-hand boundary, marked by the *Design dive speed*, or V_D (figure 42), is next. There is something a bit rule of thumb about the calculation of V_D. BCAR had three categories of glider: normal, semi-aerobatic and acrobatic (sic), where V_D was 3 x V_S (V_S is the normal 1G stalling speed), 4.4 x V_S and 5.5 x V_S respectively. JAR22 has the 'U' and 'A' categories (an equivalent 'normal' category isn't defined), and states that V_D (in kph): '... may be chosen by the applicant but must not be lower than $V_D = 18 \times \sqrt[3]{(W/S) \times (1/C_{Dmin})}$ for sailplanes of category U', or '$V_D = 3.5 \times (W/S) + 200$ for sailplanes of category A'. (W/S) = wing loading in kg/m² at the maximum all up weight, and C_{Dmin} is the estimated minimum drag coefficient – this effectively determines the glider's terminal velocity (if it were indestructible).

Whatever the criteria used to decide the value of V_D, V_{NE} is calculated from it, and V_{NE} appears on the placard, not V_D. The value of V_D is not determined by the designer saying out of the blue: 'Let's have V_D at 250kt', though in principle it could be anywhere he wished, but by the physical characteristics of the materials out of which the glider is to be constructed, among other things, and to a lesser extent whether a glide ratio of 3:1 at 170kt has any practical point. For gliders built to JAR22, V_{NE} is usually V_D x 0.9 (90% of V_D). If we assume that a particular glider in the aerobatic 'A' category has a maximum wing loading (W_L) of 5lb/ft², then, using the kt version of the formula and assuming a C_{DMIN} of 0.0075:

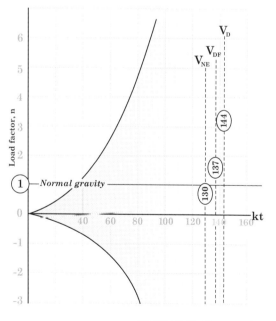

FIGURE 42 Limiting speeds

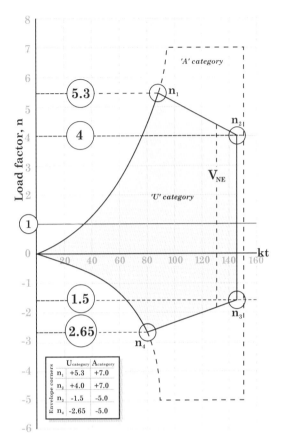

Envelope corners		U category	A category
	n_1	+5.3	+7.0
	n_2	+4.0	+7.0
	n_3	-1.5	-5.0
	n_4	-2.65	-5.0

FIGURE 43 Defining the envelope corners

JAR22.335

Design manoeuvring speed
$V_A = V_{SI} \sqrt{n_1}$ where: $V_{SI} =$
estimated stalling speed at
design maximum weight
(wing-flaps neutral, airbrakes
closed)

$$V_D = 16.5 \times \sqrt[3]{W_L}/0.0075 = 144kt$$
$$V_{NE} = 144 \times 0.9 = 130kt$$

The designer can assume a lower value of V_D from which to calculate V_{NE}, but you won't know that and shouldn't assume it was done. During flight testing the glider is flown to a *demonstrated design speed*, V_{DF}, which is approximately $V_D \times 0.95$ (95% of V_D). For the imaginary glider used in the examples, V_{DF} would be 136.8kt. The glider is *not* flown to V_D, and is only demonstrated to be structurally sound, aerodynamically stable and free from flutter, up to a speed a mere 5% beyond V_{NE}. So, if the glider's V_{NE} is 130kt, it has only ever been 6.5kt faster, once, when it was new, in ideal conditions, and flown by a specially trained test pilot.

Limit loads

The other boundaries of the manoeuvring envelope are defined by limit loads. Limit loads are the maximum loads to which the requirements assume the aircraft will be subjected during normal service. If a glider is designed to a limit load of +5.3G it should be able to sustain +5.3G indefinitely – not that non-military pilots would be conscious long enough to appreciate this! JAR22 lays down the minimum values for the limit loads – evolved over the years as the most practical – at the envelope corners (figure 43). Nevertheless, though a positive load limit of +4G for a 'U' category sailplane at V_D sounds quite large, given what could be applied there before the wing stalled, it might as well be zero.

Exceeding limit loads anywhere on the envelope isn't a good idea. Once you overstep a material's elastic limits you cause permanent damage, however slight, and once done that can only be added to. If the elastic limits are consistently exceeded by even small amounts, the material will gradually be weakened and eventually it will fail.

The negative loads allowed for are less than the positive ones, being only –1.5G at V_D. On the other hand, the background G (i.e. 'normal' weight) is +1, and from there to –1.5G at V_D is 2.5G in total, if you happen to be the right way up! Flying steadily upside down, the background G in relation to the airframe is –1, and at V_D the distance to the nearest corner of the envelope is then only 0.5G. JAR22 assumes that the average pilot neither likes nor actively seeks reduced or negative G. It also assumes that the pilot won't ever apply more than +5.3G, nor whack the controls about at high speeds.

Ultimate load

An *ultimate load* (figure 44) is what the glider will withstand, like the chair, just prior to falling apart! The *Factor of Safety* (F of S) required by JAR22 is the limit load multiplied by 1.5. The criterion is that below the ultimate load the airframe shouldn't fail, but as already described, that doesn't mean it won't be damaged. When new and/or relatively unstressed, nothing in the structure should actually break. Unfortunately, a glider's service history has a bearing on the airframe strength, and if it has been subjected to the kind of cumulative abuse mentioned above, the ultimate load may be far lower than the designer intended.

Other factors are also involved. As a glider's speed increases so too does the wing pitching moment. This created greater torsional force in the wing and an increasing download on the tailplane as it tries to prevent the glider from pitching nose-down. The F of S here is taken as 1.5 times the torque (or twisting component). These loads follow a speed-related square law, so relatively small increases in speed create large increases in load.

In all cases, if the ultimate load is exceeded, something will break, and it may be something relatively minor that triggers a catastrophic sequence of failures.

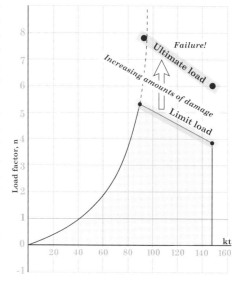

FIGURE 44 Limit and ultimate loads

Maximum manoeuvring speed (V$_A$)

Deflection of the control surfaces alters the loads on the glider's structure. Assuming the same degree of control deflection throughout, the faster the glider flies the higher the resultant loads, and at some point they will exceed first the airframe's limit loads and then the ultimate loads, with destructive results.

Stressing (working out how loads affect the structure, and what to do about it) is relatively straightforward if only one axis is involved, say pitch, but pitching and rolling at the same time is much more complicated. Firstly, deflecting the ailerons creates a torsional load on the wings, and this – as with the 'T' structure twisted in figure 18 (p. 140) – makes it less resistant to loads in the pitch plane, controlled by the elevator. Secondly, there are the fuselage loads to consider, tailplane and rudder as well, and those on the various fittings.

As defined by JAR22, the *maximum manoeuvring speed* (V$_A$) is where the 5.3G limit line crosses the stall line (figure 45). The minimum requirement the designer must meet is that at any speed up to and including V$_A$, the pilot should be able to apply full deflection of any *one* control without damaging the glider.

Take a simple manoeuvre like a loop. The entry speed required for smooth and easy execution (figure 46, see over) will put the glider beyond V$_A$ and V$_B$ to begin with, but during the initial pull-up large elevator deflections are neither needed nor desirable, and if the air is rough you probably shouldn't be doing aerobatics. The glider decelerates through the first half of the loop, and for the G or the pitch rate to remain constant, increasing amounts of up elevator are required. Shortly before the glider becomes completely inverted the stick will be fully back, but the pitch rate and speed will be low, so full elevator deflection is well within the limits.

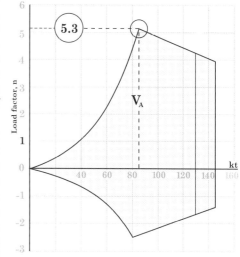

FIGURE 45 'U' category, maximum manoeuvring speed

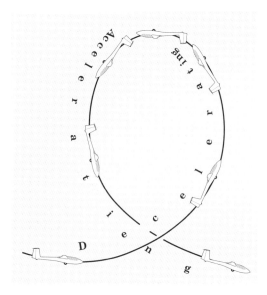

FIGURE 46 The real shape of a normal loop

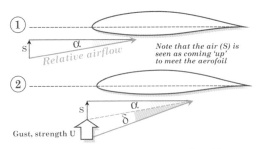

Note that the air (S) is seen as coming 'up' to meet the aerofoil

Gust, strength U

FIGURE 47 Gust effect on AoA

JAR22.333 c

(1) at . . . V_B, the sailplane must be capable of withstanding positive (up) and negative (down) gusts of 15m/s acting normal to the flight path.

(2) at .. . V_D . . . capable of withstanding positive and negative gusts of 7.5m/s . . .

Accelerating during the loop's second half, the elevator input will mirror that of the first half, so there is a progressive release of the back pressure. If, however, the stick is held fully back until the glider is again in level flight, G builds up impressively. Given the huge amounts of induced drag that result, the exit speed could easily be lower than the entry speed, though still close to V_A.

A loop is an essentially two-dimensional manoeuvre. *Chandelles*, by comparison, are three-dimensional, and demand more of the airframe and the pilot's skill. Full control deflections aren't needed for a correctly flown chandelle, and the speed should be below V_A and G positive throughout. I have observed what the pilot intended to be a chandelle become corkscrewed into an extremely tight barrel roll when, among other things, he forgot to stop rolling at the crucial moment. Luckily no damage was done, largely because the loads were positive throughout and the speed relatively low.

The basic manoeuvring envelope (figure 46) is now complete, but so far it has been based on the assumption that the air is always smooth, and this is not the case.

The gust envelope

Prior to being struck by a gust the glider is flying along at a steady Vkt with a sink rate of Skt (figure 47, ①). Note that S is upwards relative to the aerofoil (i.e. towards it). Say that a gust with a vertical component of Ukt hits the glider. The geometry of this 'hit' is straightforward. U adds to S, lengthening the vertical side of the triangle ② and increasing the AoA (angle in the opposite corner) from $\alpha°$ to $\alpha° + \delta°$. The extra lift increases the wing bending loads – very clear if you watch the wings of a glider flexing up and down in turbulence. Other parts of the structure are also affected.

If the gust doesn't stall the aerofoil, then the extra lift generated is proportional to the gust's strength and the speed of the glider – the faster you are going the greater the effect. JAR22 specifies two gust velocities: the *Strong Gust*, with a vertical velocity of 15m/s (about 30kt), and the *Weak Gust*, with a vertical velocity of 7.5m/s (about 15kt). These gust lines fan out from the 1G point. Gusts stronger than 30kt can occur, but are rare in the UK.

The theory has so far presumed that when hit by a sufficiently strong gust, the wing will stall instantly at the same AoA as it would in, say, a wind tunnel, but this isn't quite what happens. A minor airflow disturbance at the leading edge takes a short while to reach the trailing edge. Major changes, such as a very sudden increase in the AoA (gust – or pilot-induced), don't instantly stall the aerofoil, and the design assumption is that in such cases the wing can briefly generate up to 25% more lift than it would if the change had been less abrupt. The effect is not trivial, so the stalling boundaries are re-plotted to correspond to load factors 25% greater than those defining the original manoeuvring envelope.

The new envelope is called the *gust envelope* (figure 48). Note that apart from the nick in the envelope's top left corner, the strong gust line lies largely outside the envelope; in other words, if you aren't flying fast, a strong gust cannot damage the glider.

Maximum rough air speed (V$_B$)

Rough air is defined as 'all movement of air in lee-wave rotors, thunderclouds, visible whirlwinds or over mountain crests'. A far more useful rule of thumb, attributed to Frank Irving, is that if you are flying along and keep leaving the seat, then you are in rough air – and ought to slow down. V$_B$ is determined by the gradient of the strong gust line, and by the wing loading. For example, a gust might increase a wing loading of 9lb/ft^2 by, say, 1.5lb/ft^2, or 17%. The same gust striking a glider with a wing loading of 4lb/ft^2 would make a 38% difference. Crudely put, the higher the initial wing loading the less the wing is flexed by a given gust, i.e. lower wing bending moment. If the strong gust line falls outside the manoeuvring envelope (figure 49, line (X)), then V$_B$ = V$_A$, and if the strong gust line crosses the stall line and falls within the envelope (line (Y)), then it forms the envelope boundary. V$_B$ must not be lower than V$_A$. If V$_A$ were less than V$_B$ then, in rough conditions, we couldn't use the full deflection of, say, the ailerons without risking structural failure!

Gust loads add to any already being applied. At 110kt in straight flight the weak gust would subject the glider to a load of 3.3G, which is within the envelope. If we were pulling up into a loop at 110kt and +3G, the weak gust would take the total load up to 6.3G, which is outside the envelope and well into the damage area (figure 50).

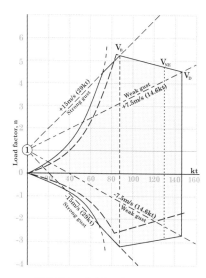

FIGURE 48 Adding the gust envelope

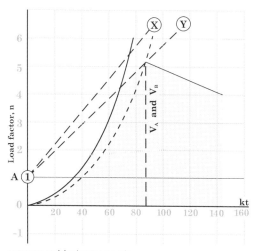

FIGURE 49 Maximum rough airspeed

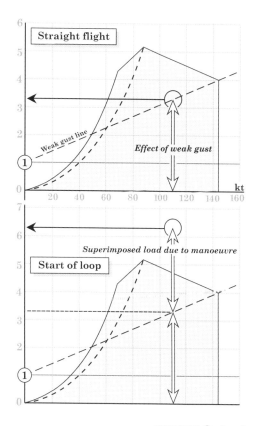

FIGURE 50 Gust and manoeuvre

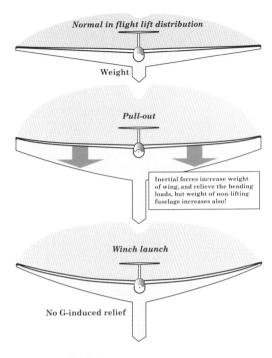

Normal in flight lift distribution

Weight

Pull-out

Inertial forces increase weight of wing, and relieve the bending loads, but weight of non-lifting fuselage increases also!

Winch launch

No G-induced relief

FIGURE 51 G relief

G relief

When a glider manoeuvres under positive G, inertial forces increase the effective weight of the entire structure (pilot included), and the wing loading increases. The fuselage hangs from the wings in flight, produces little or no lift of its own, and is largely responsible for wing bending loads. During a positive G manoeuvre, the extra bending moment created by the increased loads is partly offset by an increase in the weight of the wings – an effect known as *G relief* (figure 51). Winching, forever a special case, makes no use of G relief whatsoever because, even though the wing can be subjected to higher loads than in straight flight, there is no corresponding acceleration to create the inertial forces which will help offset them.

Max.winch/autotow (V_W) and max.aerotow (V_T)

The *design winch launching speed* (V_W; also known as max. winch) must not be lower than 110kph (59kt), as stipulated by JAR-22.335e. No minimum launch speed is specified – it is dependent on the wing loading, which differs with pilot weight and ballast. The placarded value of V_W is calculated on the basis of criteria which appear to say that since the glider has been designed to be pretty strong anyway, if you use the correct weak link – Q_{NOM} is the rated ultimate strength of the towing cable or weak link – winching or autotowing can't damage a structurally sound glider. Will any speed or load therefore be OK because the weak link will take care of anything that isn't, and how is the figure on the placard actually arrived at? In any case, does it matter? There are no cases known to me of structurally sound gliders breaking up during winch or autotow launches. Airframe limitations have no effect on launching too slowly, which is potentially more dangerous than launching too fast, which does have airframe implications. Nevertheless, all JAR22.1518 says about the maximum permitted winch speed is that it 'may not exceed the design speed V_W established in accordance with JAR22.335(e), and may not exceed the speed demonstrated in flight tests', and all that JAR22.335(e) says is, 'V_W must not be less than 110kph'! The top limit may appear open-ended, but winching subjects gliders to an unusual disposition and combination of loads, and going beyond V_W (howsoever defined) to then exceed V_A is extremely unwise, particularly if conditions are rough or gusty.

Both the winching and aerotowing criteria mention that 'excessive control forces or displacements' should not be necessary to maintain a steady flight path. Aerotowing further requires that up to V_T (which must not be less than 125kph (67.5kt)), returning from lateral or vertical displacements from the normal position shouldn't require 'exceptional skill' on the pilot's part.

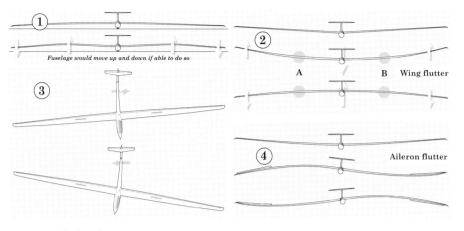

Fuselage would move up and down if able to do so

A   B   Wing flutter

Aileron flutter

FIGURE 52 Modes of airframe oscillation

Structural stiffness and flutter

Take hold of the wingtip of a rigged glider and shake it up and down. There will be at least one shaking frequency which will set the whole wing oscillating in sympathy (figure 52, ①). The shake fits the wing's *natural harmonic frequency* – part and parcel of how the structure is built, the distribution of its mass, and its rigidity or lack of it. Singing a very loud note into a piano has a similar effect and sets strings of the same pitch sounding. Obviously a glider doesn't 'sound' at the frequency of a piano string (you'd hear it if it did), the oscillations are far more leisurely, and the initiating 'shake' is usually a gust, a control surface deflection, or vortex shedding. Normally when a glider flies through a gust the wings flex up and down and any oscillations quickly damp out.

Other 'antics' will usually have been ironed out by the time a glider goes into production, but a number of factors can contribute to their reappearance: damage to the underlying structure caused by consistently exceeding limits already discussed, or heavy landings or ground looping (or both), or some unique and unusual set of circumstances which the test programme didn't cover.

Whatever the reason, in response to a gust, or pilot input, say, the wing may flex to its *aeroelastic limit* (another way of saying it can't bend any further in the circumstances) and then be propelled by a combination of structural and aerodynamic forces to shoot past the 'normal' position and hit the aeroelastic limit on the other side. The process can just keep on going and fail to damp itself out. Given the right circumstances it can get a lot worse, and may start to involve the entire airframe.

If conditions are exactly right, a gust that flexes the wings can set the fuselage bouncing up and down between the tips, with the nodes of the resultant oscillations being somewhere along the span at, say, points (A) and (B) in figure 52, ②, partly due to the mass of the fuselage springing up and down as if the wings were a trampoline. This can set the fuselage nodding, altering the tailplane's AoA, and the glider will then follow an oscillating flight path whose ups and downs are related to the frequency and amplitude of the combined fuselage bounce and wing flexing.

JAR22.583 WINCH LAUNCHING

(a) The sailplane must be initially assumed to be in level flight at speed V_W with a cable load acting at the launch hook in a forward and downward direction at an angle ranging from 0° to 75° with the horizontal.

(b) The cable load must be determined as the lesser of the following two values:

(1) 1.2 Q_{NOM} as defined in JAR22.581(b), or

(2) the loads at which equilibrium is achieved, with either:

(i) the elevator fully deflected in an upward direction, or

(ii) the wing at its maximum lift. A horizontal inertia force may be assumed to complete the equilibrium of horizontal forces.

(c) In the conditions of JAR-22.583(a), a sudden increase of the cable load to the value of 1.2Q_{NOM} as defined in JAR-22.581(b), is assumed. The resulting incremental loads must be balanced by linear and rotational inertia forces. JAR22.1518

(b) The maximum winch launch speed may not exceed the design speed V_W established in accordance with JAR22.335(e) and may not exceed the speed demonstrated in flight tests.

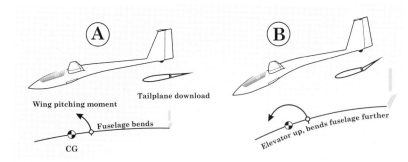

FIGURE 53 One result of inadequately rigid fuselage

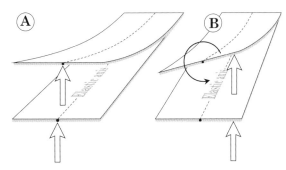

FIGURE 54 Application of load in relation to the elastic axis

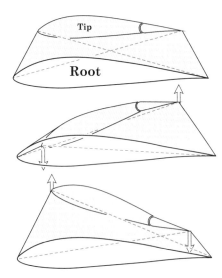

FIGURE 55 Poor torsional stiffness

Other motions which may result from lack of structural stiffness are, in the case of the wings, a rather drunken rolling motion (figure 52, ④) usually triggered by aileron input, and kept going by a combination of low bending resistance and either incorrectly balanced ailerons or control linkage problems. The tailplane assembly may then nod from side to side, pivoting around the fuselage centreline. The rear fuselage is almost always circular in section in modern gliders, and though extremely strong, even that can bend if the loads are sufficient. With lack of rigidity in the yaw plane, the glider may start to snake (figure 52 ③). This can be exacerbated by the geometry of the rudder cables causing left rudder to be applied when the fuselage bends to the right, and vice versa.

All of these are bad enough, but lack of rigidity in the fuselage's vertical plane is more serious. Increasing speed, increasing pitching moment and increasing tailplane load bend the fuselage and reduce the AoA of the tailplane. The nose then drops further, raising the speed another notch, bending the fuselage more and again decreasing the tailplane AoA. If elevator is used to raise the nose this too can bend the fuselage. Either way, the situation is divergent and at some point it will be impossible to raise the nose, and the glider will then be out of control (figure 53).

Some of these motions depend on how the resultant of an applied load, such as a gust, acts in relation to the *axis of elasticity* (the natural bending axis) of a component. For example, if the resultant acts through the axis as in example (A) in figure 54, the component will bend upwards without twisting. If able to twist, it will do so if the resultant acts to one side of the elastic axis (B).

Figure 55 represents a wing seen from the root end, looking out towards the tip. Lack of torsional rigidity can cause the tip to twist which then alters its AoA and causes it to attempt to twist even further. It may then break off, or, if the structure is sufficiently strong, and depending on where the elastic axis happens to be, the tip will twist to the other extreme. The whole process can be made very much worse if the ailerons are unbalanced, with their CG well aft of the hinge line (figure 56). Of course, with the ailerons, a gust could affect both wings at once, but not necessarily symmetrically, and the result could be a motion similar to that in figure 52 ④ – this can happen on a wing which is torsionally very stiff. Combine the motions of figures 55 and 56, and you have a serious problem.

Whatever their cause, once any of these oscillations are established, the affected part can fail. A major component with considerable mass, like the wing, can be subject to slow oscillations, but the really high frequency flutter

– literally a buzzing noise – is far more likely to affect the control surfaces. In the elevator, for example, it may begin without any warning and stop abruptly when the elevator breaks off – the entire process can begin and end catastrophically within a few seconds. Even if flexing/oscillations in the affected components are partially damped and of relatively slow frequency, structural damage can still occur.

The designer must calculate that the glider is flutter-free up to, at lowest, $1.25 \times V_D$, but only has to test its absence up to V_{DF}. In other words, fly fast enough and flutter and structural failure can occur simultaneously. Unfortunately, flutter can occur at much lower speeds than the theoretical predictions. Causes may include:

- unusual or violent control inputs at certain speeds. Pilot-induced oscillations (PIOs) can trigger flutter, and worsen it once it has begun

- sharp-edged gusts

- control circuit wear – either cumulative sloppiness throughout, or local, such as badly worn elevator hinges, or slop in an aerodynamic trimmer circuit

- poor maintenance. Could be control circuit wear, or missing or loose mass balancing

- high altitude flight (see below)

Control surface balance is important. Figure 56 shows how a poorly balanced aileron can cause serious problems, but the same could apply equally to the elevator or the rudder. The usual cure, retrospectively or otherwise, is to attach weights known as *mass balances* to the appropriate side of the control surface, shifting its CG to the hinge line or slightly to the wing side of it. Control surfaces are usually very light, and the practice these days is to attach a strip of some suitably dense material, not necessarily lead, to the leading edge (figure 57). The control surface's leading edge may be thickened with more material, which has the same effect. Older aircraft often had the mass balance on the end of a kind of stalk; in the case of the ailerons this was usually buried in the wings. Rudder and elevator may also be mass balanced.

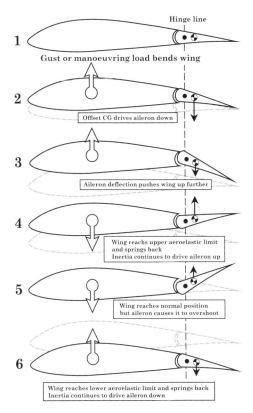

FIGURE 56 Flutter created by unbalanced ailerons

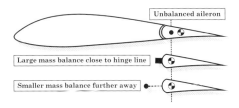

FIGURE 57 Mass balancing

The effects of changes in air density

TRUE AND INDICATED AIRSPEEDS (TAS & IAS)

High altitude flight as a cause of flutter needs explaining because it can affect *any* glider, no matter how well maintained.

FIGURE 58 ASI

Atmospheric pressure at sea level is 15lb/in^2 – the result of the weight of a huge column of air, 50 miles or more high, sitting on that particular square inch. As you climb there is less of the column above you (less weight of air pressing down), so the local pressure drops and the air gets colder.

Whether due to temperature or altitude, changes in air density don't alter how an aerofoil generates lift, but they do have an effect. The formula $L = C_L \frac{1}{2} \rho V^2 S$ provides a clue. Assuming unaccelerated straight flight, weight doesn't alter with altitude, so L is constant, as is the wing area, S. The air density ρ decreases with altitude, so for L to continue being equal to W, either V or C_L has to increase. C_L remains constant because if the glider flies at the same *indicated airspeed* (IAS) then the AoA won't change – broadly speaking, the aerofoil is as efficient high up as low down. Which leaves V, and that's where the problem lies.

THE PROBLEM

Imagine that you are flying a glider at 1,000ft and 50kt. A small wireframe box outside the cockpit counts the air molecules as they pass through. For the sake of argument, let's say that at 50kt IAS the box measures 50 molecules passing through every second. Now you climb to 20,000ft. The air is less dense up here but your ASI still says 50kt, and the box continues to count the passage of 50 molecules a second. You check the stalling speed. According to the ASI it is the same as it was at 1,000ft. But today there is no wind at altitude, and a glance at the GPS shows your ground speed to be 68kt. What's going on?

The difference lies in the fact that for the lift to stay equal to the weight, the same mass of air must pass over the aerofoil every second, regardless of the ambient air's density. The box count, as it were, is correct, and the GPS isn't lying. The air is less dense at altitude (fewer molecules by volume), so the glider has to fly faster to get the same number (mass) per second through the box and over the aerofoil. Is the ASI lying? No, it isn't. The name 'airspeed indicator' may suggest that it measures airspeed directly, but it is actually measuring the dynamic energy (pressure) of the air molecules as they rush in through the pitot and are brought to a dead stop inside the instrument. The *true airspeed* (TAS) is the speed at which the glider flies past each air molecule (68kt), as opposed to the IAS of 50kt, which is in effect telling you the number of molecules you are passing in a certain time. One of the consequences is that for every aircraft there is a combination of altitude and speed where they can simultaneously stall and exceed V_{NE} – the latter is modified at altitude by flutter constraints, as noted below.

OTHER CONSEQUENCES

Until glider pilots begin to make climbs that require pressure suits, the altitude-induced coincidence of V_S and V_{NE} is theoretical, but there's still a problem. Flutter is more dependent on the velocity of the airflow than its density, and there is an altitude/IAS combination where flutter *will* occur. At sea level, 100kt IAS is a TAS of 100kt, but at 20,000ft, the same IAS is a TAS of 150kt. As you climb, so does the TAS. Eventually it exceeds V_{DF} and something will flutter. Descending at a high IAS from a wave climb, or doing high IAS, high altitude cross country flights in wave, could put the aircraft outside its design limits, whatever the ASI says. Notice that the phrase is not 'outside the placarded limits', because the placard may not mention it. Most handbooks do.

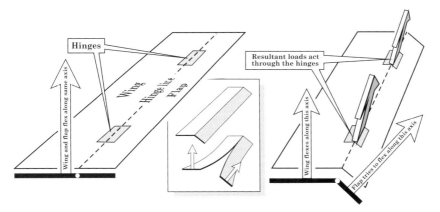

FIGURE 59 Flap loadings

One further effect which isn't immediately obvious is that the higher you go the wider the radius of any turn made at a given IAS and angle of bank – worth remembering if flying in the mountains.

AVOIDING FLUTTER

The practical rule of thumb is that you should reduce the glider's V_{NE} by 1.5% for every 1,000ft above sea level. If your glider's V_{NE} is 128kt, then at 20,000ft the ASI reading corresponding to a TAS of 128kt is 90kt, and at 30,000ft it will be 70kt. (At 36,000ft V_{NE} is half its value at sea level.) In fact, because pressure almost never falls off linearly with altitude, it's possible for the situation to be worse than these figures suggest. It's worth working out the relevant figures before making high climbs because as the air gets colder and thinner with height, pilots usually get colder and thicker. The weather needs taking into account. Meteorological highs and lows and air temperature changes make a difference to the TAS and hence to V_{NE}, though not usually by much.

Other considerations

This chapter has so far taken the commonsense line that gliders don't change shape in flight, even though this isn't quite true. Movement of the controls does alter the aerodynamic shape, however marginally, and without that we wouldn't have any control. Flaps are also shape-changers, and their effects on the loadings have to be taken into account. The same is true of lift-destroying/drag-producing devices like spoilers, airbrakes, or the various flap/airbrake combinations.

FLAP LIMITING SPEEDS

The flaps may have speed and/or G limitations on their use. These limitations may depend on the straightness or otherwise of the flap hinge line. Under load, the wings bend and the hinge line develops a significant curve. With the flaps in anything other than the neutral (0°) position the effect on the structure is the same as adding a kink or fold to a sheet of material in order to stiffen it (figure 59). When the wings bend upwards under load they do so along one axis while the deflected flap tries to bend along another, subjecting the

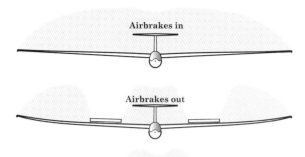

FIGURE 60 Lift/load distribution,
various configurations

hinge fittings to very high loads which can break or tear them out of the structure. Flaps are often operated at their midpoint via a single push/pull rod from a bell-crank in the wing. High aerodynamic loads may twist the flap on either side of the bearing. The flap may flutter if it is too flexible, or there is too much slop in the actuating mechanism. The loads produced by negative or cruising flap are nowhere near as high as the landing flap loads, and it is commonly the positive, and in particular the landing flap configurations, that have specific limiting speeds and/or loads.

LOAD DISTRIBUTION CHANGES WITH USE OF AIRBRAKES

Airbrakes and spoilers reduce lift and increase drag, but each to differing degrees. Spoilers create some drag, but since their main effect is to destroy lift they aren't speed-limiting. Airbrakes also destroy lift, but their main effect is to create drag simply by sticking up at right angles to the airflow and being as un-streamlined as possible. At high speeds most of the drag produced by the airbrakes is profile drag, whereas at low speeds it is mainly due to a large increase in induced drag.

Either way, both spoilers and airbrakes take a chunk out of the lift distribution curve (figure 60) and redistribute the loads. The increased bending loads caused by, say, the deployment of airbrakes can produce a marked upward flexing of the wings, not at the root, where the overall vertical loads stay much the same, but outboard of the air brake boxes. This effectively weakens the structure, and the design case only calls for a 3.5G loading limit here.

During the approach and landing the opposite can happen in flapped gliders, where the positive settings – particularly when the interconnect between flaps and ailerons has disengaged – alter the effective washout angle of the tips, causing them to bend down-wards. With all types of airbrakes the rearward loads (figure 61) are a consequence of having airbrakes that work. The torsional effects are minimal. A further effect of using

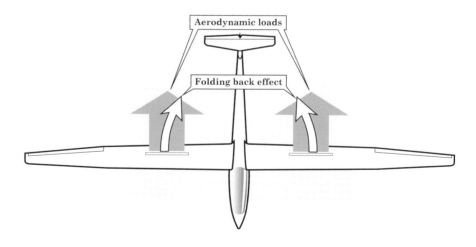

FIGURE 61 Rearward loads
created by airbrakes

the airbrakes can be an increase in the stalling speed, and in some gliders the brakes-in, brakes-out stalling speeds can differ markedly.

JAR22 has some slightly curious default requirements for airbrakes. The pilot must be able to open them at speeds up to V_D without causing structural damage, but there is no requirement to be able to close them again until the speed drops below 75% of V_{NE}. This might prove impossible for some gliders not designed to JAR22, because at the highest speeds the airbrakes suck out extremely violently and do cause damage to the structure and themselves. Equally, the aerodynamic loads may be so high that the airbrakes can't be retracted until the speed has been drastically reduced. A classic example was the early versions of the SZD Pirat. If the airbrakes were opened at, or above, 60kt, it was impossible to close them again unless you were either tremendously strong or first slowed down. The mandatory modification for this feature was the addition of a strong spring into the airbrake circuit.

Summary of chapter five

Page	Subject	
–	**Equivalent air speed (EAS)**	IAS corrected for height and temperature. *See Indicated airspeed.*
154	**Factor of Safety (F of S)**	'just in case' extra built into load calculations.
137	**Fatigue**	failure response of material to repetitive load.
141	**Fillet**	**aerodynamic**: extension to a surface (e.g. wing root trailing edge) to promote smooth flow (*see* chapter 3, pp. 73–4) **structural**: additional material used to reinforce a joint (gusset).
146	**Flush rivet**	rivet head countersunk to provide a smooth surface.
159–61	**Flutter**	uncontrolled oscillation of an aerodynamic component.
136, 137	**Gel coat**	'plastic' equivalent of paint.
138	**Girder**	name for beam or spar, usually, but not necessarily, square section
156–7	**Gust envelope**	replotted manoeuvring envelope taking gusts into account.
159	**Harmonic frequency**	component's frequency of oscillation, of which there may be several.
136	**High tensile steel**	iron alloy with strong resistence in tension.
162	**Indicated airspeed (IAS)**	measure of amount (by mass) of air passing the aircraft in a given time.
128, 129	**JAR22**	Joint Airworthiness Requirements, section 22. Airworthiness criteria for gliders and powered gliders.
132	**Limit load**	design load which is a specified proportion (Factor of Safety) of the ultimate strength of the component.
155	**Limiting speeds**	*see* also end table, p. 169.
131	**Load bearing**	structure or component carrying a load.
129–30	**Loads (types of)**	**torsion**: twisting loads **compression**: squashing loads **tension**: pulling loads **shear**: sliding loads. Also occurs when materials are under tension **bending**: combination of *compression*, *tension* and *shear* loads.
–	**Load path**	direction of load through structure.
144	**Longeron**	longitudinal member carrying loads through a structure; or a support for, say, fabric covering.
136	**Low maintenance**	marketing analgesic to smother pain of purchase price.

Page	Subject	
152–3	**Manoeuvring envelope**	the 'outside' limits of a glider's manoeuvring performance defined by its strength and/or aerodynamics.
161	**Mass balancing**	helps prevents flutter by making a surface's CG coincident, or nearly so, with hinge line/axis of elasticity, etc.
141, 142	**Monocoque**	type of construction where the external shell is the major load bearer.
–	**Neutral axis**	structural: *see Axis of elasticity.*
128	**OSTIV**	Organisation Scientifique et Technique Internationale de Vol a Voile. Set of airworthiness criteria (*see also JAR, BCAR*).
146	**Oxidation**	chemical reaction between oxygen and a material (e.g. rust).
134, 135	**Plywood**	laminated wood with grain of each layer running in a different direction.
141, 142	**Semi-monocoque**	partial monocoque that needs additional reinforcement (see monocoque).
132	**Set**	permanent deformation.
130	**Shear stress**	*see loads/shear.*
136	**Simple curve**	single plane curve, i.e. a tube.
152, 153	**Stall line**	leftmost boundary of manoeuvring envelope.
143	**Sternpost**	rear vertical spar in the fin to which the rudder hinges attach.
140	**Stiffener**	something to reinforce a member.
–	**Stress**	force per unit area.
155	**Stressing**	process of working out effects of loads on the airframe.
137	**Stress fracture**	crack propagated from a point of high stress.
144	**Stringer**	sticklike component, usually no-load-bearing, for shaping and support.
147	**Torque tube**	tube transferring torsional forces.
140	**Torsional rigidity**	measure of resistance to twisting stresses.
149, 150	**Tost hook**	release hook. Another hook type, no longer in use, is Ottfur.
162	**True airspeed (TAS)**	the speed at which airflow passes an aircraft (*see* also *IAS*).
154–5	**Ultimate load**	maximum load just prior to failure.

Page	Subject	
146	**Zinc chromate**	anti-corrosion compound used between dissimilar materials.
	SPEED	**REMARKS** (NB: all units are metric)
(154) V_{NE}	**Never exceed**	Do not exceed this speed in any operation, and do not use more than one-third of full control deflection (of one control).
(157) V_{RA} (or V_B)	**Maximum rough air**	Do not exceed this speed except in smooth air, and then only with caution.
(155) V_A	**Maximum manoeuvring** ($V_A = V_{SI}\sqrt{n1}$, where V_{SI} is estimated stalling speed, clean, at max AUW)	To avoid overstressing the glider, do not make large or abrupt control movements above this speed.
(163) V_{FE}	**Maximum flap extended**	Do not exceed these speeds with the given flap settings.
(158) V_W	**Maximum winch launch**	Do not exceed this speed during a winch or autotow launch.
(158) V_T	**Maximum aerotow**	Do not exceed this speed during an aerotow.
V_{LO}	**Maximum landing gear operating**	Do not extend or retract the landing gear above this speed.
(153) V_D	**Design dive** Category 'U' sailplanes: $V_D = 18 \times \sqrt[3]{(W/S)} \times (1/C_{Dmin})$ Category 'A' sailplanes: $V_D = 3.5 \times (W/S) + 200$	(for ft, lb and kt, use 16.5 not 18 for 'U').

CHAPTER 6
STABILITY AND CONTROL

CHAPTER CONTENTS ★ should know ☆ useful

CHAPTER CONTENTS ★ should know ☆ useful

6 STABILITY AND CONTROL

Stability

All post-war airworthiness standards for gliders outline *stability* and *handling characteristics* broadly similar to those required by JAR-22, and frown upon anything which requires 'exceptional piloting skills, alertness or strength', or anything which, on a regular or irregular basis, might terrify the pilot.

STABILITY, STATIC AND DYNAMIC

Stability is the tendency of an object which has been disturbed to return unaided to its previous state. Chapter 1 discussed stability in relation to why some things fall over (the box) and others don't or can't (the ball). But a description of stability requires rather more than just saying an object or situation is stable, neutrally stable or unstable. For example, when placed on a level surface the ball in figure 1 will stay where it is put, and has *static stability*; neutral in this case because if disturbed it won't come back to where it started. Given a push the ball will roll, and theoretically would keep on rolling forever were it not for the usual draggy forces. In terms of *dynamic stability* (i.e. what happens when it's been disturbed), it has *neutral dynamic stability*, so again it won't come back. The same would apply to the behaviour of an aircraft which had neutral static and dynamic stability.

Stability has a good deal to do with control, and were an aircraft designed to have the static stability characteristics of the cube in the figure, it wouldn't matter how furiously the pilot waggled the controls about – nothing would happen. Pilots aren't usually happy to go along just for the ride, and like to feel that they have some influence over the course of a flight, even if the result is a crash. In their view, control is whatever they can cope with, so in practice there mustn't be too much or too little stability, either statically or dynamically. On the other hand, 'cuboid' stability characteristics would suit a free-flight model glider very well, allowing it to right itself automatically after any upset.

As for the dynamic stability characteristics of the cube, to its right in figure 1 sits a ball in a deep bowl. Push the ball up the side to, say, position (A), as in figure 2. When the ball is released it rolls back towards the central position, overshoots several times, and eventually comes to rest there (B). The oscillations are *convergent*, and the whole process *dynamically stable*. Just how many times the ball rolls through the central position before coming to rest there depends on the bowl's curvature; the flatter that is, the more leisurely the process of return. Either way, the deeper bowl represents a more dynamically stable set-up than the shallower one.

Whereas the sphere or ball is neutrally stable, statically and dynamically, the cone is

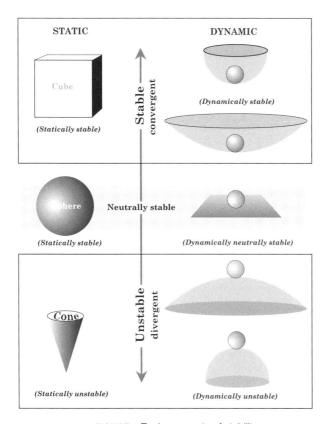

FIGURE 1 Basic concepts of stability

JAR-22.181
DYNAMIC STABILITY.
Any short period oscillation occurring between the stalling speed and V_{DF}, must be heavily damped with the primary controls:
(a) Free
(b) Fixed.

JAR-22.173 STATIC
LONGITUDINAL STABILITY
(1) The slope of the curve, stick force versus speed, must be positive and have a value such that any significant speed change will cause a variation in stick force plainly perceptible to the pilot
(2) The slope of the curve, stick displacement versus speed, must not be negative, except that a negative slope may be acceptable provided that the slope of the curve, stick force versus speed, is adequate and provided that it can be demonstrated that there is no difficulty in control
(3) The air speed must return to within ±15% or ±15kph of the original trimmed speed, whichever is greater, when the control force is slowly released at any trimmable speed up to V_{NE}.

not. In an unstable situation nothing stays put, and tends to escape at ever increasing speed in whatever direction suits it best. The cone, and the ball opposite it sitting on the upturned bowl, represent static and dynamic instability respectively. Theoretically there is an exact point of balance for both, but so atom precise are these positions that the slightest disturbance will cause the cone to fall over and the ball to roll off the bowl, never to return. In both these cases the situation is *divergent* (i.e. whatever it was you didn't want to happen, gets worse).

Any combination of static and dynamic stability is possible, if not always desirable. The ball in the bowl has static and dynamic stability. Let's assume that it can have positive static stability, and neutral dynamic stability. When pushed up the side of the bowl and released, every attempt the ball makes to return to the

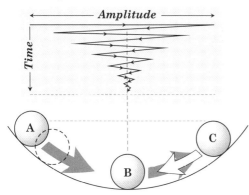

FIGURE 2 Convergent oscillations

central position results in an overshoot to exactly the same height on the other side, theoretically forever. Extending the example a bit further, assume that the ball can be both statically and dynamically unstable. In this case each overshoot will be larger than the previous one, and eventually the ball will fly out of the bowl. Both these scenarios are impossible for the ball because more energy is coming out of the 'system' than has been put in. Aircraft are perfectly capable of both the behaviours described, but avoid the 'no-no' of perpetual motion by fuelling the oscillations with energy from other sources such as petrol, or, in the case of a glider, losing height (i.e. potential energy).

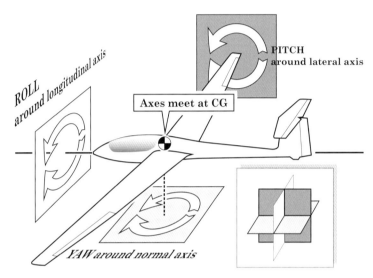

FIGURE 3 Axes of stability

The axes of stability

An aircraft can be thought of as sitting inside a box of three-dimensional space, with each of its major axes acting like an axle at right angles to the surface of the relevant plane. The axes are:

- **pitch**, which refers to movement around the *lateral* axis

- **roll**, which refers to movement around the *longitudinal* axis

- **yaw**, which refers to movement around the *normal* axis.

In practice, the roll and yaw axes constantly interact, so they are usually discussed as one item. The three axes meet at the glider's CG, which is the pivot point around which attitude changes normally take place. Each axis needs to have stability to some degree, even if only neutral stability. Pitch stability, often referred to as *fore and aft* stability, is the hardest to achieve. Automatic balance around the roll and yaw axes is relatively easy because each has a plane of symmetry (e.g. left mirrors right), unlike the pitch axis.

BALANCE

The stability of an aircraft depends on the balance and interaction between the forces of mass/weight, with their balance point at the CG, and the aerodynamic forces (figure 4). The balance point of the aerodynamic forces is placed at the CG by adjusting the elevator to achieve steady flight equilibrium. Their overall *Aerodynamic Centre* (AC), or *Neutral Point* (NP), is critical to stability, and we'll be looking at the relationship between these two in more detail later.

THE CG

The position of the CG depends on the distribution of the airframe's weight/mass and its contents, which include instruments, oxygen bottle, and so on. The pilots have to be

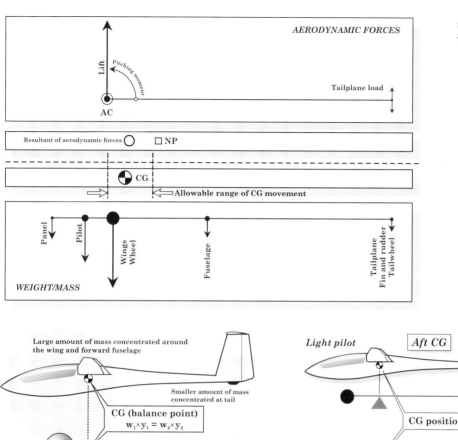

FIGURE 4 Two systems: aerodynamic and mass

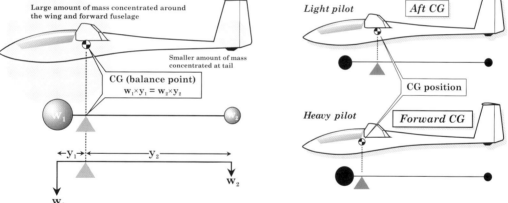

FIGURE 5 Mass concentration and the CG

FIGURE 6 CG position, heavy and light pilots

included as well, of course, and since pilots aren't a standard weight, each will alter the balance equation in figure 5. A heavy pilot will shift the CG nose-ward, while a light pilot will move it aft (figure 6).

Taken purely by itself it wouldn't matter much where the CG was, but since its relationship with the aerodynamic forces is so critical, it can't be just anywhere. The allowable range of CG movement will only be a few inches each side of a datum, and defined largely by the effective leverage of the control surfaces. Having the CG outside of these designed limits can have very serious consequences. For example, with a pilot below the minimum placarded weight the glider may be uncontrollable in pitch, but this won't be obvious until after take-off! Because the CG position is the important variable – the NP position is essentially fixed at the design stage – all changes to it have to be taken into account, though some won't require any action. Pilot apart, any of the following can affect the CG position:

- adding or removing panel instruments

- removing or fitting oxygen equipment or fixed ballast

- badly done repairs which use too much material or put the right amount in the wrong place. This can have a much larger effect than one might think, particularly if it involved work around the tail

- respraying or regelling

- taking off with the taildolly on (big effect because of the long *lever arm*)

- adding water ballast and dumping it. Using a fin tank.

In some of the above cases the glider will need reweighing (*see* Appendix B, pp. 293–4) and the CG position recalculated to make sure it remains within the prescribed limits.

LONG AND SHORT PERIOD OSCILLATIONS IN PITCH

When a trimmed aircraft (*see* p.189) that is both statically and dynamically stable is disturbed in pitch and then left to its own devices, it will try to home in on its original flight path. Two distinct motions are involved: a long period oscillation and a short period oscillation.

A characteristic of the long period oscillation is that the AoA stays very nearly constant throughout. Partly because the forces involved are so small, the motion is leisurely, poorly damped, and may never die out completely (figure 7 ①). In essence, slight changes to the lift – triggered in the illustration by an initial acceleration – cause the glider to pitch gradually

FIGURE 7 Oscillations following a pitch disturbance

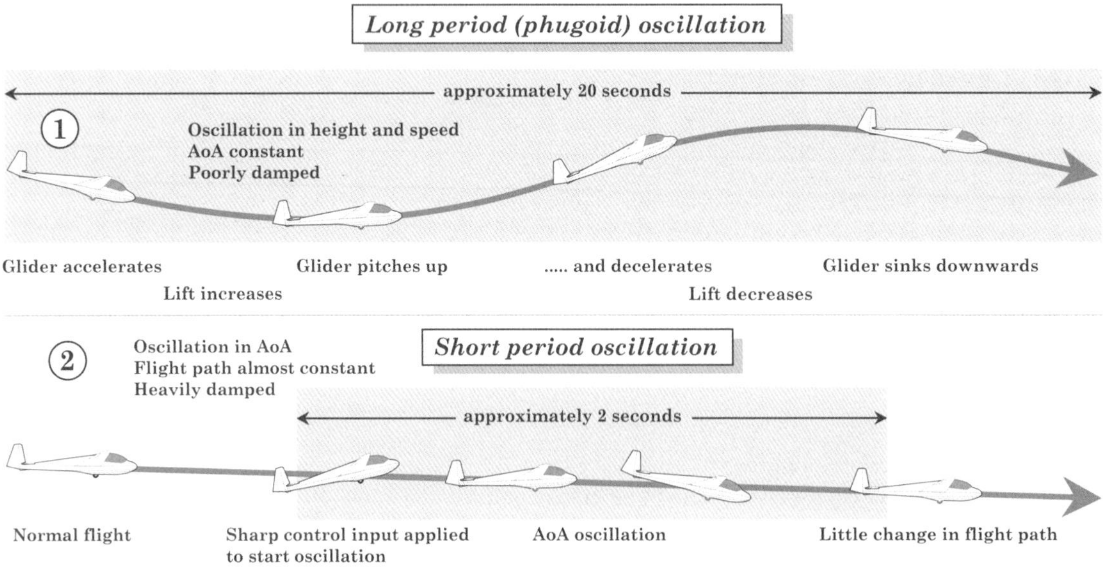

Long period (phugoid) oscillation

approximately 20 seconds

① Oscillation in height and speed
AoA constant
Poorly damped

Glider accelerates   Glider pitches up   ..... and decelerates   Glider sinks downwards

Lift increases   Lift decreases

② Oscillation in AoA
Flight path almost constant
Heavily damped

Short period oscillation

approximately 2 seconds

Normal flight   Sharp control input applied   AoA oscillation   Little change in flight path
                       to start oscillation

into a gentle climb and slow down. As the lift decreases, the glider starts to sink and pitch gently nose-down, accelerating once more. The entire process repeats itself.

By contrast, the short term oscillation has more to do with the AoA and the tendency of the tailplane to try and align itself with the direction of the local airflow, exactly as if the pitch axis were balanced by a spring. If the pilot moves the stick quickly aft and then returns it to its original position, the flight path remains fairly constant, but the AoA (and the glider) oscillate about it in the manner illustrated (figure 7, ②). JAR-22 requires that this motion be *dynamically stable* and well damped. In other words, any oscillations resulting from the original disturbance must either die out quickly – as happens with most gliders – or not occur at all. Though the designer can alter the nature of the short-term oscillation, very little can be done about the long-term one.

THE NEUTRAL POINT (NP)

Every aerodynamic component of an aircraft, including the fuselage, has its own AC. Providing all these components make up a reasonably rigid structure, then the resolved ACs of all the 'working' components plus some factor allowing for their mutual interaction will give the aircraft an AC of its own, called the *Neutral Point* (NP). Figure 8 shows where the NP might be located in relation to the individual ACs of the wings and tailplane of a tandem winged aircraft, and the more conventional layout typical of a single-seat GRP glider. The NP is located at the point where the sum of all the aerodynamic moments is zero, and in normal circumstances (glider nowhere near the stall) it is regarded as fixed.

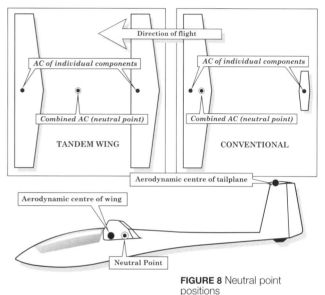

FIGURE 8 Neutral point positions

THE STATIC MARGIN

The distance between the CG and the NP is known as the *static margin* (figure 9), also called the *stability margin*. The smaller the static margin, the less inherent stability the glider will possess. If the static margin is negative, i.e. the CG is behind the NP, then the glider's stability and handling characteristics may be very poor.

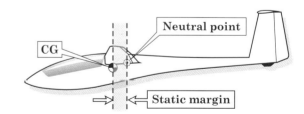

FIGURE 9 The static margin

Pitch stability

THE CG AND NP

In figure 10 (see over) a glider is flying along and is hit by a sudden gust. The pilot holds the stick fixed while all this happening and does nothing else. In example (A) the NP and the CG coincide exactly, though they could equally lie along the same vertical line. Any increase in

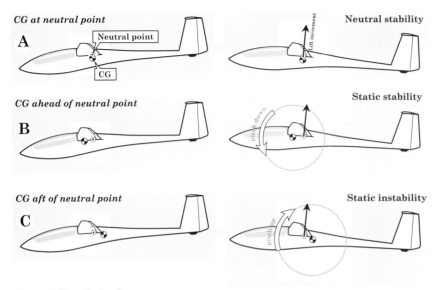

FIGURE 10 The effects of different NP positions on pitch stability

lift, being an aerodynamic force, acts through the NP and about the CG, but in (A) the NP and the CG coincide, so there is no resultant pitching moment. In the short term, at least, the glider will stay in whatever new attitude it finds itself. The static margin here is zero and the glider is described as being *neutrally stable* in pitch.

In example (B) the CG lies ahead of the NP. The gust may pitch the nose up but the resulting increase in lift causes a nose-down pitching moment which tends to restore the glider to its original flight path. The static margin is positive, and the glider is statically stable in pitch. In example (C) the CG is some way behind the NP. The 'restoring' moment now increases the original pitch-up, increasing the AoA even further and with the same result, so the motion is divergent. Left to its own devices the glider will eventually stall. The static margin is negative and the glider is *statically unstable* in pitch.

With the CG very slightly aft of the NP the glider will be dynamically stable but statically unstable, which in practice means that it will diverge mildly in pitch when hit by the gust – the correction required is so small that the pilot may not even be aware of making it – but not tend to tighten up of its own accord when turning or pulling out of a dive. The most obvious effects of this mild static instability are that the glider won't maintain a constant speed. As the speed reduces the stick will have to be moved forwards slightly, and backwards slightly as speed increases. Again, the pilot may not be aware of making a correction. The stick forces will also be lower than normal, though the glider will remain perfectly controllable. The potential danger in a high performance sailplane with this degree of static instability is that it may start to run away if the pilot's attention is elsewhere.

With the CG even further aft there will come a point where any pitch change, commanded or not, will have a greater moment about the CG than can be countered by full deflection of the elevator. However, assuming the placarded weights are correct, it is difficult to achieve the loading error that puts the CG far enough aft to make the glider completely uncontrollable in pitch.

In the case of an extreme forward CG (again outside the placarded limits), full back stick may only prevent the nose dropping when the speed is high. The AoA of the wing may be quite low and the glider isn't actually stalled (*see* chapter 7), but if the speed falls below a value determined by just how overweight the cockpit load is, then the tailplane can't provide the aerodynamic download needed to maintain the associated attitude. It is the ability to flare (or not) which determines the forward CG limit, but in this case rounding out for landing will be problematic.

Though the addition of water ballast can alter the CG position, the limit to the amount of water carried may be to do with not exceeding the AUW rather than with stability. A fin tank is a different matter altogether. Its sole purpose is to shift the CG. There are several reasons for wanting to do this, the main one being to reduce *trim drag* (*see* p. 197). Shifting the CG aft also makes the glider easier to spin, and the fin tank is used for that purpose in at least one modern two-seater.

Finally, the nearer the CG approaches the NP from some initial point forward, the smaller the static margin and the degree of elevator deflection required to produce a given response rate in pitch. The pilot will see the glider as becoming increasingly 'twitchy'.

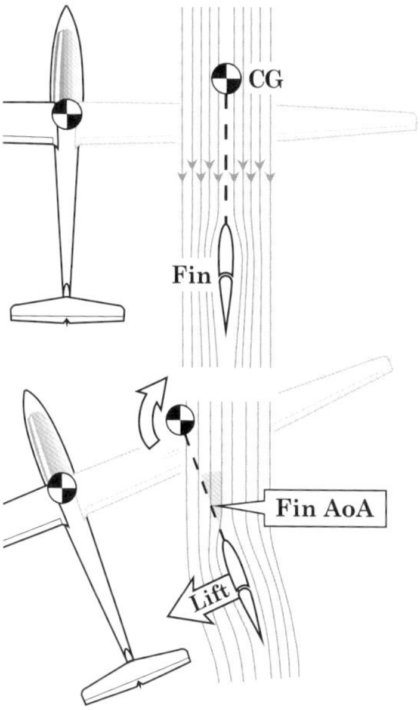

Directional and longitudinal stability

YAW

By itself and without a fin, the fuselage would tend to turn broadside on to the direction of flight. The fin fulfils the same function as the flight feathers of darts and arrows, keeping the fuselage pointing in the direction in which it is going. Weathercocks also 'point into wind', and so this tendency is sometimes referred to as *weathercock* stability. It is fairly strong on most gliders.

The aerofoil comprising the fin and rudder is symmetrical because it has to work equally well to left and right. When the glider yaws, the skewed airflow gives the fin/rudder aerofoil an AoA. This creates a 'lift' force (sideways perhaps, but still 'lift') which swings the glider back parallel to the relative airflow (figure 11). If the glider swings too far, the resultant restoring force swings it back again, but for the majority of gliders any oscillations that there might be damp out extremely quickly.

FIGURE 11 Yaw stability (weathercock)

ROLL

Good roll stability would mean that when tipped left or right by a gust, the glider would automatically roll back wings level. While all gliders possess a degree of resistance to roll, the genuine self-righting effects are actually quite weak.

The wings are by far the heaviest part of the overall structure and their mass extends well out along the lateral axis (figure 12 (A)). By comparison, the distribution of mass in pitch (glider seen from the side) is concentrated more closely around the CG (B). As a result, there is a greater inertial resistance to rolling than there is to pitching. By the same token, once roll has begun, *angular momentum* (*see* chapter 7, p. 221) tends to keep it going.

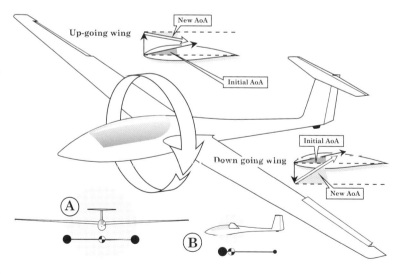

FIGURE 12 Lateral damping and inertial effects

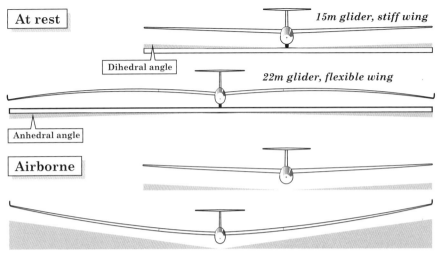

FIGURE 13 Wing flexing and changes in effective dihedral

Barring ineffective controls, the most significant contribution to roll resistance is *lateral* or *roll damping*. When roll is initiated, the down-going wing's AoA increases and so does its lift, whereas exactly the opposite happens to the up-going wing. The AoA changes are highly exaggerated in figure 12, but both act against the direction of the roll and slow it down. Lateral damping becomes stronger the greater the wing span, but at best produces only neutral stability in roll.

DIHEDRAL AND SIDESLIP (SPIRAL STABILITY)

Viewed along the longitudinal axis the wingtips of most gliders in steady straight flight are higher than the wing roots. This upward tilt is called *dihedral*, and the angle between the centre line of the wing and the horizontal is called the *dihedral angle*. The wings of modern gliders, particularly those with large spans, flex upwards in flight and change the effective dihedral (figure 13). Very flexible wings can easily have *anhedral* during the initial stages of take-off and at the end of the landing run, but for the smaller, stiffer winged gliders, dihedral angles average about 3°.

If a gust tips the glider right wing down (figure 14 ①), the glider will shortly afterwards start to slip towards the lowered wing, propelled by a loss of the vertical component of lift and the glider's weight ③. If the wings have dihedral, sideslip creates a greater AoA on the into-slip wing, so there is a tendency for the glider to roll upright again ④. The best way to see how it works is to first cut out a strip of card and give it dihedral, like a wing (figure 14 ②), but preferably slightly exaggerated. Take a pencil to literally point out the direction of the relative airflow, from slightly below

FIGURE 14 Sideslipping and roll stability

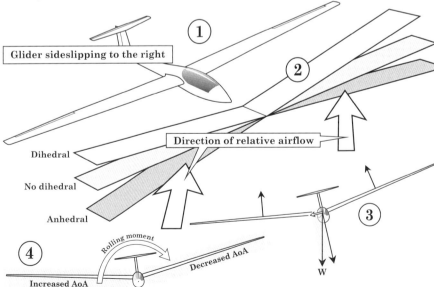

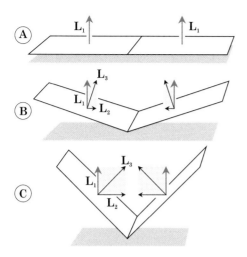

FIGURE 15 Effects of increasing dihedral

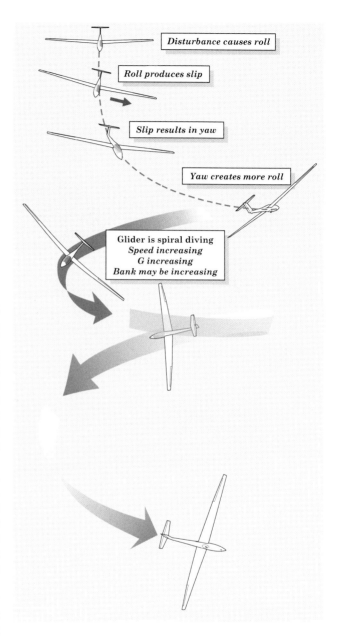

Disturbance causes roll

Roll produces slip

Slip results in yaw

Yaw creates more roll

Glider is spiral diving
Speed increasing
G increasing
Bank may be increasing

FIGURE 16 Spiral instability

and to one side, as illustrated by the two arrows. Tilt the card slightly, like a sideslipping glider, and then 'slip' it towards the pencil. The leading into-slip 'wing' always has the greater AoA, and the consequent lift increase on that side and decrease on the other will tend to roll the wings back level again. When there is no dihedral, slip results in both 'wings' having the same AoA, so there is no self-levelling tendency and roll stability is neutral. Anhedral has a destabilising tendency, causing the glider to bank into the sideslip and, in this case, roll stability is negative.

However, while more dihedral will produce a stronger tendency for the glider to roll wings level, there are practical limits. As viewed along the longitudinal axis, lift always acts at right angles to the plane of the wing's surface, so that for a wing with no dihedral and in balanced straight flight, all the lift generated supports the weight. Small dihedral angles make little difference to this.

As dihedral increases, the wing has to work harder and harder to maintain the vertical component (figure 15, (B) and (C)), while at the same time it becomes more difficult for it to operate at an efficient AoA. Stating the obvious perhaps, but in the extreme case, where the dihedral angle is 90°, the wing can't operate at any AoA capable of producing a vertical component of lift.

When the majority of gliders sideslip and are just left to get on with it, they wind themselves with varying degrees of rapidity into a *spiral dive*, as illustrated in figure 16.

FIGURE 17 The fin rolling moment

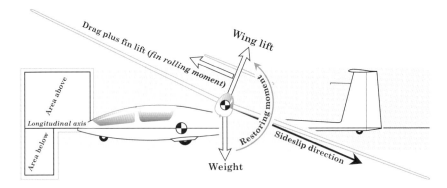

This tendency is known as *spiral instability*. The increased AoA of the into-sideslip wing increases the induced drag on that side, yawing and also rolling the glider into the slip. The nose is already dropping, but the inclination of the yaw axis helps here, and the speed starts to increase, along with the G and the bank. At some point the bank won't increase any further, but speed and G will just keep piling on. Failing sensible recovery action the glider will first be seriously damaged and then very likely break up. Rare though the characteristic is among gliders, if, instead of tightening up, the angle of bank reduces and the speed and G fail to increase significantly, the glider is said to be *spirally stable*.

Dihedral doesn't affect the roll rate, providing there's no sideslip. Sideslip increases drag.

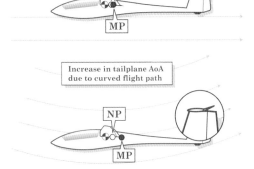

FIGURE 18 Increasing manoeuvre stability in pitch

OTHER CONTRIBUTIONS TO ROLL STABILITY

A large proportion of a glider's side area, much of it belonging to the fin and rudder, lies above the longitudinal axis that runs through the CG. The fin and rudder extend well above the longitudinal axis and are a long way back from the CG. When sideslip develops, the relative airflow over the fin and rudder creates a sideways force comprising increased fin lift and some additional drag. This produces, the *fin rolling moment*, which tends to roll the glider upright again (figure 17). The strength of the effect depends in part on the degree of sideslip, but because of the fin's position in relation to the CG it also creates yaw.

Miscellaneous items

THE MANOEUVRE POINT (MP)

NP to MP distance = ((tail area x tail arm²)/weight) x a constant factor

During any manoeuvre which increases the AoA there is an increase in downwash from the wing, but at the same time the nose may be pitching up, as it would in, say, a turn. This pitch up alters the direction of the airflow over the tailplane – as if it were sat in a curved airflow – and the net result is a change in the tailplane's AoA (figure 18). Assuming that the glider was correctly trimmed (*see* p. 189) before the manoeuvre, it responds to what is now an out of trim situation by trying to pitch nose-down, and to counter this more up elevator is needed. The stick loads will also be higher and the glider will feel as if it has become more 'stable'.

The NP, CG and AC are all balance points, so the moments of any appropriate forces acting about them are zero. The MP is no different in this respect. For example, if you are having to keep a strong back pressure on the stick during a turn, then the MP is where you would need to put the CG to get rid of that back pressure. For reasons already discussed, the CG is not normally located at this point, but well ahead of it, and this forward location also helps to create the higher stick loads. Something similar occurs if the glider is being flown at or above its maximum AUW.

The MP lies behind the NP by a distance proportional to the tail geometry and other factors common to all gliders. A typical unballasted glider has its MP approximately two inches aft of the NP. Gliders with large weight ranges have an MP which, unlike the NP, does change position significantly with the weight.

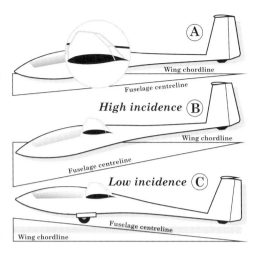

FIGURE 19 Angle of incidence of win

ANGLE OF INCIDENCE

The *angle of incidence* is the geometric angle between the chord-line of the wing or tailplane and the fuselage centre line. The fuselage's drag will always be lowest when it sits at a specific angle to the relative airflow. This 'sit' is determined by the wing's angle of incidence and the airspeed. Figure 19, (A) represents the 'standard' arrangement, with the fuselage more or less parallel to the relative airflow at a mid range of speeds. By contrast, when glider (B) flies fast, the AoA may be small, but the fuselage sits nose-down at an inefficient and draggy angle to the relative airflow, and during the take-off or landing run, glider (B)'s wing will be at a very high AoA, making wing-dropping much more likely. Glider (C)'s fuselage also sits at a draggy angle, but the low incidence means that the glider won't take off until it is going very fast, and that a fully held-off landing will result in the glider touching down tail first. A two point landing, will, like the take-off, be very fast.

The tailplane also has an angle of incidence, normally smaller than the wing, which is sometimes referred to as *longitudinal dihedral*, but it has nothing to do with stability.

Control

GENERAL POINTS

At their simplest, control requirements boil down to (1) will the controls have any effect when they are used, and if so, (2) can the pilot cope with the results? There are measurable limits to the speed of thought and to reaction times. An aircraft that responds extremely quickly or in a highly exaggerated fashion to control inputs (I sneezed and it did six flick rolls) can be uncontrollable simply because the pilot can't keep up. Very sluggish responses, on the other hand, may prompt further pilot input (nothing happened so I pushed a bit harder) before a previous input has had any discernible effect. Either way, pilot and aircraft end up completely out of phase, and the result is *pilot induced oscillations*,

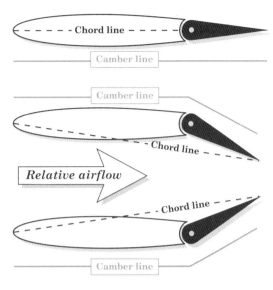

FIGURE 20 A control surface

or PIOs. Pilots can be trained to deal with aircraft which respond sluggishly, but not those which are too quick.

That aside, aircraft require positive control in the three major axes, and an appropriate control surface to deal with each. Flying wings and aircraft with Vee tails may appear to be the exceptions to the need for three separate sets of control surfaces, but the major axes are still there regardless, so one control will certainly be doing the job of two. The Vee tail (*see* p. 193) combines the function of rudder and elevator in a 'ruddervator'. Modern jets often combine the function of elevator and aileron in a 'taileron'.

All the primary flight controls work in the same way. The generic control surface in <u>figure 20</u> could be an elevator, an aileron, or a rudder. Deflecting the control surface alters the camber and hence the 'lift' of the aerofoil of which they form a part so that, for example, it is not pressure on an up-going aileron that lowers a wing, but a 'lift' force acting downwards. The following two points are important:

(1) the AoA changes that created roll damping also create damping in pitch and yaw

(2) because the primary control surfaces form part of aerofoils and rely on this fact for their effectiveness, they can all be stalled.

Mechanical aspects of control

Trite though the observation is, for there to be any control at all there must be some physical connection between the pilot and the control surfaces. Were the control system required to take an active part in the pilot's conduct of a flight – as in a modern air-superiority fighter, where the computer juggles the pilot's demands against what is starting to look suspiciously like the system's desire to survive – then fly-by-wire (or why-by-flier?) might have some point in sporting aviation. But, on a cost-effective basis if nothing else, old-fashioned direct links via rods, cables, bell-cranks, pulleys and so on, are both cheaper and more reliable than batteries or hydraulics.

Most glider control systems are now rod operated, with the exception of the rudder which, largely for reasons of simplicity, is usually cable-operated. The norm in older gliders, cables:

•   are susceptible to corrosion

•   only work in tension, so each control surface needs two of them

•   are sensitive to temperature changes. Adjusted to the correct tension during the winter, they go slack in the summer, and vice versa. Too slack and there's too much 'slop'. Too tight and the controls become stiff, and pulleys and fairleads (guide tubes) can be dislodged.

Control rods, on the other hand, are hollow tubes, usually made of corrosion-resistant materials, and are:

- relatively rigid

- light

- able to push and pull, so an individual control only requires one rod to operate it (forgetting any bell-cranks, changes of direction, and so on).

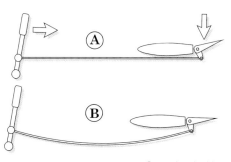

FIGURE 21 Control rod whip

Careful choice of materials minimises the effects of temperature, but small changes in the length of a push rod or torque tube are not critical, and are usually automatically compensated for by the pilot. Temperature changes ought to have some effect on the sit of rod-operated ailerons, either depressing or raising both very slightly, but I have never seen any evidence of this.

Control rods that are long and/or insufficiently rigid are very likely to bend when the aerodynamic forces on the control surfaces and those applied biologically at the stick act in opposite directions, which is most of the time (figure 21). Normally these forces aren't that high, but if a rod does bend it will limit the angle through which the attached control surface can move. The rod can also whip and make the control surface more susceptible to flutter. The longer rods are usually supported somewhere along their length by wheeled bearings similar to those in figure 22. Control rods can sometimes buckle, but the necessary degree of bending and brute force is usually only available during rigging or de-rigging.

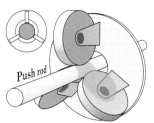

FIGURE 22 Control rod support

Figure 23 (see over) illustrates some of the ways in which the pilot can be mechanically linked to the control surfaces.

Aerodynamic aspects of control

THE TAILPLANE AND ELEVATOR

The majority of gliders spend almost no time at all upside down, so there's no advantage to be gained from having a symmetrical wing section. On the other hand, the tailplane is regularly required to fly 'upside down' in the sense that it is subjected equally to up, down, or no loads as the occasion demands, and here a symmetrical section – or one nearly so – makes sense.

Pitch control requires (1) that when the pilot moves the stick fore or aft of the neutral position something happens, and (2) that – following the convention – moving the stick forward pitches the nose down, and moving it back pitches the nose up. Deflection of the elevator alters the tailplane's camber and creates the appropriate 'lift' force which then alters the attitude.

The stick/elevator movement determines the wing's AoA and the glider's speed. For a given glider at a given weight and CG position, the relationship between a particular pitch attitude and a particular speed is unvarying. There is normally therefore a stick position for each speed/attitude and a specific elevator deflection. The pitch rate is determined by the degree of any additional elevator deflection, the tailplane moment arm, the area of the elevator and the glider's speed. Basically, a rapid and large forward movement of the stick at a moderate airspeed results in a

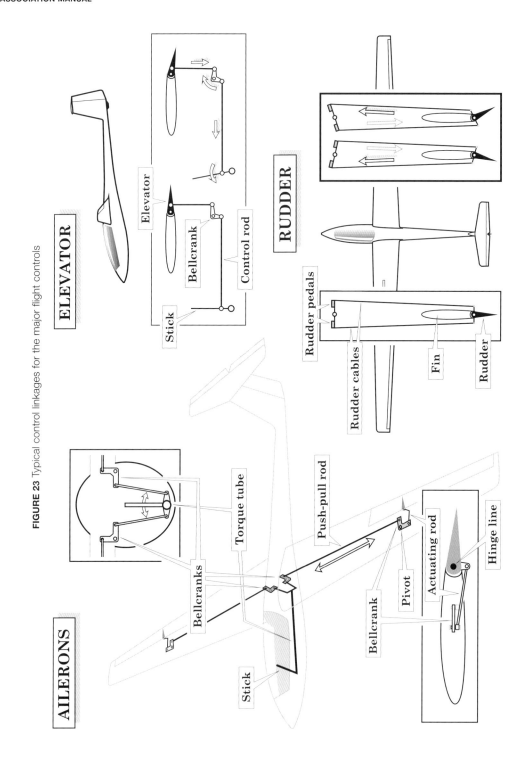

FIGURE 23 Typical control linkages for the major flight controls

ELEVATOR

Elevator

Bellcrank

Control rod

Stick

RUDDER

Rudder pedals

Rudder cables

Fin

Rudder

AILERONS

Torque tube

Push-pull rod

Bellcranks

Bellcrank

Pivot

Actuating rod

Hinge line

Stick

violent pitch-down, but a similar movement at a low speed has a less drastic effect.

One purpose of the tailplane and elevator is to help balance the lift and pitching forces of the wing and provide efficient control of the AoA. The pitching moment of normally cambered aerofoils changes with the speed squared i.e. at four times the speed there's twice the pitching moment. This is offset by the tailplane being set slightly nose-down in relation to the wing so that it produces an opposing pitching moment, which also increases with the speed squared. Whatever the actual magnitude of the resultant forces, the tailplane is there to balance them, but that doesn't mean that the tailplane is always under load. The glider will have been designed so that at a particular CG position and speed the tailplane load will be zero.

Let's say that the glider is statically stable and that the zero tailplane load occurs at 60kt (figure 24 (A)). The wing pitching moment is exactly balanced by the couple between the lift at the AC and the weight at the CG. When the pilot lowers the nose and increases the speed above 60kt the opposed pitching moments of the wing and tailplane remain in balance, but the lift/weight couple alters, creating a pitch-up moment. To hold any new attitude and speed above 60kt, therefore, the pilot has to move the stick forward (B), or retrim (*see* below). Interestingly enough, this means it's perfectly possible to have both a tailplane download and the stick forward. When the pilot reduces the speed to, say, 45 kt, the wing and tailplane pitching moments remain in balance and decrease, but the change in the lift/weight couple turns the tailplane download into an upload, and creates a pitch-down moment. To hold the new speed and attitude the pilot has now either to pull the stick aft continuously, or retrim. Again, it's perfectly possible to have the stick back and an upload on the tailplane.

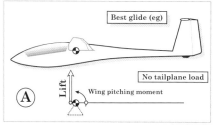

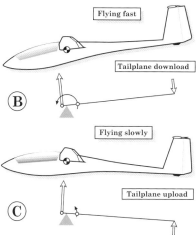

FIGURE 24 Tailplane loads

THE TRIMMER

Unlike powered aircraft, gliders (figure 25) aren't subjected to the yaw and roll associated with engine torque or asymmetric thrust, and need trimming in pitch only. The trimmer is an aid to stability, but from a pilot's point of view it is a workload management tool. Having to keep a constant fore or aft pressure on the stick to maintain any particular speed/attitude is tiring. The trimmer's function here is to reduce the stick loads to zero at whatever speed the pilot has chosen, but for reasons already discussed that won't necessarily change the loads on the tailplane. The new trimmed speed/attitude becomes the stability datum to which the glider will try to return after a disturbance.

There are two types of trimmer: *aerodynamic* and *spring*. Aerodynamic *trim tabs* are small elevators on the elevator. Adjusted by the trim lever in the cockpit, the standard

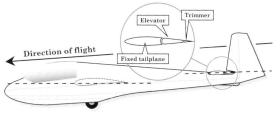

FIGURE 25 Elevator trim

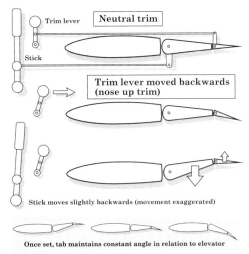

FIGURE 26 Standard aerodynamic trim tab

aerodynamic trim tab then maintains a fixed angle in relation to the elevator. In <u>figure 26</u> it is being used to produce a nose up trim.

Modern gliders may have their stick-free stability increased by curving the trailing edge of the elevator down slightly to form a permanently deflected tab (for example, the SZD Junior), or giving a slight 'dish' to the elevator under-surface, and then balancing the resultant up-elevator force against a spring in the elevator/trimmer circuit (<u>figure 27</u>). When the glider flies faster than the trimmed speed (whatever it is), the pilot has to push against the fixed tab even if the actual position of the stick remains unaltered.

THE TRIM TAB AS A LEVER

The large effect that an item as small as an aerodynamic trim tab has on the elevator is due to the greater leverage offered by its *moment arm*. The principle is similar to that of a wheelbarrow. The elevator is the equivalent of the barrow's contents (W), and the trimmer has the same function as your hands on the handles (L in <u>figure 28</u>). For an aircraft, L doesn't have to be up, nor W down.

To balance W, L's and W's moment about the pivot must be the same (L × b = W × a). For example, say that to maintain a particular speed the elevator needs to be held slightly up by the trim tab, and that this results in a force on the elevator of 1.5lb. We'll assume this force acts 4in back (distance [a]) from the elevator hinge, and that the trimmer's hinge line is 1ft 2in back (distance [b]) from the same point. To hold the elevator in the new position the trimmer has to provide an upward force L, equal to W × a ÷ b, which is 1.5 × 0.33(ft) ÷ 1.16(ft), or just under 0.43lb. For this particular trim condition, therefore, the trim force has to be approximately one third of the elevator force.

An *anti-balance tab* is designed to increase the stick force per G (*see* below) in cases where it would otherwise be too light and the glider could be easily overstressed. Anti-balance tabs

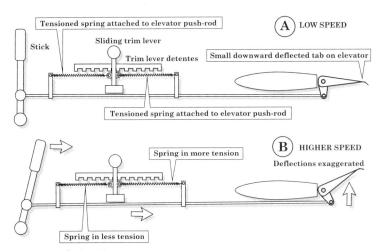

FIGURE 27 Spring trimmer setup

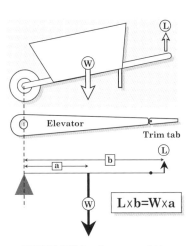

FIGURE 28 Wheelbarrow and trim

JAR-22.155

ELEVATOR CONTROL

FORCES IN MANOUEVRES

The elevator control forces
during turns or when
recovering from manoeuvres
must be such that an increase
in load factor causes an
increase in control force

usually also function as a trimmer, adjustable from the cockpit, but once set don't remain fixed in relation to the elevator; figure 29 will make this clearer. Anti-balance tabs can increase the elevator's effectiveness.

Aerodynamic trimmers have a more positive action than spring trimmers, but their big drawback is that, partly because of their narrow chord, the deflected tab adds significantly to the total drag. Less drag is produced overall if the tab is set to neutral, in line with the elevator, and the pilot accepts the changed stick loads. For a modern glider 1lb of extra drag due to an aerodynamic trimmer could easily be 5% of the total, so spring trimmers which act directly on the elevator are preferred. Spring trimmers tend to feel a bit 'vague', and if one of the related springs breaks the stick loads will change abruptly, not necessarily becoming zero, and stick free stability may be affected.

Trim tab set like standard trimmer, but changes angle relative to elevator when that moves

FIGURE 29 Anti-balance tab

STICK FORCE PER G

Stick force per G refers to the amount of force a pilot has to apply to the controls to produce a 1G increase in load. The lower the stick force per G, the lighter the control forces, and vice versa. The JAR-22 requirements refer to the desirability of the curves 'stick force versus speed' and 'stick displacement versus speed', being positive. In other words, the control forces should increase as the glider speeds up, making it harder for the pilot to overstress the glider, and producing a given pitch rate should not require larger and larger control deflections.

Pilots tend to assume that a glider with heavy controls is more stable than one with lighter controls, but it may not be so. High stick forces may simply reflect a poor *mechanical advantage* (lack of leverage) between stick and control surfaces.

Elevator or rudder loads can be lightened by aerodynamic balances, or horns (figure 30). Often the horns are there to

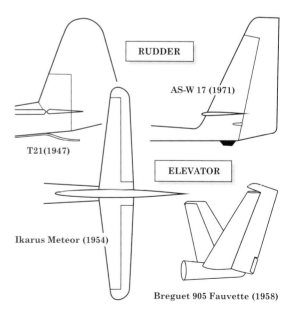

RUDDER

AS-W 17 (1971)

T21(1947)

ELEVATOR

Ikarus Meteor (1954)

Breguet 905 Fauvette (1958)

FIGURE 30 Horn balances

hold mass balance weights, so the aerodynamic effects are secondary. Servo tabs are sometimes added to ailerons to reduce the stick loads in roll.

STICK-FIXED AND STICK-FREE STABILITY

The degree of stick-fixed stability relates to how far the stick needs to be moved fore or aft to produce a given increase or decrease in G. When stick-fixed stability is low, a small movement of the stick takes little effort and results in a large increase in G. On the other hand, if the stick-fixed stability is high the stick may need to be moved quite a long way to get the same increase.

Stick-free stability, on the other hand, refers to the actual control loads themselves, and a high degree of stick-free stability will lead to high stick force per G. Although JAR-22 requires positive stick-free stability it accepts that zero stick fixed stability is an option. So, it is OK for the stick position to remain fixed over a range of speeds – i.e. the speed not directly related to stick position – providing a push force is needed to hold a higher speed and a pull force is needed to hold a lower speed.

ALL-MOVING TAILPLANES

As the name suggests, the all-moving tail (figure 31) fuses the tailplane and elevator together and swivels the entire unit. The pivot point is usually close to the tailplane's aerodynamic centre, i.e. the quarter chord point, and the basic aerofoil is either symmetrical or very nearly so. As a result, changing the tailplane's AoA can require very little stick movement and very little effort, though the latter is by no means universal among gliders with all-moving tails.

Very low stick forces per G are not an entirely desirable characteristic, particularly at high speeds and with all-moving tailplanes – which tend to have fairly high control surface inertia – so the loads may be increased by incorporating the following modifications:

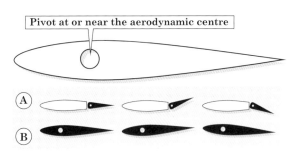

FIGURE 31 All-moving tailplane

(1)   some camber may be incorporated. As the glider speeds up, the tailplane's pitching moment tries to tilt the tailplane nose-down (up elevator) and pitch the glider nose-up. The forward stick loads required to prevent this can be very high

(2)   the pivot point may be moved forward of the AC, which can create other problems

(3)   the loads are artificially enhanced by anti-balance tabs (Dart 15 and 17) or a spring trimmer (K6e, Standard Cirrus).

In the conventional tailplane/elevator set-up only the elevator can float stick-free in the airflow, whereas with an all-moving tail the entire unit is free to do so, helping to reduce drag. For any given pitch rate an all-moving tail deflects through a smaller angle than a normal elevator – compare figure 31, (A) and (B) – but this doesn't lead to a reduction in induced drag. Unless mounted on top of the fin, an all-moving tail has a leakage drag inducing gap between it and the fuselage or fin, and, as mentioned earlier, it has a higher inertia than an elevator, making PIOs more likely.

THE VEE TAIL

The original intention of the Vee tail was to reduce interference drag by doing away with the standard set-up. Each surface of the Vee acts both as a rudder and an elevator, and somewhere in the control circuit there has to be a 'mixer box' which decides how to move each in response to the pilot's control inputs. Left rudder requires the port surface Vee to go down, effectively pushing the tail to the right and lifting it up at the same time, while the starboard Vee goes up and has the opposite effect. The up and down components cancel out, and what's left is an appropriate sideways force, plus some small tendency to roll to the right. Add down elevator into this mix and things start to get complicated (figure 32). On the whole, Vee tails, whether all-moving or not, don't work that much better than conventional tail units and are mechanically complicated.

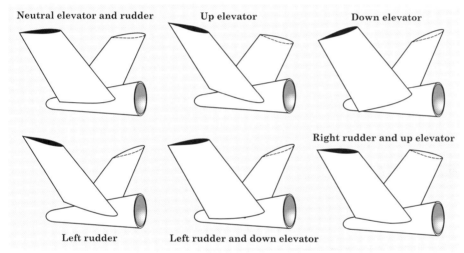

Neutral elevator and rudder

Up elevator

Down elevator

Right rudder and up elevator

Left rudder

Left rudder and down elevator

FIGURE 32 'Ruddervator' movements for Vee tail

THE FLAT TAILPLANE

Chapter 3 mentioned that curved edge flat plates weren't used as wing sections largely because they were overly inefficient, but failed to say exactly why they are very frequently the sections of choice for the tailplane and elevator, and fin and rudder sections of many light aircraft. Despite their drawbacks they are (1) simple to make, and (2) generally don't have to work very hard, so their working range of AoAs tends to be small and the drag levels acceptable, if high.

The ailerons

For reasons already discussed in relation to the elevator and rudder, the ailerons are not usually part of a symmetrical aerofoil. Roll control requires that when the aileron on one

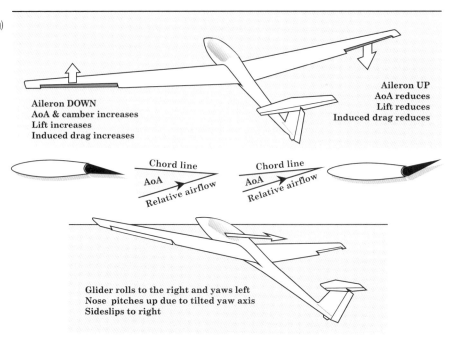

FIGURE 33 The ailerons, roll and adverse yaw (aileron drag)

side goes up, the other goes down, or, at least, that they don't both go up and down together. Moving the stick to the right, for example, should raise the right aileron and lower the left one, and vice versa. The resulting changes in lift on each wing should then roll the glider in the direction of the stick movement, and at a rate related to the degree of stick displacement. The more aileron you apply, the faster the rate of roll, though in a very few gliders the maximum possible roll rate may not be with the stick fully deflected, which suggests the ailerons are stalling.

ADVERSE YAW (AILERON DRAG)

As the glider rolls to, say, the right, it also wants to yaw off to the left (*adverse yaw*). Because the yaw plane is tilted (figure 33), adverse yaw can raise the nose above the horizon and affect the speed, though by rather less than the attitude might suggest because the glider is usually side-slipping at that point (figure 34). Adverse yaw is much worse at low airspeeds and/or high AoAs because it is largely a result of induced drag.

AILERON DESIGN

Various types of aileron have been designed to minimise adverse yaw, but there's usually a penalty involved. Frise ailerons (figure 35) are shaped and hinged so that the

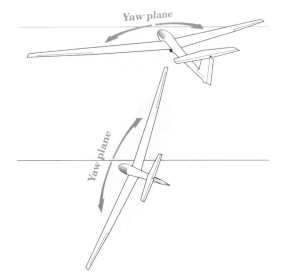

FIGURE 34 Inclination of yaw axis

leading edge of the raised aileron protrudes into the lower surface airflow. This increases the drag of the up-going aileron, partially counteracting the increased drag from the down-going aileron on the other side. They have occasionally been used for gliders, but the additional drag is a drawback.

The method of reducing adverse yaw used by most glider designers is *differential ailerons*. Clever design of the actuating mechanism causes the up-going aileron to deflect through a greater angle than the down-going one, so that the up-going aileron provides more of the rolling moment than the drag-producing down-going one.

Some of the larger span gliders incorporate a spoiler which deploys in conjunction with, and on the same side as, the up-going aileron. The drag and reduction in lift help to offset adverse yaw and increase the roll rate, but this adds significantly to the total drag. The penalty is only incurred when the glider manoeuvres in roll, and the overall loss is small because the bigger gliders are those able to fly in more or less straight lines for the longest times. Smaller gliders of lower performance may have to circle more often, but lateral damping and inertia are less of a problem, adverse yaw is usually less marked, and as a result their manoeuverability doesn't suffer.

HOLDING OFF BANK

In turning flight the glider describes a circle on the surface of a cone (figure 36), with the outer wing tracing out a wider arc than the inner one. The outer tip has the higher airspeed and creates more lift than the inner one – which will also be at a slightly higher AoA – and the overall effect is to roll the glider further into the turn. As a result, once at a desired bank angle, and even with the ailerons centralised, the glider may try to keep rolling. So, in practice, the stick may need to go slightly beyond the neutral position and some small amount of opposite aileron applied – known as *holding off* the bank. The amount of hold-off required does depend on the glider's speed and bank angle, but is usually small. Generally speaking, if hold-off is large and has to be increased to prevent the bank steepening, and at the same time the stick has to be moved back to prevent the nose dropping, then the glider is about to spin.

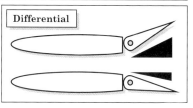
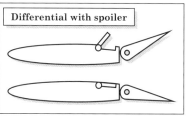

FIGURE 35 Types of aileron

AILERON FORCES AND AILERON REVERSAL

It is a requirement of most airworthiness standards that the aileron forces increase with the speed, and are always positive. In older wooden gliders (T21s, Olympia 2bs) the ailerons could become heavier and less effective as the speed increased. The wings on these gliders were not very rigid torsionally, and as the speed increased, the ailerons acted more and more like servo/trim tabs, twisting the wing in the opposite direction to the aileron movement. The effect was disconcerting, but not a serious problem if such aircraft were flown within placarded limits.

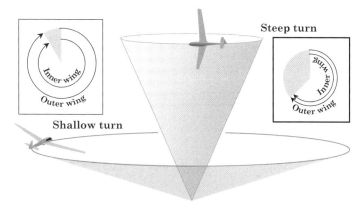

FIGURE 36 Difference in tip speeds for steep and shallow turns

The rudder

The only time when the rudder is used genuinely to steer the glider is on the ground. In flight its primary function is to counteract the adverse yaw created by the ailerons.

For some gliders balanced flight during a turn may require a small amount of into-turn rudder for a continuous shallow turn, slightly more for bank angles up to 45°, and less from there until at 90° of bank there won't be any because the turn will be all pitch (*see* chapter 4, p. 113). This is not an invitation for glider pilots to rudder round turns!

Rudder loads aren't normally very high, but may become so during sideslip, and in some gliders the rudder can then lock over and considerable force may be needed to centralise it again. Since the rudder also forms a large proportion of the total fin/rudder area, losing it will result in a significant, and possibly total, loss of directional stability.

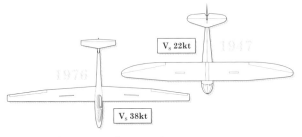

FIGURE 37 Changing stalling speeds

Flaps

A side effect of the aerodynamic qualities that lead to better glide ratios over the entire speed range has been higher stalling, take-off and landing speeds. The unaccelerated stalling speed of a Slingsby T21 is about 22kt, but a Grob G103 stalls at 38kt, about 60% higher (figure 37). One of the simplest ways to keep the high speed gains and reduce the speeds at the other more critical end of the range is to use adjustable flaps.

The primary function of flaps is to increase lift and reduce the stalling speed. As with the other control surfaces, flaps are camber-changing/lift-altering devices offering the pilot a multiple choice of aerofoils, each with a different C_L and C_D. The aerofoil is in its datum configuration with neutral or *zero flap*. As the flaps are lowered (+x°, or positive flap), and depending somewhat on the aerofoil and the glider's speed, 0° to approximately +6° produces a large increase in lift for a relatively small increase in drag. Beyond that, up to about +30° of flap, lift and drag increase more or less in parallel. Anything more than that and the lift increase tails off while drag continues to rise. The flaps can also be raised above the zero position (–x°, or *negative flap*), which has an effect on high speed performance, as described later. In a typical flapped glider the pilot can select from five or so flap positions ranging between –15° to +20°.

Split flaps (figure 38) increase lift and also create very large amounts of drag at the same time. *Fowler flaps*, as used on the Blanik, increase the wing area and alter the camber by sliding backwards out of the wing. Both Fowler and *slotted flaps* use the gap between the flap and the wing as a channel or slot to divert some lower surface air over the top of the flap, making it more efficient. The theoretical benefits of Fowler and slotted flaps are seldom realised in gliders, partly because of the extra weight of the sliding/tilting mechanism, and partly because leakage drag occurs even when the flaps are retracted. The overwhelming majority of flapped gliders use the *simple* or *plain* flap, which is moderately efficient and easy to construct and seal.

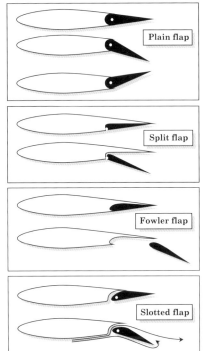

FIGURE 38 Types of flap

POSITIVE FLAP

The smaller positive deflections give a high C_L and a relatively low C_D, useful for thermalling. The lower stalling speed allows smaller radius circles for any given angle of bank. Any increase in drag and sink rate is offset by the ability to fly slightly slower and tighter in the thermal core. Larger positive deflections, beyond *thermalling flap* and up to the maximum deflection for which the design allows, are used for landing (*landing flap*), where the lower stalling speed is accompanied by the, in this case, useful extra of higher drag levels.

Positive flap can provide slightly better visibility on the approach by altering the sit of the fuselage, making it more nose-down than it would be without flap (figure 39). Lowering flap may result in automatic alterations in pitch, depending on changes to the downwash angle and the aerofoil pitching moment.

Most flapped gliders are also equipped with airbrakes, but a few have none in the conventional sense and rely entirely on a very wide range of flap movement for both speed and approach control. The Pik20b's flaps, for example, went in steps of about 2° from −15° to +90°, and were very effective.

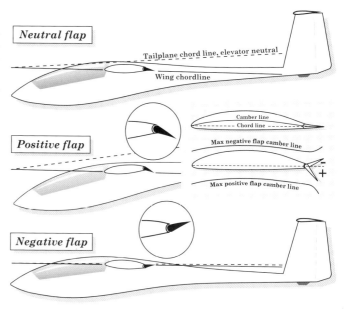

FIGURE 39 Camber changes created by flap

NEGATIVE (CRUISING) FLAP AND TRIM DRAG

To keep a high and constant airspeed the pilot will usually have to maintain a continuous forward pressure on the stick, or use the trimmer. Both actions lower the elevator, even though they will usually be at the same time as a tailplane download. In other words, the tailplane has an AoA and is creating 'lift' and induced drag (figure 40, see over). The extra drag created by the combination of down elevator and tailplane download is known as *trim drag*. All-flying tails reduce trim drag by operating at a lower effective AoA than the conventional tailplane set-up. Alternatively, flaps can be used. Negative flap gives the wing section a *reflex curve*, which lessens the wing-pitching moment and decreases any balancing tailplane load. Usefully, the fuselage will stay at or near the angle relative to the airflow which gives it the lowest C_D.

It is usual to describe flap settings in terms of camber and pitching moment changes, and not in terms of incidence and AoA.

Approach control

Glider performance in the early days was so bad that there was no need to make it any worse. However, as glide ratios improved and speeds in general rose, the flatter approach angles that resulted began to be a problem. The earliest form of approach

FIGURE 40 Use of negative flap to remove trim drag

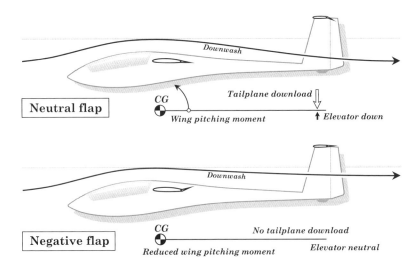

control was *sideslipping*, which, though effective, requires considerable skill. Sideslipping to a spot-landing isn't easy, and if the speed has built up during the approach then, when the wings are levelled for the round-out, the glider is skating along fast in ground effect (*see* Appendix D, p. 298) and in no hurry to either touchdown or stay down. At the other end of the speed scale, decreases in total drag make it much easier to exceed the limiting speeds. Sideslipping is not a practical answer here because, apart from anything else, the fin applies huge torsional loads to the rear fuselage.

One solution to the control of the approach angle is *spoilers* (figure 41). They increase drag, but their biggest effect is to destroy lift. They are not speed limiting. *Airbrakes* fulfil both the approach angle and speed limiting functions by destroying lift, but their biggest effect is to increase the total drag. Both airbrakes and spoilers are simple to adjust and have the added advantage that, unlike sideslipping, the glider doesn't have to go sideways.

Just how effective airbrakes are depends on their area and their chordwise location on the wing. The depth of the wing can restrict the airbrake paddle depth if they are located near the trailing edge – a double or split paddle arrangement helps here – and may affect the leverage available from the actuating mechanism. Many early generation GRP gliders (e.g. Libelle and Kestrel) had rearward-positioned airbrakes and poor approach control, which is why most of them were also equipped with a braking parachute. Airbrakes near the leading edge are not a good idea. If they don't fit flush or seal properly when closed they will trigger turbulent flow well before the normal transition point. Very occasionally

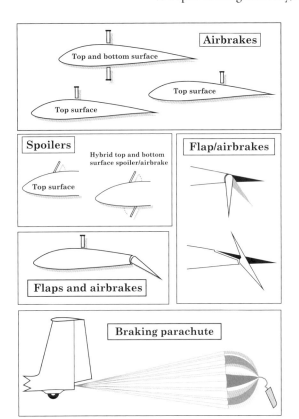

FIGURE 41 Approach control

airbrakes can seem too effective by half (AS-K7), but any problems that arise are usually those of usage.

How effective spoilers or airbrakes are depends on their chordwise location on the wing, whether they are upper and lower surface, or lower surface only, plus their overall effect on airflow and lift distribution. Deploying airbrakes or spoilers may cause pitch changes, almost invariably nose down. Trailing edge airbrakes that pivot along their centre line (e.g. Vega and Mosquito) have no effect on pitch, nor do they increase the stalling speed like conventional airbrakes. They are slightly less effective at low speeds because, unlike conventional airbrakes, they don't change lift and so don't affect induced drag. Conventional airbrakes seem to have an effect on pitch stability, which may be due to the larger pitch changes required for a given increase or decreases in speed.

Of the other devices used for approach and speed control, there are various flap/airbrake combinations, flaps only, and that last ditch device, the *braking parachute*. With every device, the braking chute apart, there is a minute chance that when you pull the operating lever nothing will happen – brakes iced up, for example. Despite the parachute's complete lack of finesse and the good chance that it will fail to deploy correctly, at least one early GRP glider's only means of approach control, apart from sideslipping, was a braking parachute.

Summary of chapter six

Page	Subject	
194	**Adverse yaw**	*see* Controls, secondary effects.
194	**Aileron drag**	*also known as adverse yaw.*
197–9	**Airbrakes**	drag-producing devices, also destroy lift.
192	**All-moving (all-flying) tail**	'fused' tailplane and elevator (single unit).
182	**Anhedral**	*see Dihedral.*
176	**Axes of stability**	*see Stability.*
176–8	**Centre of gravity (CG)**	*see* also chapter 1 summary (p. 23).

185	**Controls**	Type	Primary effect(s)	Secondary effect
		elevator	pitch (lateral axis)	none
		ailerons	roll (longitudinal axis)	yaw
		rudder	yaw (normal axis)	roll
		flaps	lift and drag	
		airbrakes	drag and glide ratio	
		spoilers	drag and glide ratio	

Page	Subject	
174	**Convergent oscillation**	diminishing oscillation about a mean.
182	**Dihedral**	upward angle in relation to horizontal from root to tip (opposite is *anhedral*
175	**Divergent oscillation**	increasing oscillation about a mean.
174	**Dynamic stability**	tendency of a displaced object to return to a given position.

CHAPTER 7
STALLING AND SPINNING

CHAPTER CONTENTS ★ should know ☆ useful

7 STALLING AND SPINNING

A brief history

Cayley referred to his gliders as 'governable parachutes' and, like all the earliest pioneers of aviation, assumed that aeroplanes that flew too slowly – when they could be made to work – would behave exactly like a parachute and float gently to earth. The first person to fall victim to the much less comfortable reality was Otto Lilienthal in 1896, killed as the result of an unintentional stall and subsequent loss of control. 'Sacrifices must be made,' he had said, and in the years that followed, stalling accounted for large numbers of them, largely because no one knew what was happening. Lilienthal himself did not know about stalling, as the following quotation from his 1893 article 'The carrying capacity of arched surfaces in sailing flight' makes clear:

"Beginners are also easily tempted to utilize the momentum which the easy downward glide gives them for bold upward flight. They are likely to forget, however, that at the summit of the rising curve their apparatus becomes a mere parachute. They do not lean far back enough and incur damages requiring considerable repairs to the machine."

During their gliding experiments prior to the historic first powered flight in 1903, the Wrights stalled and/or sideslipped into the ground on several occasions. Partly due to being very low and slow – modern glider pilots who try this are likely to kill themselves – and with no little luck, they always hit the ground before things had 'developed', and so managed to escape serious injury. Orville Wright, describing one flight, used a phrase which in one form or another appears often in pilots' accident reports: 'I was sailing along smoothly without any trouble at all', when shortly afterwards, as he recounted, he had stalled and crashed. By1905, the brothers had discovered how to recover from stalls. This did not mean, unfortunately, that the aerodynamic facts were in any better order than they had been before, and sorting them out took several years. In the spirit of 'more of one thing probably means less of the other', in the early days the approved method of avoiding what was known rather dramatically as the 'sudden dive', was plenty of speed.

Even when stalling began to be understood, no-one made any direct connection between it and spinning. A recommended practice in 1910, or thereabouts, was to skid aircraft round turns using the rudder alone; a potentially suicidal technique along the lines of Lilienthal's well intentioned remonstration that beginners 'do not lean far back enough'. Not for the first time, the major problem was, in part, the lack of an adequate theory. Initially, the only obvious difference between a recoverable spiral and something far more deadly was that some spirals ended with a fatal crash. No-one had much idea why there was a difference, so it was impossible to say exactly why the actions taken by surviving pilots had or hadn't worked. Understandably, it was some while before pilots took to spinning deliberately, though Cecil Lewis in his book *Sagittarius Rising* does talk about service pilots from 1915 onwards proving their manhood by doing just that, and usually recovering. Given the flying characteristics of most early aircraft, such sporting japes amounted to Russian roulette.

As to who was the first to recover successfully from a spin, there are several candidates, but the honour is generally given to a Lieutenant Parke. In August 1912, having spun his Avro biplane at about 500ft, by 50ft he had found a recovery action that worked, and eventually levelled out at 5ft – which seems to have been cutting it a bit fine! Nevertheless, despite his surviving to provide useful advice to others on how to avoid killing themselves, by 1914 there was still no general or consistent spin recovery procedure, and a curious lack of communication between those who had spun and survived, and those who were about to, and probably would not.

A handbook called *Practical flying*[1], subtitled *Complete course of flying instruction*, first published in 1918 and written by Flight Commander W. G. McMinnies RN, defines stalling as 'losing flying speed', and in the half page spent discussing it makes no mention of angle of attack or load-related factors. Spinning is 'to go round and round in a small circle with the nose of the machine pointing directly downwards. A corkscrew descent'. For spin recovery the book advises placing the stick and rudder central, whereupon the aircraft will 'take on a nose dive'. There is a later mention that some machines might require the pilot to move the stick forward of the elevator neutral position, but in a book of 200 pages, spinning occupies less than one.

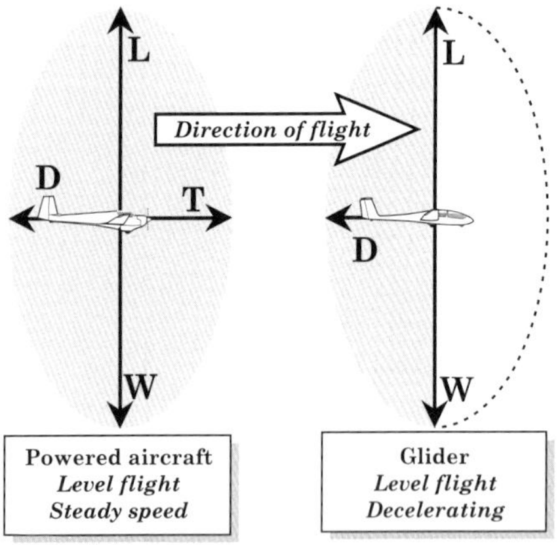

As far as I can ascertain, flight-testing and research undertaken from 1916 onwards at the Royal Aircraft Factory (later to become RAE Farnborough), helped tie up most of spinning's theoretical and technical loose ends. By the mid-1920s there was a standard recovery procedure for stalls and spins which, with some small modifications, is still in use today.

In the early days the loss of life from stalling and spinning accidents was of epidemic proportions, yet today, when the 'why's and wherefore's' are understood, pilots continue to maim or kill themselves by spinning in. Depressingly, the most common comment from survivors is that, like the earliest victims, they didn't realise what was happening.

FIGURE 1 Forces in level flight

Powered aircraft
Level flight
Steady speed

Glider
Level flight
Decelerating

Direction of flight

Stalling

Aerofoils create lift by a combination of their speed through the air (airflow velocity), their shape (camber), and the angle at which they sit in relation to the direction of flight (AoA). There are limits to how much lift an aerofoil can generate.

In true straight and level flight gliders inevitably decelerate (figure 1) and the speed generated component of lift decreases. If the pilot holds the level flight attitude (figure 2, (A)) as the speed decreases, then the glider's sink rate and AoA increase. If, instead, the pilot tries to maintain a constant height rather than a constant attitude, the lift shortfall from the decreasing speed component must be made up by gradually raising the nose

[1]Reprinted as part of Empire Interactive's 1996 World War One flight simulation, *Flying Corps*.

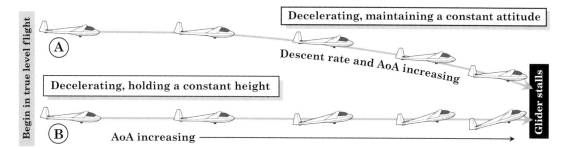

FIGURE 2 The stall approached in two different ways

and increasing the AoA (B). In both of these decelerating scenarios the aerofoil will stall when the AoA reaches a *critical angle specific* to the aerofoil.

Pilots are apt to talk about the stalling speed as if it only had one value, but given a high enough load factor, any aircraft can stall at any speed and in any attitude. All that's required is that the AoA exceeds the critical angle. Technically, the stall occurs either at or just after the point of maximum C_L, i.e. where AoA-generated lift is at its greatest (figure 3). The behaviour of aerofoils at the stall can vary a good deal, with a few suffering an abrupt reduction in lift just beyond the point of maximum C_L (figure 3, (A)). Their stall can be sharp and the automatic pitch-down which follows (*see* p. 209) can be just as abrupt. The C_L curve of other aerofoils may be very flat at the maximum value (figure 3, (B)), and by comparison they have a much softer stall.

Stalling can be divided into two areas. The first covers the mechanics of the airflow over the aerofoil at various AoAs, and the detailed causes of flow breakdown. The second area is concerned with how the aircraft as a whole responds.

AIRFLOW BREAKDOWN AND THE STALL

Aerofoils were originally designed either by guesswork or in wind tunnels, which occasionally amounted to the same thing. Early in World War One the British used wind tunnels to design an aerofoil known as RAF No 6 (figure 4). Almost entirely due to its sharp leading edge, RAF No 6 had an exceedingly vicious and comprehensive stall and was probably responsible for the deaths of many pilots. It could have been so different!

In 1892, Lanchester, a prominent theoretician of the time, realised that there was, in essence, a circular flow round aerofoils (*see* Chapter 3, p. 77). He finally published his theory in 1907, whereupon it was completely ignored by aerofoil designers in the UK, who continued to use wind tunnels. The Germans understood it, however, and Prandtl and other theoreticians refined and elaborated it, using it to design aerofoils like the Göttingen 298.

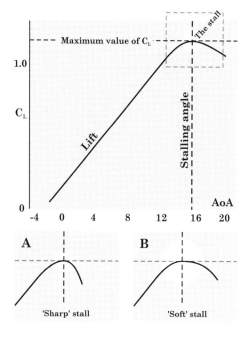

FIGURE 3 'Sharp' and 'soft' stalls

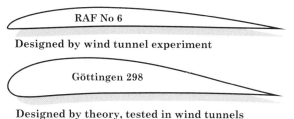

FIGURE 4 Aerofoils, circa 1916

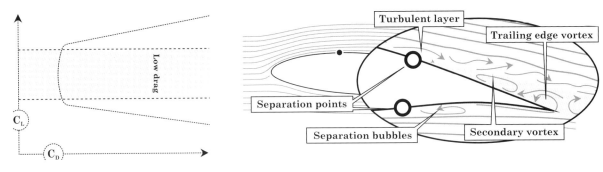

FIGURE 5 Low drag 'bucket'

FIGURE 6 The separation point(s)

With a large radius leading edge and greater depth, this aerofoil not only had infinitely better stalling characteristics than RAF No 6, but allowed the use of a much more substantial main spar, fewer bracing wires and struts, and opened the way for semi-monocoque construction. Redundant wires and struts were sometimes retained to reassure pilots that the wings weren't going to fall off.

AoA is the most important factor in stalling, but as the above tale shows, so too is the shape of the aerofoil because it determines the nature of the flow, the location of the peak suction point and the transition points, and how they move as the critical angle is approached. The aerofoil shape will also determine the location of the separation point, which is where the airflow leaves the surface. On modern aerofoils separated flow doesn't normally occur until the AoA is quite high but, as described in chapter 3, laminar flow can separate prematurely. We'll assume here that there is nothing on the surface of the aerofoil to cause this, and that it is a turbulent boundary layer that separates.

FIGURE 7 Changing airflow as aerofoil approaches the stalling angle

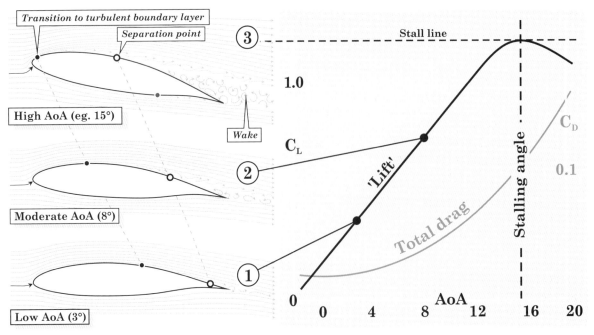

The drag coefficient (C_D) curves for modern laminar flow aerofoils usually have a low drag '*bucket*' (figure 5), so called because of the shape of the curve. The bottom of the 'bucket' represents the aerofoil's designed working range of AoAs (strictly C_Ls) where the drag levels are low and don't change very much, and the aerofoils are consequently operating at peak efficiency. Once the AoA strays outside that range there can be quite steep drag rises for comparatively small AoA changes. Initially these are largely the result of the upper surface transition point moving towards the leading edge, so more of the boundary layer over the wing is turbulent. For real-world aerofoils the drag rise would also include induced drag.

At an AoA specific to the aerofoil, the turbulent boundary layer will separate, but a vacuum does not form underneath it. Instead, air from the undersurface spills round the trailing edge and travels forwards along the upper surface, often setting up a series of spanwise standing vortices (figure 6). Separation causes steep increases in drag levels, affects the position of the AC (and the NP) and causes symmetrical and normally cambered aerofoils to pitch nose down more strongly.

Figure 7, examples 1-3, illustrates the gradual breakdown of flow as the AoA approaches the *critical* or *stalling angle*, and the forward movement of the upper surface transition and separation points. Note the steep rise in the drag level with AoA.

THE STALL, AIRCRAFT BEHAVIOUR

It is surely stating the obvious, but the aircraft behaviour that glider pilots take to be normal at the stall has to be designed in and doesn't just happen. Since good behaviour is 'put in', there is also the potential for anything which alters a glider's designed ('safe') and tested configuration to take it out again, however temporarily. For example, aerofoils with sharp stalling characteristics make poor sense from a handling and safety point of view, particularly for thermalling, and are not deliberately chosen for gliders. You can, however, get bad stalling characteristics by default from an otherwise exemplary aerofoil if the glider ices up or is splattered with bugs.

The desirable automatic pitch-down at the stall occurs only if there has been a significant loss of lift from the wing, caused either by an abrupt application of elevator suddenly increasing the AoA, or by the speed being insufficient, or by some combination of both.

Take a straight and *unaccelerated stall* (figure 8, see over). The glider has been trimmed for straight and steady flight at, say, 50kt. We'll assume that initially there's a small download on the tail ①. The pilot eases the stick back, pitching the decelerating glider up at a rate which keeps it in more or less level flight, i.e. the loading as near to 1G as possible. (The unaccelerated 1G stall is the datum stall.)

As the glider decelerates, the pilot has to make a deliberate effort to keep the nose pitching up because the resultant of all the other forces is trying to pitch it down – to return it to the prior trimmed condition. At some point the wing's AoA will reach the critical angle, the C_L will be at its maximum,

JAR-22 (STALLING)

JAR-22.201 Wings level stall

a) Stall demonstrations must be conducted by reducing the speed by approximately 2km/h per second until either a stall results as evidenced by a downward pitching motion or rolling motion not immediately controllable, or until the longitudinal control [the stick] reaches the stop. It must be possible to produce and correct roll and yaw by unreversed use of the controls until the stall occurs

c) Stalling behaviour must not be unduly sensitive to sideslip

e) With the sailplane in straight flight at 1.2 V_s in the configuration appropriate to winch launching, by pulling rapidly on the control stick a pitch attitude approximately 30° above the horizon must be achieved and the resulting stall must not be severe and such as to make prompt recovery difficult.

JAR-22.207 Stall warning

a) There must be a clear and distinctive stall warning with airbrakes, wing flaps and landing gear in any normal position, both in straight and in turning flight

b) The stall warning may be furnished either through the inherent aerodynamic qualities of the sailplane (eg. buffeting) or by (the addition of) a device that will give clearly distinguishable indications A visual stall warning alone is not acceptable

c) The stall warning must begin at a speed between 1.05 and 1.1 V_s, and must continue until the stall occurs

d) A sailplane which does not give warning of the approach of the stall may, however, be acceptable provided that when a stall occurs from straight flight –

1) it is possible to produce the correct roll by use of the ailerons, the rudder being held neutral; and

2) no appreciable wing drop occurs when both aileron and rudder are held neutral.

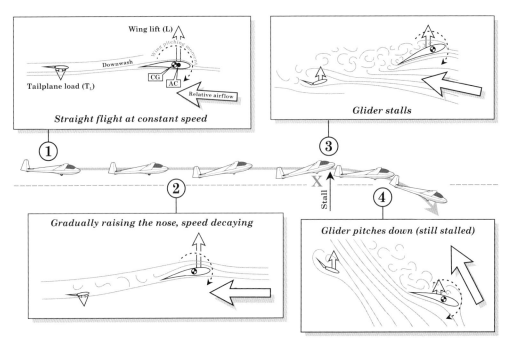

FIGURE 8 The straight stall

Straight flight at constant speed — **1**

Gradually raising the nose, speed decaying — **2**

Glider stalls — **3**

Glider pitches down (still stalled) — **4**

and the glider will be stalled. Apart from the *mushing stall* (*see* p. 214), it then becomes impossible to prevent the nose dropping, even with the stick fully back.

At the stall the tailplane produces an upload, largely due to the change in direction of the relative airflow. The AC, meanwhile, has slid back to somewhere near the 50% chord position. Despite this shift, the overall pitching moment at the stall for aerofoils where the C_L curve has an extended peak, may reduce slightly. On older sections it typically increased slightly. In both cases the wing-pitching moment does not suddenly increase, nor is it solely responsible for the pitch-down. The tailplane is set up to stall long after the wing, and it is the combination of its now relatively large moment, plus the wing-pitching moment, both about the CG, which automatically lowers the nose.

STALL RECOVERY

Before dealing with the symptoms of an approaching stall we'll look at the recovery procedure. Stalls are caused by trying to operate the wing at too high an AoA, so the first action is to reduce it by easing the stick forward and lowering the nose. Following any stall, the rate at which the glider accelerates and the AoA decreases depends on the glider's attitude, and the lower the nose the quicker the changes. Failure to lower the nose sufficiently results in slow acceleration, or none at all, and the possibility of a further stall. There is also the drag level to consider, and having the brakes open when you stall will, for a given recovery attitude, slow any acceleration.

The key recovery action should always be the same, but exactly how much forward stick is required depends on the glider's attitude when it stalled, its speed at the time, what it did shortly afterwards, and your understanding of what's happening. For gliders, pushing the stick vigorously to the front stop can count as overkill. On the other hand, you won't know exactly what the AoA is – except that the glider has stalled so the AoA must be high – and slightly overreacting is a better strategy than not reacting enough. In any event, it is important to reemphasise the two fundamental points:

(1)   you can't unstall without reducing the AoA

(2)   the glider can stall at any airspeed and in any attitude. All it requires is a high enough AoA.

Symptoms of the stall

Gliders spend a significant part of their flying time close to the stall, so predictable behaviour there is preferable, as well as unambiguous symptoms that show that a stall is approaching. Some of the more usual symptoms are, in no particular order:

(1)   nose high, relative to the normal flying attitude

(2)   low or reducing airspeed

(3)   low, reducing or occasionally changing airflow noise

(4)   buffeting

(5)   changes in the way the controls normally operate

(6)   elevator failing to raise the nose.

Of all the above, the only symptom present in every stall is (6). If you can't raise the nose with the elevator – excepting a failure to connect it, or the cockpit weight being way over the placarded maximum – then you are stalled. The elevator will always lower the nose unless the glider is moving at a ridiculously low airspeed.

Even those symptoms which are present at the stall won't necessarily be shouting for attention. Of the first three, for example, (1) won't be at all obvious visually if the glider is about to high speed stall during a dive recovery, or during a well banked turn. In fact, symptom (1) probably ought to read, 'nose high relative to the flight path'. Changes in airspeed (symptom (2) can go unnoticed unless the ASI is being monitored, and even then may not tell true. For example, if the glider is flying sideways, pressure changes caused by crossflow across a nose-mounted pot-pitot can wind the ASI needle backwards by 20–30kt, which can be misread either as the glider going far too fast, or too slow!

Changes in airflow noise (3) can be subtle. Separated airflow often has a characteristic hiss, or may differ in pitch from the usual airflow noises. An imminent stall during a tight thermalling turn may be signalled by nothing more than a whooshing noise apparently just behind the pilot's head.

Gliders are designed so that airflow over the wing begins separating from the root end first (see p. 218). With a low set tailplane, the first streamers of separated and turbulent flow run down the side of the fuselage and hit the tailplane and elevator, causing fore and aft shaking of the stick. This

FIGURE 9 The mechanics of pre-stall buffet

211

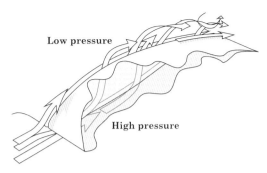

FIGURE 10 Flow through wing root gap

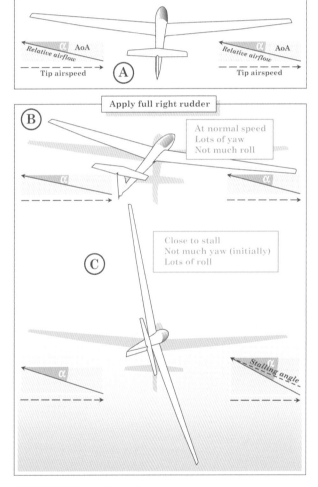

FIGURE 11 Effects of yaw at different speeds

symptom (4) is usually referred to as *pre-stall buffet* (figure 9, see previous page), and in gliders such as ASK13s can also make a low rumbling noise clearly audible in the cockpit. With T-tailed gliders the tailplane sits well above the turbulent wake, so any pre-stall buffet is felt through the rudder, perhaps with the glider wagging its tail. Side to side shaking of the stick is not particularly good news, because it suggests that the ailerons are being affected and that the tips are about to stall. This symptom, or any uncommanded but not necessarily marked rocking of the wings can precede a very sudden wing drop. Immediate action needs to be taken to reduce the AoA, even if this only amounts to relaxing the back pressure on the stick.

Buffet and juddering don't always signify a high AoA, even though in the majority of cases this is their cause. In some gliders opening the airbrakes can create pronounced buffet. Similarly, if the wing/fuselage gap isn't sealed with tape or foam (figure 10) through-flow from the high to low pressure area can cause local flow breakaway, sending a turbulent wake rolling back to buffet the rear fuselage and tailplane. Failing to tape the junction between tailplane and fin in modern sailplanes can result in continuous low levels of vibration through the stick. Such apparent 'pre-stall' buffets can occur in straight flight at speeds well above the nominal unaccelerated stalling speed without the glider actually being stalled (or suffering from flutter). They imply increases in drag; large and planned in the case of the airbrakes, smaller and unplanned in the others. It's worth doing something about getting rid of the unplanned ones. Other causes of buffet are more intractable. The glider may vibrate or 'buzz' if it has been rained upon or is covered with ice or insects. Either way, it is likely that the stalling speed will have increased, though not necessarily by much.

Symptom (5) boils down to control effectiveness at or near the stall. It is not true to say that what the controls do changes, even though they can stop working altogether. Take the rudder. It always produces two effects: the yaw it was designed to provide, and the unwanted roll induced by the yaw. These relative proportions do change with speed.

Assume that we are flying along in a straight line (figure 11, Ⓐ) at a speed below V_A, and abruptly put on full right rudder and let everything take its natural course. The glider will do one of the following:

(1)   at best glide, say, it will yaw markedly, but with little roll. Apart from the effects of the abrupt initial

swing, and despite the resulting sideslip, the differences in AoA and lift between the wings will be small, as will the amount of roll ⑧

(2)   close to the stall, both wings are already at high AoAs. The rudder will be sluggish at such low speeds, but the swing will create a relatively large speed and AoA differential between the tips ©. The AoA and induced drag of the accelerating left wing decrease, while the opposite happens to the right wing, increasing the yaw rate and rapidly worsening the situation. The changes are quick to show themselves. The right and rearward going wing stalls, and the glider then rolls rapidly towards it – perhaps rolling through a partially inverted position – and enters an upright spin

(3)   everything happens as in (2), except that the wing drops and the glider enters a spiral dive (*see* p. 223) instead of a spin.

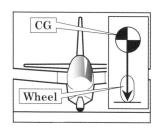

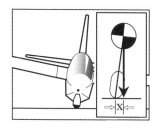

FIGURE 12 CG/wheel couple

A couple of related practical points ought to be mentioned here. First, the fin and rudder can stall, and if they do so the glider will try to swap ends – this might be an additional factor in example ②. Second, at extreme yaw angles the fin can aerodynamically blank off part of the tailplane. If the tailplane is being subjected to a download, then effectively taking away half of it will cause the glider to pitch nose-down. With an initial upload the blanking will cause the glider to pitch nose-up. An obvious conclusion is that any glider with a tendency to do either should not be sideslipped close to the ground.

SLOW FLYING

Exercises that involve keeping the wings level during slow flight by using the rudder are no longer taught. However, current teaching notwithstanding, a dropping wing can be picked up by using opposite rudder, but only if the stick is eased forward at the same time. Failure to lower the nose can result in the glider rolling rapidly into a spin in the direction of the rudder input.

AILERONS AGAIN

Most glider airworthiness standards specify that the ailerons continue to work, however sluggishly, right up to the stall and preferably beyond. The requirement seems to be aimed largely at gliders in flight,
but is just as applicable to the ground run, where stalling a wing can drop it onto the ground – at take-off in particular – and cause ground loops or worse.

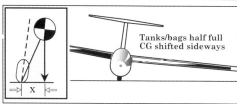

FIGURE 13 Effect of water ballast on lateral CG position

The sole function of the ailerons during the ground run is to keep the wings level. When the wings aren't level the couple created by the wheel and the offset CG is small, even when the wing is on the ground (figure 12). Pick up the wing of a parked glider and see for yourself. At very low airflow velocities the ailerons don't work well enough to provide even that small amount of force. More critically, it is easy during the early part of a take-off roll to stall a dropping wing by simply whacking the stick over to pick it up.

The wheel/CG couple of a water-ballasted glider will be far stronger, and markedly so if the bags or integral tanks are only part filled (figure 13). The wings have to be held absolutely level for several seconds just prior to the launch to allow the water to stop sloshing around, even out the load, and lessen the likelihood of a wing drop.

FIGURE 14 Changes in the AoA, C_L and C_D at the stall

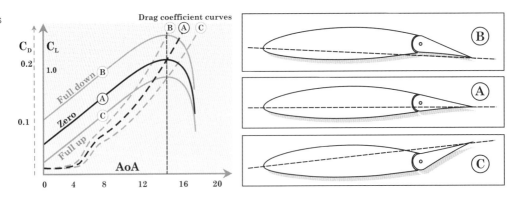

The results of trying to pick up a stalled wing with aileron are more safely observed in flight. Figure 14 shows three different aileron positions: B – full down; A – central; and C – fully up. Lowering or raising the aileron alters the section camber and gives us, in effect, as many aerofoils – and C_L and C_D curves – as there are aileron positions.

Close to the stall, with aileron neutral, the C_L of the section including the aileron (curve (A)) will be near to its maximum. Though down aileron does slightly reduce the critical stalling angle of the wing at that spanwise location, it still shifts the C_L curve up to (B), and since this also increases the effective AoA, that part of the wing is now operating on the (B) curve, but to the right of the stall line, where there is both less lift and more drag.

FIGURE 15 Stall with no clear break

THE MUSHING STALL

If a glider approaches the stall with a very gentle pitch-up rate (figure 15) there may be no obvious stall break. Despite some initial nose drop the elevator may be able to prevent it

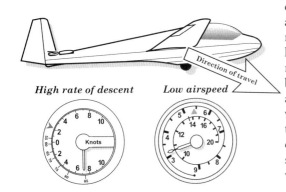

FIGURE 16 Mushing stall, instrument indications

dropping very far, but not be quite powerful enough to take the aerofoil past the critical angle. The glider then descends at a high rate, usually at a low airspeed, but not necessarily with the stick hard against the back stop. The AoA remains constant. This is the mushing stall. The symptoms aren't very dramatic, and there may be no buffet. If drag levels are high enough and the glider isn't accelerating (brakes out, say), a mush stall can occur with the nose well below the horizontal. In either case, an inattentive pilot may think that everything is fine, though the stick position can be a bit of a giveaway (figure 16). If yaw is introduced during a mushing stall, the glider can roll with astonishing rapidity into a spin. As with all stalls, the nose must be lowered to reduce the AoA.

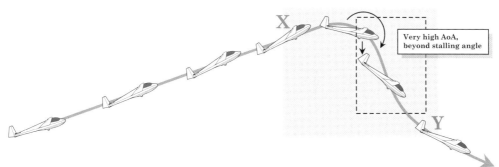

FIGURE 17 A steep or 'ballistic' stall

EXTREME AOAS AND BALLISTIC STALLS

When a glider already close to, or at, the stall is hit by a gust, or the pilot suddenly puts on full-up elevator, or the glider does a *ballistic* or *hammerhead* stall, the AoA can temporarily be much greater than the nominal critical angle. Strictly speaking, 'ballistic stall' is a misnomer. The glider can climb steeply (<u>figure 17</u>), come almost to a stop – as would any object which had more or less been thrown there (the ballistic bit) – and then simply drop. Only then does the glider stall in the aerodynamic sense, with the AoA going briefly way beyond the critical angle. At the peak of what can be part of a freefall parabola, the ASI will indicate correctly, but misleadingly, speeds way below the normal stalling speed, even zero.

When the glider's initial trajectory is extremely steep (<u>figure 18</u>) and the glider very nearly comes to a halt at the peak, the subsequent interaction between the aerodynamic

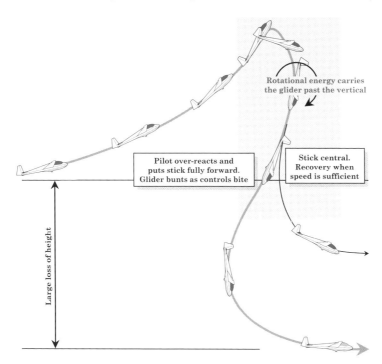

FIGURE 18 'Hammerhead' stall

forces and the CG as the glider falls will cause it to pitch sharply nose-down. The rotational energy this generates can take the glider past the vertical before it is moving fast enough for the controls to have enough 'bite' to prevent it. In this case the stick must be moved forward at the very least to the neutral elevator position. Moving it much further than that can result in the glider starting a *bunt* as the elevator takes effect. This is easy to correct, but the pilot will leave the seat, and the further the glider goes beyond the vertical the greater the arc to pull through to level flight, and the higher the speed during the recovery.

$$\text{Stalling speed} = \sqrt{n} \times V_s$$

Unaccelerated stalling speed is example only

Bank angle	Load Factor	Stalling speed (kt)
	0	0
	0.1	12
	0.25	19
	0.5	27
0°	1	38
15°	1.035	39
30°	1.15	41
45°	1.41	45
60°	2	54
75°	3.8	74
80°	5.76	91
85°	11.5	129

FIGURE 19 Stalling speed and 'n'

STALLING, REDUCED AND ZERO G

When the load factor is less than one the glider can fly, and to some extent be controllable at speeds below the nominal stalling speed. If G (or n) is less than one then the wing loading will be lower than normal (<u>figure 19</u>), the wing won't have to work so hard, and consequently the AoA will also be lower, possibly well below the critical angle. It hardly needs saying that this is only a temporary state of affairs, but reduced or zero G is fairly common after winch cable breaks.

STALLING OFF A FAILED WINCH LAUNCH AND REDUCED G

Many pilots have no clear idea of how long it takes to pitch from 50° nose-up at 54kt – normal for an AS K13 winch launch – to, say, 20° nose-down. This 70° attitude change and return to an adequate speed can take over 10 seconds, even with the stick initially fully forward. Experiment! At a safe altitude in a two-seater, simulate a cable break. Either you or the other pilot should time what happens. Points to note:

(1)   however good your reflexes – even if you are instantly aware of what's happened – after a genuine break there is a short pause before your muscles fire up and do anything

(2)   the glider will continue to decelerate until the nose is below the horizontal

(3)   the elevator will become less and less effective during the deceleration, and the pitch down rate will slow

(4)   when the pitch-down stops, G immediately returns to normal along with the wing loading and the stalling speed. If the airspeed is then insufficient, the glider will stall.

In <u>figure 20</u> both examples represent a glider on a winch launch, established in a 50° climb at 54 kt. The cable breaks. Pilot (A) responds by lowering the nose well below the normal flying attitude, but not excessively so. Though initially the AoA is high, as illustrated by the brief sag in the flight path, it quickly reduces as the glider accelerates rapidly away. Pilot (B) responds equally quickly, but only lowers the nose to the normal flying attitude, or something less, and then attempts to hold it there. The glider immediately starts to sink, and if it accelerates at all, does so only slowly. It may already be stalled, or nearly so. Either way, initiating a turn will increase the wing loading and introduce yaw. With the AoA already high, one wing will go beyond the critical angle, the stall will be asymmetric and the glider will spin.

Some caution needs to be exercised if, unlike the ASK13 in the example, the glider has a high maximum winch speed (V_W) and is flying close to that when a break occurs. Pushing the stick fully forward can fly the glider under either the parachute or the broken cable.

MINIMUM SAFE SPEED AND STALLING ON THE LAUNCH

The minimum safe winching speed was introduced to help pilots avoid the risks associated with climbing at high AoAs and/or low airspeeds. Defined as 1.5 x V_S, the speed is equivalent to a load factor slightly greater than two. A reliable value of the unaccelerated stalling speed (V_S) is required to calculate it. The basic idea is that if you don't fly the launch slower than 1.5 x V_S then, no matter how hard you pull back on the stick, the weak link will break before the glider stalls. You can still stall effortlessly off the break, however, and failure to lower the nose sufficiently or in time is a major cause of winching accidents. The minimum safe speed applies to every winch launch – even those where being somewhat slower wouldn't matter – and can lead to an absurdly small operating window between it and the placarded maximum winch/autotow speed (V_W) (<u>figure 21</u>).

For example, assuming a 36kt stalling speed for an SZD Puchacz, the minimum safe winching/autotow speed works out at 54kt, leaving a dolls house letterbox slot 5kt wide between it and the 59kt V_W (Max winch). For an AS-K21, however, V_S is about 38kt and V_W 81kt, so the launch window is 24kt wide. It's worth repeating that too slow on a winch launch is potentially far more dangerous than too fast.

Rapid pitch-ups on a winch launch are bad news. Rotating far too quickly after take-off can put the AoA dangerously close to the stalling angle. The same can be said of sitting on the launch with the stick hard back; if the weak-link or cable breaks, a very sharp, albeit brief pitch up may stall the glider. Given that the instantaneous load factor

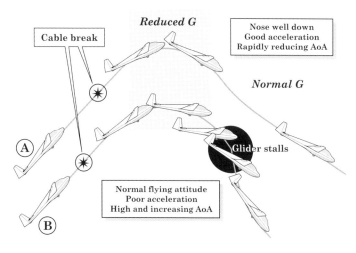

FIGURE 20 After the cable break

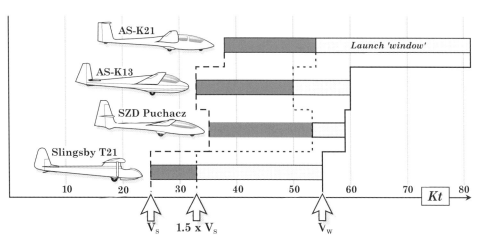

FIGURE 21 Comparison of stalling speeds, minimum safe and speed and maximum winch speed

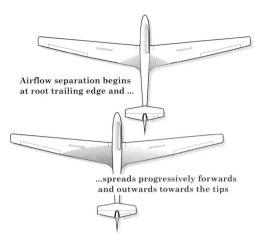

Airflow separation begins
at root trailing edge and …

…spreads progressively forwards
and outwards towards the tips

FIGURE 22 Progressive stalling

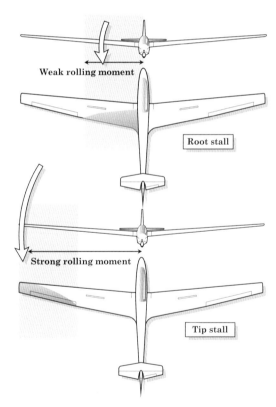

Weak rolling moment

Root stall

Strong rolling moment

Tip stall

FIGURE 23 Asymmetrical stalling
and the rolling moment

in both an over-rotation or stick on the back-stop situation can be quite high, anything unpleasant that follows a stall at this point can happen very quickly, and the glider may well *flick*. At low altitude the situation is irrecoverable.

HIGH SPEED (ACCELERATED) STALLS

There isn't too much to say about these that hasn't been said or implied elsewhere. Again, all that's required is that the AoA be high enough, and if you pull enough G at any speed (bearing in mind the loading limitations) then you stall.

Aspects of good behaviour at the stall

WASHOUT AND WING DROP

Good behaviour at the stall, as described earlier, begins with choosing the right aerofoil. Equally importantly, when an aerofoil does stall it is not a good idea to have the whole wing do so at the same instant. One might imagine that that's what happens anyway, but a glider's wings are designed to stall progressively, starting at the root and working out towards the tip (figure 22). Some while before the automatic pitch-down occurs, a fair portion of the wing will already have stalled.

It's usual to arrange for the root to stall first, so that any rolling moment resulting from an *asymmetric stall* is small. Furthermore, a desirable handling characteristic required by most airworthiness criteria is that the ailerons continue working right up to and beyond the stall; tip stalling can result in impressively swift and uncontrollable rates of roll (figure 23).

In order to get the good characteristics described it is usual to reduce the AoA of the tip in relation to the root by building a twist or *washout* into the outboard sections (figure 24), though the same effect can be achieved by changing the section towards the tips. Either way, washout's good behaviour gain is paid for by higher torsional and bending loads on the wing and extra drag, particularly at speed. Inverted flight, of course, turns washout into *wash-in*, changing the lift/load distribution, and when the inverted wing stalls, the tips do so first – why inexperienced aerobatics pilots tend to flick out from inverted flight.

Structural washout is fixed. A more elegant solution can be seen in the Ka 6CR, 6E, 7 and 8, and the ASK13 series of gliders, with the geometry of the control linkages in the fuselage providing the washout. As the stick is moved aft from the central position, the elevator goes up, and so, by a few degrees, do both ailerons. When the stick is moved forward of the central position, both ailerons go down slightly. An advantage of relating washout to the fore and aft stick position is that you tend to get it when you want it, such as during the round-out and hold-off for landing. There is, however, still the drawback of increased torsional loads at speed.

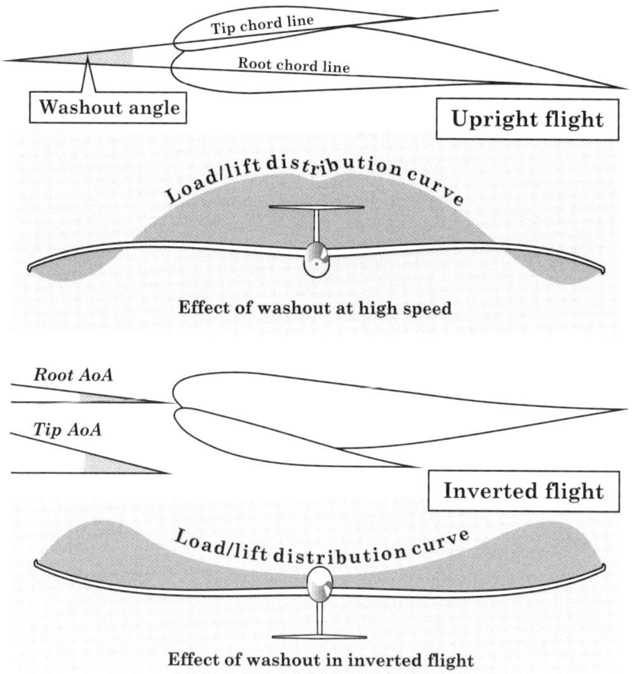

The Spin (auto-rotation)

Spinning is dynamically complex, so whatever an airworthiness standard says shall happen, there is no cast-iron guarantee that it always will. The chances of totally unexpected behaviour are extremely small, but that doesn't mean they are impossible. There are cheery souls who insist that such-and-such a glider won't spin, but what they mean is that it doesn't seem to spin with them in it, which is not the same thing and could be for any number of reasons. The intelligent response to 'doesn't', 'won't', or 'can't be made to', is 'not so far'. Contradictory as it may sound, it is only after the event that a glider's behaviour during stalling and/or spinning can be said to have been completely predictable, and that is so of every aircraft until it is pensioned off, never to fly again.

The technical term used to describe spinning is *auto-rotation*. Auto-rotation is a self-sustaining and, as far as most gliders are concerned, more or less stable condition of flight where:

(a)   the glider is pitching, rolling and yawing simultaneously

(b)   the forward speed is low

(c)   the vertical speed is high – easily 100ft/second (60kt)

(d)   the glider may rotate approximately one full turn every four seconds (figure 25).

(A) is hard to believe, but take each axis in turn and imagine how the glider would behave if that were the only axis involved. With an entirely pitch-based motion, the result would be a skewed loop from any of the positions illustrated. If only roll was involved then the glider would continue on in a straight line, but rolling! With only yaw involved the glider would be flying backwards at regular intervals.

SPIN RECOVERY

The recovery technique is standard and, as far as is known, works in all circumstances with all gliders certified to JAR-22 or a similar standard, and being flown within their design weight and CG limitations. The recovery sequence is:

FIGURE 24 The effects of washout

Labels in figure: Tip chord line, Root chord line, Washout angle, Upright flight, Load/lift distribution curve, Effect of washout at high speed, Root AoA, Tip AoA, Inverted flight, Load/lift distribution curve, Effect of washout in inverted flight

SPINNING – JAR-22.221

(b) The sailplane must be able to recover from spins of at least five turns or such lesser number at which the spins turn into a spiral dive.

(c) The sailplane must be able to recover . . . in not more than one additional turn by applying the controls in a manner normal for recovery and without exceeding either the limiting airspeed or the limiting positive manoeuvring factor for the sailplane.

(d) It must be impossible to obtain uncontrollable spins with any use of the controls.

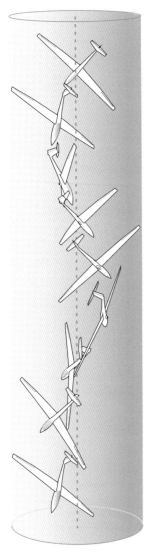

FIGURE 25 The spin

(1)   centralise the ailerons

(2)   apply full opposite rudder (i.e. against the direction of the spin)

(3)   pause (not normally necessary in gliders, but part of the standard recovery technique for powered aircraft)

(4)   move the stick progressively forwards until the rotation stops. If spinning at an aft CG the stick may have to be fully forward before anything happens

(5)   when the rotation stops, centralise the rudder

(6)   ease smoothly out of the ensuing dive.

The application of rudder helps to slow the rate of rotation and makes use of *inertial cross-coupling* (see below) to help pitch the nose down. Centralising the ailerons reduces the AoA and drag of the stalled wing. Easing the stick forward reduces the AoA. Centralising the rudder helps to:

(a)   prevent the glider spinning in the opposite direction

(b)   pitch the nose down, and

(c)   avoids high sideways loads on the fin when the glider accelerates during recovery.

A major problem with spin training is that at least one popular two-seater appears impossible to spin, and with the others recovery can often be affected by the pilot simply letting go of the controls. This is a dangerously flabby technique, if it can even be called a technique, and is definitely not recommended because (a) it doesn't work with every glider, and (b) it can't even be relied upon with the same one. Always take the correct recovery actions, and in the specified order.

GYROSCOPIC EFFECTS

A rotating object, such as a bicycle wheel, contains energy due to its rotation, usually referred to as its *angular momentum* – this is like 'ordinary' momentum, but restrained to a circular path and measured, not in terms of mph, say, but in degrees per second, or something similar. Both linear and angular momentum have the same 'can't stop' problem, and objects which are rotating and have either a large mass and/or are spinning at high speeds are very resistant to any kind of change, particularly to the tilt of their rotational axis (figure 26). A further complication is that rotating objects, like gyroscopes, *precess* – the axis of rotation itself moves round in a circle.

When any aircraft spins there are, in effect, three gyroscopes involved, one perpendicular to each of the major axes. Altering the manner of rotation of any one of these gyroscopes will affect the others via *inertial cross coupling*. For example, during a spin, if the rotation of the yaw 'gyroscope' is slowed by the application of full opposite rudder, crosscoupling will tend to affect the pitch 'gyroscope' and lower the nose.

The effects are more marked in powered aircraft whose span is usually shorter and mass more concentrated. Consequently, they tend to rotate a lot faster than gliders, and the dynamics of the spin are also affected by complicated couples created by rotating propellers and such like.

CONSERVATION OF ANGULAR MOMENTUM

Skaters and dancers spend quite a lot of time spinning around, and their rpm is partly determined by the distribution of their mass in relation to the axis of rotation (figure 27, see over). For example, with arms outstretched a skater will revolve fairly slowly, but as his/her arms are brought inwards the rate of rotation starts to increase, and is greatest when the mass is as close to the rotational axis as possible.

Much the same applies to a spinning glider, which can be thought of as two separate masses (like an asymmetric dumbbell), with one mass (W_2) at the tail and the other (W_1) near the wing leading edge. The spin's axis of rotation is ahead of the glider's nose, and W_1 and W_2 spiral around this axis. Conservation of angular momentum requires that if the glider goes from situation (A) to situation (B) (figure 27), where the masses are closer to the rotational axis, the amount of rotational energy remains the same, so (B) will rotate faster than (A). This is an over-simplification, but the practical result is that pitching the nose down to reduce the AoA may temporarily speed up a spin's rate of rotation.

If the relationship between the aerodynamic and inertial forces is unbalanced, a spin can flatten, and the flatter it gets the more prolonged the recovery is likely to be. Despite the fact that JAR-22 compliance requires a glider capable of carrying water ballast to have been spin-tested fully 'tanked-up', spinning with water ballast on board is, in one way or another, putting yourself in harm's way. The detail features of a fully developed spin are:

- the AoA is above the stalling, or critical angle

- at least one wing is stalled

- the CG describes a vertical spiral whose radius is small relative to the pitch axis

- drag, acting vertically along the flight path, balances the weight – hence the steady vertical velocity – whereas the wing lift provides an inward force, towards the axis of the spin, which prevents the helix traced out by the glider's CG from widening

- the aircraft is subject to gyroscopic moments about each of the body axes, balanced by corresponding aerodynamic moments. These intereactions are complicated, but if the forces involved balance out, the spin is stable, and the yaw, pitch and roll rates remain constant. When these forces don't balance, the spin becomes unstable. In a glider you're not very likely to come across anything really complicated, but there is plenty of film footage of spinning military jets which shows just how chaotic the results can become.

SPIN ENTRY

The kick-off for a spin is an asymmetric stall, which can happen with the glider in any attitude, including upside down. The manner of entry to a potential spin can have a bearing on:

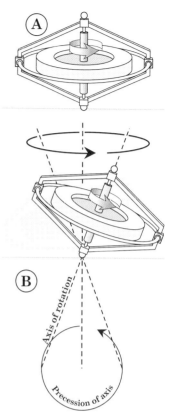

FIGURE 26 A gyroscope

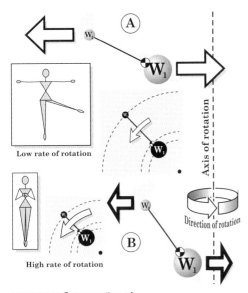

Low rate of rotation

High rate of rotation

FIGURE 27 Conservation of angular momentum

- whether the glider spins at all

- how rapidly it enters the spin

- the character of the spin once it is established

- the delay between recovery action being taken and the recovery taking place.

The position of the controls is important in all of the above – misuse of the ailerons is a very common cause of spins – as is the entry attitude and the instantaneous load factor. One report on a well-known 'unspinnable' two-seater, suitably ballasted to change all that, noted that from unaccelerated stalls the spin rotation was fast, well nose-down and stable, and that recovery was positive. From an *accelerated stall*, however, the pitch attitude in the spin cycled over five seconds between +30° and –30° of 40° nose-down, and if recovery was initiated at the wrong point in this cycle it could take up to five seconds before the glider responded.

A glider may also have two or more upright spin modes independent of entry, so that having spun in one mode through, say, three turns, the spin might flatten, or the rate of rotation increase, and the spin then stabilise into a new mode. Prolonged spins may take longer to recover from than those of only two complete rotations, for example.

Assuming that the glider has no serious design flaws, there are other factors which can affect the spin characteristics:

(1)   CG position is by far the most critical factor. At an aft CG (i.e. a light pilot near or on the lower weight limit) a glider is both easier to spin and takes longer to recover. In the worst case recovery can be impossible

(2)   the proportionate area of the flying and control surfaces. This includes the amount of leverage available to the elevator and rudder

(3)   the spatial relationship of the various surfaces to each other. One component may aerodynamically shield another

(4)   random configuration changes such as wet wings, bugs on the leading edge, dust, etc. Any of these can alter the aerodynamics and effectively put you into another glider with different spin and recovery characteristics

(5)   deliberate configuration changes. It is an unfortunate fact of life that the majority of flapped gliders will spin readily with positive flap, and increasingly readily the more positive flap is deployed. Having the undercarriage down, though good for landing, may not help much. In other words, close to the ground, when spinning is the last thing anyone wants to do, the glider is configured to do it both easily and well. Deploying the airbrakes can also delay or even prevent recovery.

SPIRAL DIVES

The recovery actions for a spin and a spiral dive are different. Trying to roll off the bank before recovering from a spin which you thought was a spiral dive virtually guarantees that you won't recover. Recovering from an unrecognised spiral dive by using spin recovery can overstress the glider.

SPIRAL DIVE	SPIN
G increases	G remains more or less constant
bank tends to increase	bank either stays constant or lessens
airspeed increases	airspeed stays constant (the ASI may read backwards, giving an artificially high or low value)
the rate of descent may not be that high	the rate of descent is very high
rate of turn depends on bank angle and speed but a high rate of turn will be accompanied by considerable G	the rate of rotation will usually be high, but inconsistent if the spin is unstable
all the controls work	the ailerons don't work and . . .
. . . pulling back increases the G	. . . pulling back has no effect whatsoever

The recovery action from a spiral dive is to first level the wings, or at least take off some of the bank before using the elevator. The order is important because:

- if the bank angle is already steep, pulling back on the stick simply tightens the turn and increases the G

- if speed and G are high then pulling and rolling at the same time subject the airframe to very high loads

- most gliders become increasingly unstable spirally as the C_L increases, and beyond a certain critical angle of bank increasing the AoA and the wing loading may cause the glider to roll into an even steeper bank and descend at a much higher rate.

Summary of chapter seven

Page	Subject	
208	**Separation point**	*see* chapter 3 summary (p. 83).
219	**Spin recovery**	(1) centralise the ailerons (2) apply full opposite rudder (3) pause (not usually necessary in gliders) (4) ease the stick steadily forwards until the rotation stops (5) centralise the rudder (6) ease smoothly out of the ensuing dive.
219	**Spin**	triggered by asymmetric stall. Glider descends vertically in steep nose-down attitude, simultaneously rolling, yawing and pitching.
223	**Spiral dive**	can be confused with spin, but see differences, table p. 223.
223	**Spiral dive recovery**	reduce bank first, then ease out of dive.
211	**Stall symptoms**	(1) nose-high relative to the normal flying attitude (2) low or reducing airspeed (3) low, reducing or changing airflow noise (4) pre-stall buffet (5) changes in the way the controls normally operate (6) stick well back (elevator full up) but cannot raise the nose.
210	**Stall recovery**	ease the stick forward progressively until the wing unstalls; reduce the AoA.
206	**Stall**	**unaccelerated**: 1G stall **accelerated**: stall where the load factor is greater than 1. Also applies to load factors less than 1 (decelerated stalls?).
209, 210	**Stall break**	Pitchdown occurring at stall.
209	**Stalling angle**	AoA at maximum C_L (lift coefficient): also *critical AoA*.
205	**Sudden or death dive**	early names for stall.
218	**Wash-out**	twist and/or section change built into the outer wing to reduce AoA in relation to the root. The opposite is wash-in.

CHAPTER 8
GLIDING PERFORMANCE

CHAPTER CONTENTS ★ should know ☆ useful

8 GLIDING PERFORMANCE

Glide angle and glide ratio

The terms *glide angle* and *glide ratio* crop up frequently in gliding conversation. They refer to the same thing, but one of them isn't correctly used. Ask a glider pilot the best glide angle of his or her glider and the reply won't be *1.5° at 55kt*, but something like *37 to one at 55kt*, which is a glide ratio – forward speed to sink rate – not an angle. The most frequently quoted performance figure is the *best glide (ratio)*, which is the shallowest possible glide slope down which the glider can run. Best glide gives maximum distance through the air mass, but not necessarily maximum distance over the ground.

The glide ratio is usually referred to as the lift/drag ratio, or L/D. For example, if a glider has an L/D of 37:1, 37 units of total lift are being produced for every unit of total drag (figure 1). The speed for best L/D also happens to be the *minimum drag speed* (minimum total drag). If the speed is increased beyond best L/D, profile drag increases and induced drag reduces. If the speed falls below best L/D, then induced drag increases and profile drag decreases. Either way, flying slower or faster than the best L/D increases the total drag and worsens the glide ratio in relation to the airmass.

There is another specific, and lower speed, where the sink rate will be at its lowest. Even though the glider won't go as far as it would at the best L/D speed, it will nevertheless remain airborne for slightly longer. This speed is called the *minimum sink speed*, usually abbreviated to *min sink*.

Assuming that a best L/D of 37:1 occurs at 55kt, the associated rate of sink will be 55/37 = 1.5kt. If the sink rate of the same glider at 75kt is 2.5kt, then its L/D at that speed is 75/2.5, or 30:1 (figure 2, see over). The angles of such glides are remarkably shallow. At 55kt, angle CAB in figure 2 will be about 1.5°; check how small that is against a protractor. Even when the glider is flying at 75kt, angle CAB will only increase to about 1.9°.

The geometry tells us that even though the triangle BDE (representing the combination of lift, drag, and the total reaction) is much smaller than triangle ACB, they contain exactly the same angles between their sides, and are similar triangles. In practical terms this means that the lift and drag forces represented by the lines BD and DE respectively, bear the same relationship to each other as the sink rate BC does to AC, which is the distance the glider travels.

There are a number of simple ways of calculating the best glide ratio, or L/D, and any of those in figure 3, see over, will give a correct answer, though there is a small proviso about the first. L/D is definitely distance travelled over height lost (figure 3, ②). However, method ① isn't quite correct. Although sink is along BC, airspeed is along AB, rather than AC (figure 2). So, if you fly very fast indeed, method ② will give you the right answer –

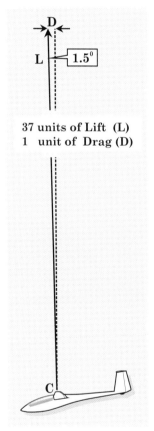

37 units of Lift (L)
1 unit of Drag (D)

FIGURE 1 Lift and drag ratios, to scale

FIGURE 2 Lift and drag ratios, angles involved (not to scale)

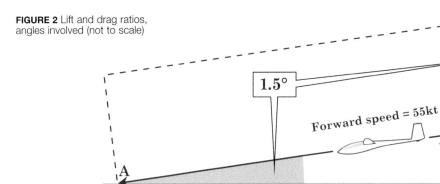

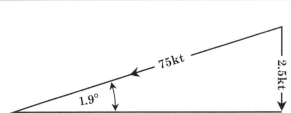

$$L/D = \begin{array}{l} \textit{(1) Airspeed/Sink rate} \\ \textit{(2) Distance travelled/Height lost} \\ \textit{(3) Lift/Drag} \\ \textit{(4) Weight/Drag} \end{array}$$

FIGURE 3 Working out L/D

that the glide ratio is poor – but method ① won't because it is based on the length of the glide slope, not how far you've travelled over the ground. It is a quibble; at normal speeds all the formulae give near enough the same answer.

By measuring the sink rate at several different speeds and plotting the results on a graph, we can create a performance curve known inaccurately, but unchangeably, as a *polar* (figure 4). It is important to realise that the polar doesn't change unless the glider is physically altered in some way. In other words, the relationship between the glider's forward speed and sink rate *through the air mass* will always be the same.

The more points we can use to plot the polar the better, but there are problems. An accurate, calculated polar is almost a contradiction in terms, so flight tests are needed to determine the sink rates at various speeds. If the air is not completely still, an entire airmass gently rising at $^1/_4$kt (25ft/min) will inflate a realistic best glide of 37:1 through the air to a more impressive 46:1 over the ground. The same airmass sinking at $^1/_4$kt would reduce 37:1 to a less saleable 31:1. Since completely calm conditions, in so far as they ever occur, are much more likely early in the day and at altitude, flight tests usually take place from very high early morning tows, and the results are the mean of several flights, corrected for altitude, temperature and position errors[1].

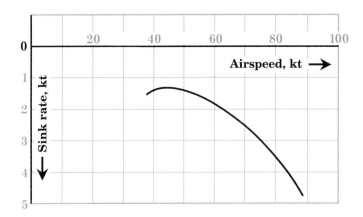

FIGURE 4 The basic polar curve

[1]Position errors are ASI errors caused by local variations in pressure and airflow velocity around the pitot and static. The percentage error they create can vary with speed and may be significant.

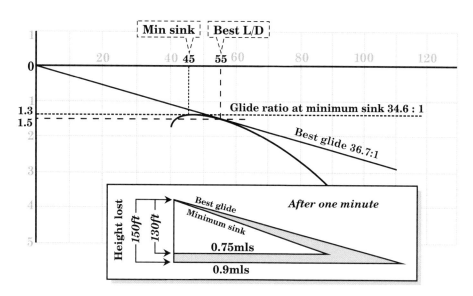

FIGURE 5 Minimum sink and best L/D speeds

In practice, most polars are *best fit* curves which arc smoothly through a splattering of physically measured points. Alternatively, the tests can be pair flown against a glider whose performance is accurately known, and with which comparisons can be made.

A reasonably accurate performance curve provides much useful information, and is the basis for fairly sophisticated calculations – some of which we'll look at later. Assuming the polar is accurate ('best fit' from a manufacturer tends to mean 'best possible visual interpretation without big fibs'), it can be used to determine the best L/D and minimum sink speeds.

FINDING THE MINIMUM SINK SPEED

Finding the minimum sink speed is straightforward. The polar curve peaks where the glider's sink rate is lowest (figure 5). Any other point on the curve will always give a larger value for the sink rate. Draw the horizontal tangent to the top of the curve, and read off the sink value where the tangent hits the vertical (sink) axis of the graph. Then, from the point where the tangent touches the polar, draw a line vertically upwards and read off the speed from the horizontal axis. Using the polar in the illustration, the minimum sink for this particular glider is 1.3kt at 45kt. In relation to the air, it can never be any less. The glide ratio at the minimum sink speed is 45/1.3, or 34.6:1.

FINDING THE BEST GLIDE SPEED

To find the speed for best glide, draw a tangent with the shallowest possible slope from the intersection of the speed and sink axes (the zero), to the curve. There is only one line that fits these criteria. Leaving aside for the moment exactly why this construction gives you the right result, draw the line and read off the values as you did for minimum sink.

FIGURE 6 Duplicate glide ratios

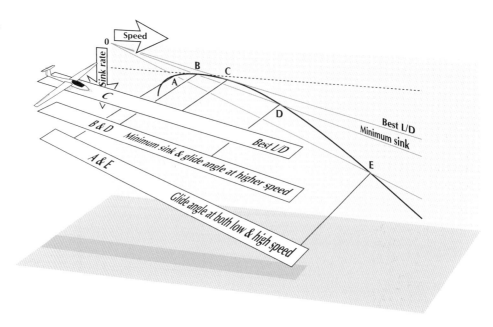

In this case the sink rate is 1.5kt at 55kt. The best L/D is therefore 55/1.5, or 36.7:1. The tangent from the origin to any other point on the curve will always give a worse glide ratio, so in still air (or through the airmass, whatever that's doing) this glider will never do better than 36.7:1.

We get these results because if the speed and sink axes on the polar diagram were to the same scale, then the best L/D tangent would have exactly the same slope as the one down which the real glider will fly at best L/D, and the same goes for any other L/D. Because it is proportionally so much longer than the sink axis, the speed axis is usually compressed, but that doesn't alter the numerical ratios (ie. 30:1), only the angle of the tangent to the horizontal, and we aren't measuring that.

In one minute, flying at the minimum sink speed, our glider will travel 0.75 miles and lose 130ft. Flying at best glide for one minute it will travel nearly a mile and lose 150ft. You might think that losing 150ft as against 130ft isn't that much, or that it is actually better to fly to lose the minimum amount of height, but the choice depends entirely on what you are trying to do.

You are flitting moth-like over the only sunlit spot in the entire country, waiting for it to breath off the thermal that will get you high enough to reach home. In this case it pays to conserve height and fly for maximum time, not distance. Minimum sink speed is the obvious choice[2]. Equally, if you have just climbed up in the day's last thermal and want to get as near home as possible, then you need the longest possible glide, not time, so it makes more sense to fly at best L/D. There are other factors involved, such as the wind strength and direction. We'll return to them later.

The polar allows us to work out the glide ratio at any speed, or conversely, the speed to fly for a particular glide ratio. For instance, what would the glide ratio be if we flew at, say,

[2]Regardless of the strategy you are using, in sinking air you will still need to fly more or less according to the MacCready Ring. *See* pp. 239–40.

75kt? There is no need to draw a tangent. Just look along the speed axis, find 75kt, drop a vertical line down to the polar and then horizontally back to the sink axis. The sink is 2.5kt, so the glide ratio at 75kt is 75/2.5, or 30:1. Being able to work out the L/D for any speed is crucial to *speed to fly* theory and to creating a *speed to fly ring* (*see* pp. 238–40).

What should be noted about the polar is that apart from best glide, nearly every tangent to the curve will cut the polar at two points, and that at both points the glide ratio will be the same. For instance, in figure 6, the tangent AE cuts through the curve at a 'slow' point to the left of best glide, and again to the right at a 'fast' point. In both cases the glide ratio is identical, whatever its value. However, in still air there are two differences between them:

(1) the time taken by the glider to cover a given distance

(2) the kinetic energy of the glider during the glide.

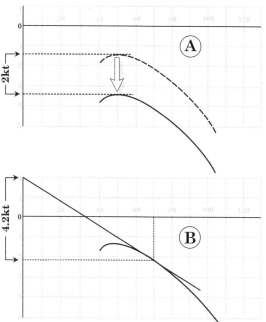

FIGURE 7 The polar in sinking air

Taking account of lift and sink

So far everything has assumed completely still air, which isn't much use for cross country flying. If there is lift about then there will be sink, and some account has to be taken of both, along with the effect of the wind. We will deal with sinking air first.

Flying at the best glide speed gives maximum range in still air, but if the air is sinking we need to change tactics. Sinking air reduces our glide ratio, not in relation to the air mass, but in relation to the ground, and in that respect the glider will perform rather worse than in still air. By flying more slowly we lose height by dawdling in the sink. On the other hand, if we flew very fast to get through it as quickly as possible, our glide ratio through the air would be steep, so we would again lose a lot of height. Either way we'd increase the chances of an outlanding. Somewhere between flying too slowly and too fast there has to be a speed which gives us the best possible glide ratio *in relation to the ground*.

Imagine we are flying through air that is descending at 2kt (200ft/min). This has the same effect as shifting the glider's polar down by 2kt. The best glide tangent now touches the displaced polar at a point further down the right hand side of the curve. It is still best glide, but that of a glider of poorer performance in still air, or our good glider passing through 2kt of sink (figure 7, (A)). Of course, shifting the polar down is awkward (particularly if you have just drawn it in a different position), and the easiest way to go about deriving the new value of best glide in sinking air is to leave the polar where it is, and simply move the zero point (the origin) up the sink/lift axis by 2kt, as in example (B)). The results are the same.

The new tangent tells us that if we fly at 70kt we will cross a given area of 2kt sink in the quickest possible time and with the minimum loss of height. Dividing our airspeed by the combined sink rates of the glider and the air (70/(2 + 2.2)) gives us a new glide ratio of 16.6:1. Once again, any other tangent to the curve (i.e. flying slower or faster) gives worse results. We can verify this by simulating a glider passing through an area of sink (figure 8, see over).

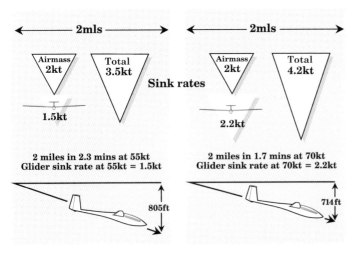

FIGURE 8 Effect of an area of sink in otherwise still air

The sink is a steady 2kt over a distance of 2NM. By flying at the speed for best L/D (55kt), we will spend 2.3 minutes in the sink, and in that time the glider's overall sink rate would be its own, 1.5kt, plus 2kt for the air; a total of 3.5kt. The height lost over 2NM would therefore be 2.3 × 3.5 × 100 (1kt is approximately 100ft/min), or 805ft. By flying at 70kt, we cross the area of sink in 1.7min. At 70kt the glider's overall sink rate is its own, 2.2kt, plus 2kt for the air; a total of 4.2kt. Over 2NM we lose 714ft. Though flying faster makes the glider descend faster, we crossed the area of sink more quickly. The net result is a 13% reduction in the height lost (a difference of 91ft), and a speed gain of 27%. This is the best possible result in this particular case. Flying any faster will shorten the time in the sink, but since the glider's own sink rate will be correspondingly worse, more height will be lost.

There are further considerations to take into account when flying for maximum speed, but before looking at these we need to examine the effects of head and tail winds on the glider's performance.

The effect of the wind

Neither a head nor a tail wind affects the glider's progress to the next thermal. The glider, the thermal, and any associated clouds, are all carried along in the same block of air. All other things being equal, reaching the next thermal should be just as easy up, down, or crosswind.

The situation is quite different if the glider is trying to reach a specific point on the ground, such as a turning point or home base. In this case the direction and strength of the wind, and exactly how fast you fly, are the factors deciding whether you get there or not.

Flying at a constant airspeed to reach a ground point five miles upwind takes longer than going to one five miles downwind, as you would expect, but by the same token flying upwind reduces your glide ratio in relation to the ground, whereas the reverse is true for flying downwind (figure 9). In other words, if you were trying to reach your home airfield from somewhere downwind, then you would need more height to get there than if you were trying to reach it from the same distance upwind. In neither case would you fly at the notional best glide speed.

FIGURE 9 Effects of wind on glide ratio over ground

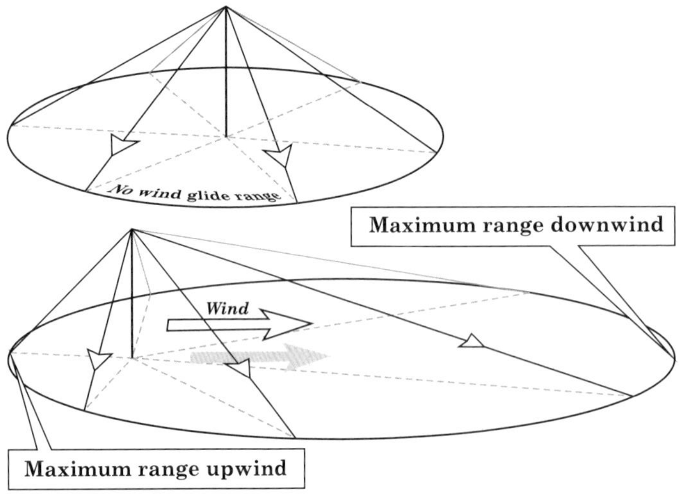

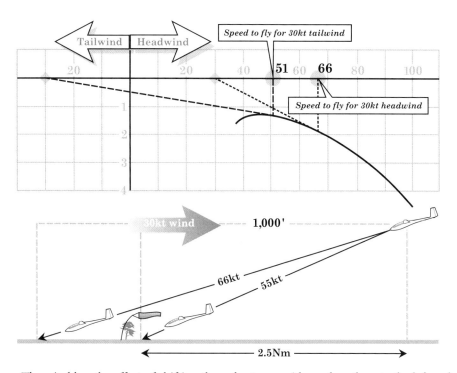

FIGURE 10 Glide ratio and speed to fly into a headwind

The wind has the effect of shifting the polar to one side or the other; to the left and nearer the origin if there is a headwind, and to the right and further away if there is a tailwind. To avoid having to move the curve, head and tailwind components can again be accommodated by the simpler expedient of shifting the origin to the left or right (figure 10).

In still air, our glider (L/D 37:1 at 55kt) will travel 37ft forward through the air mass for every foot of height lost. From 1,000ft it will glide 37 × 1000 = 37,000ft, or just over 6NM, descending at 150ft/min and taking 6.5mins to reach the ground. If the same glider flies at the same speed (55kt) into a 30kt headwind, its ground speed falls to 25kt (55–30). The effect on the glide ratio in relation to the ground is to reduce it to 16.6:1 (25/1.5). The sink rate is still the same as in the previous example, but now the glider will only travel 2.6NM from 1,000ft.

Still flying into the same wind, putting the airspeed up to 66kt increases the ground speed to 36kt. The glider's sink rate at 66kt is 2kt, and its L/D through the airmass is now 33:1. Despite this apparent worsening of the glide ratio, increasing the speed has improved it in relation to the ground from 16.6:1 to 18:1 (66 – 30 = 36 and 36/2 = 18). This may not seem like much, but from 1,000ft the glider will now go a further 0.4NM, or 3NM in total, before meeting the ground. The difference may be small but it could be that between being buried in the downwind boundary hedge, or overflying it comfortably.

Working out the effect of a tailwind is a similar process, except that we move the origin of the polar in the opposite direction to the headwind case, and fly more slowly. The polar in figure 10 shows that we should fly slightly slower than best glide if we are trying to make the greatest distance, but never less than the minimum sink speed, and strictly speaking we would only fly at that if there was an infinitely strong tailwind.

Flying for speed

You don't have to be competition flying to need speed. Any cross country flight has to take into account the available soaring period and the strength of the wind and of lift. Average speed is calculated from the total time taken in climbing and gliding, divided by the distance travelled. To complete a given task our average speed must at least equal the task distance divided by the length of the soarable period. For example, at an average speed of 70kph, a 300km triangle takes just over 4 hours to complete. It will take six hours at 50kph, and if soaring conditions expire after 5? hours, you'll be ringing for a retrieve.

Average speeds can be increased by spending less time circling, but that doesn't mean not climbing. Let's say you are going to take our glider on a 300km flight. For some totally obscure reason you can only take one gigantic climb at the beginning of the flight, and must glide out the rest at best L/D. In completely still air the height needed for this epic downhill trundle would be 26,600ft (300km = 984,297ft, and 984,297/37 = 26,600). So, at an absolute, and indeed an impossible minimum, you must climb a total of 26,600ft (five miles) during a flight of 300km. The more time you spend circling to climb, the slower your average speed. Since you can't avoid *having* to climb in one way or another, you must either do so as fast as possible, or spend as much time as you can flying in lift while going in a more or less straight line towards your goal. In the context of isolated thermals, climbing well means using only the strongest lift[3], which we'll discuss in more detail later.

Another way to increase average speed is to fly between thermals at the correct speed. The correct speed is related to the earlier flying through sink examples, but there is an awkward twist here to what would otherwise be a relatively simple calculation. On any given day the inter-thermal speed to fly for the highest possible average speed depends, not on the strength of the thermal you are in, nor the one you have just left, but of the one towards which you are heading – and how strong is that? You can make an educated guess about its likely strength, based upon the look of the clouds and so on, but you can't really be sure. Quite a conundrum! However, what one can say is that regardless of how strong or weak the lift turns out to be, if you fly towards it too fast you either won't get there, or all the height you've thrown away must at some point be made up by additional climbing. On the other hand, flying too slowly will result in time wasted during the glide. Luckily there is a strategy which, while not perfect, can be adopted to make the best of what is essentially chance, and we'll come to it in a moment.

RATE OF CLIMB

First, what constitutes a rate of climb? What the variometer says at any instant during a climb is of little value. It might indicate 10kt, but for only 10% of the time. The other 90% could be 3kt, even −3kt. We need to know the average rate of climb for the entire thermal, from the moment we start looking for the core to the moment we straighten up to leave it. The best way to get this is to have an electric variometer fitted with an *averager*. This will give an indication of the *achieved rate of climb* over the last 20 or 30 seconds. Some variometers allow you to start and stop the averager whenever you want, so it is a simple matter to get an average for the entire climb. The reason for including everything,

---

[3]The situation is somewhat different for Dolphin flying (see pp. 241–2). While there is no doubt that you do have to climb, you are under no obligation to circle in order to do so.

including the bumbling about looking for the core, is that during your search you will have slowed down or even stopped moving along track. Being more or less stationary, or worse, being blown backwards, won't increase your average speed for the task! Whatever you do, a pattern will begin to emerge over a number of thermals – perhaps most of them average about 2.5kt, so the 6kt one you just left may not be representative. Of course it has been known for conditions to improve but they can also get worse.

Assuming that the next thermal will provide a climb averaging, say, 4kt, the polar can help work out the correct speed to fly towards it. Draw a tangent to the polar from the 4kt line above the zero (figure 11). The vertical line from the tangent tells us that for best average speed we must fly to the next thermal at 80kt.

How can we be sure that this inter-thermal speed yields the highest average speed? Take a very simplistic example. If we average 2kt climbs in every 4kt thermal round our task, and fly between thermals at 70kt (which produces a glider sink rate of 2kt), then we will spend exactly half our time climbing, and half gliding. Our average speed will therefore be exactly half our inter-thermal speed. Figure 12 shows that the theoretical highest average speed from achieved rates of climb of two knots is 33.5kt (62kph), a speed that corresponds to the point at which the tangent from +2kt cuts the speed axis. Applying the same method to the example in figure 11, our average speed will be 46kt (85kph). Flying faster or slower than this will give a lower average speed.

If we assume that the achieved rate of climb is always going to be 4kt, figure 13 shows how flying too fast, too slow, or at the correct theoretical best inter-thermal speed affects the average cross country speed. By flying towards a 4kt thermal at 60kt – a speed the theory suggests is slightly too slow since the theoretical best is 74kt – our average speed would be 41kt (75.9kph). If we flew at 90kt, which is too fast, then the average speed would be slightly lower, at 40kt (74kph). The best we can do, theoretically, is 43kt (79.5kph), and both too fast and too slow give averages about 7% slower than this.

Of course, all this assumes that we get the thermal we want, but what is the effect on the cross country speed if we expect 4kt, and instead find only 2kt? The optimum inter-thermal speed for an expected 4kt climb is 74kt, but the result of, in effect, flying too fast (figure 14, see over), is that the average speed for the current glide and slower climb will be 31kt (57kph), a decrease of about 28%. During a long flight, one miscalculation like that isn't serious – unless it causes you to land out – but make too many more and it's a different story, perhaps making it impossible to complete the task in the remaining soaring day. On the other hand, if we expected a 2kt thermal, flew towards it at 63kt, and then found a 4kt climb instead, our average speed for the glide and climb would be 42kt (77.8kph), which is only 1kt (1.85kph) slower, or 2.3% less than the theoretical best for a 4kt thermal.

In terms of average speed, the penalty is slight if we fly expecting weaker climbs. Less height will be lost during the glide, unless there's lots of sink about, and because we'll arrive in thermals higher up, less time will be spent climbing. In addition, that extra height will give us the option of rejecting a thermal if it fails to come up to the mark, and flying on to find one that does. If there is lift

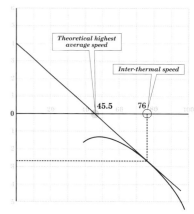

FIGURE 11 Best inter-thermal speed for a 4kt climb

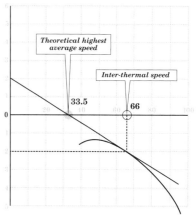

FIGURE 12 Best inter-thermal and highest average speeds for a 2kt climb

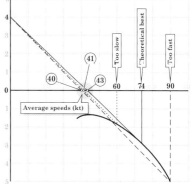

FIGURE 13 Effects of flying too fast or too slow

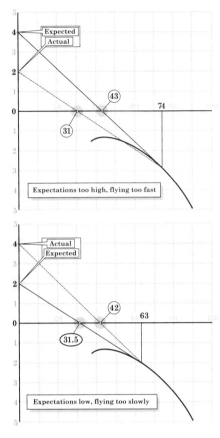

FIGURE 14 When expected and actual differ

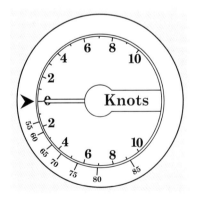

FIGURE 15 The MacCready speed to fly ring

about and we are flying too slowly, pottering along at best L/D, we have more or less assumed that the average rate of climb is zero, in which case one might be tempted to ask why we're going cross country at all. Flying at or above the theoretically correct speeds is high risk flying. At 70kt our glider can fly 5.2NM for a 1,000ft loss of height, but at 80kt it will lose the same height in 4.5NM. The faster speed reduces our chances of reaching any thermal, however good, increases the possibility of an outlanding, and may force us to take weak climbs just to stay airborne.

The MacCready speed to fly ring

It would be tedious and impractical to have to draw a new tangent to the polar every time we entered sink or lift and wanted to know how fast to fly, so information derived from the polar is displayed in the form of a moveable ring around the variometer (figure 15). Some modern electronic variometers can be programmed to do the same job. Dr Paul MacCready, who is equally famous for creating the world's first really successful manpowered aeroplane, Gossamer Condor (p. 31), invented what is known, unsurprisingly, as the *MacCready ring* (figure 15).

MAKING A RING

The ring must be calibrated from the glider's polar, and for a specific wing loading. Transferring the values from the polar to the ring isn't entirely straightforward, and the various tangents and lines that you must draw are best done on a polar curve which is as large as you can possibly make it. If the polar is too small, accurate tangents to the flatter sections of the curve will be more difficult to draw, and small errors here can have a significant effect on the results. The following steps show how the values are calculated and added to the ring.

Step 1
Draw a series of tangents to the glider's polar from a number of different values of lift (figure 16). Note down the best speeds to fly, which is where the various tangents cut the speed axis.

Step 2
Construct a second curve above the speed axis by taking a lift value of, say, 4kt on the vertical axis, and use this as the origin for a tangent to the polar curve. From where this tangent touches the polar, draw a vertical line back up through the speed axis until it reaches the 4kt lift line. Mark that point in some way. Do the same for a number of other values of lift, and then draw in a curve that fits all the marked points smoothly together.

Step 3

Make a table to help you transfer the information you need to the speed to fly ring. Choose a number of suitable speed values, in steps of 5 or 10kt, from best glide upwards. The ring opposite shows 55 to 85 in 5kt steps. Find each of the speeds on the horizontal axis of your graph and measure the *total* sink rate; that is, the sink rate of the glider plus the sink rate of the airmass (the values circled in figure 16). The sink rate of the glider is the distance between the horizontal axis and the polar, and that of the airmass is the distance between the horizontal axis and the curve you constructed above it.

Step 4

This involves no calculation but is fiddly. Remove the ring from the variometer and mark on it a datum arrow. Reattach the ring. Place the datum arrow opposite the variometer's zero, and use the table you made previously to help you place the appropriate speeds to fly – use Letraset or something similar – on the ring opposite the related total sink rates. Once done, remove the ring again and spray it with a matt varnish to help prevent the figures being worn off by constant resetting, and to cut down on reflections. Put it all back together again.

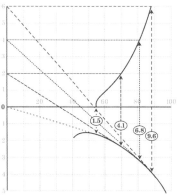

FIGURE 16 Constructing a MacCready ring from the polar

USING THE SPEED TO FLY RING

If you are trying to maximise time in the air, place the datum arrow, which represents the glider's minimum sink speed, opposite the glider's minimum sink rate (figure 17, (A)). You may not know what this is, so a little experimentation during a still evening may be required. You can take the manufacturer's estimate, but unless the value has been measured recently it may be optimistic.

When sink is encountered, increase the speed to the ring value opposite the indicated sink rate. If the variometer system is a bit basic you can find yourself chasing the needle. As you speed up, it registers more sink. You put on speed to catch up but the variometer then registers more sink. You do get there eventually, but cranking up the speed bit by bit can lead to a greater loss of height than would result from going straight to the correct speed. Chapter 9 (p. 251) describes how the variometer setup is modified to make this possible.

If you are trying to make the maximum distance in calm air, then set the ring to zero, as illustrated in example (B), and again fly the indicated speeds. If you are trying to fly for best average speed through the air, and bearing in mind the remarks made earlier about average rates of climb – the ring setting in example (C) is for an exceptional day in the UK – place the datum arrow opposite a value which is half or less than the anticipated average strength of the next thermal. Increase the speed to the ring value opposite the indicated sink or lift rate. Unless you must, don't circle in any thermal weaker than the anticipated average.

The technique is high risk because the theory assumes things which, in the real world, you can't dismiss, namely that:

- the next climb will be at least as strong as anticipated (at best it's an educated guess)

- on entering a thermal you will instantly achieve the highest possible rate of climb. Even the best pilots take some time, however minimal, to centre. Any

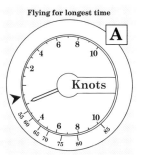

Flying for longest time — A

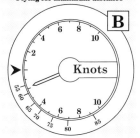

Flying for maximum distance — B

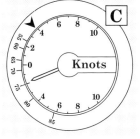

Flying for highest average speed — C

FIGURE 17 The ring in use

time spent in weaker lift while trying to find something stronger reduces the overall rate of climb

- there is no ground. You have infinite height and can fly on for as long as it takes to reach the next thermal

- thermals are of constant strength throughout their depth. This is not always the case. Normally the higher you are the stronger and larger the centres tend to be and the easier they are to find, but there can be any number of variations to this.

Bearing in mind the earlier proviso about the unrepresentative 6kt thermal, most pilots get round the 'guessing ahead' problem and speed to fly's assumptions by reckoning that the next thermal will be between a third and a half of the strength of the current thermal, and set the ring accordingly. Settings of ?–1kt on an average day, 1–2kt on a good day, and 2–3kt on the very best days, will cost little in terms of average speed.

ADDING WATER BALLAST

The polar is only valid for one particular wing loading. For instance, a glider with an AUW of 650lb and a wing area of 100ft^2, has a wing loading of 650/100, or 6.5lb/ft^2. Pumping 300lb of water ballast into the wings raises the wing loading to (650 + 300)/100, or 9.5lb/ft^2.

Altering the weight by adding water ballast has two significant effects on the polar, one of which is well worth having and the other you get regardless. These effects are:

- the extra weight, and consequently the higher wing loading, push the polar down the sink axis and increase the minimum sink speed and the sink rate. This is probably what you would expect even if it isn't exactly what you want; the glider is heavier and the wing is obviously being asked to do rather more work to keep it airborne. The downside is that the glider won't climb quite as well in thermals

- not so obviously, the polar is also shifted off to the right along the speed axis[4]

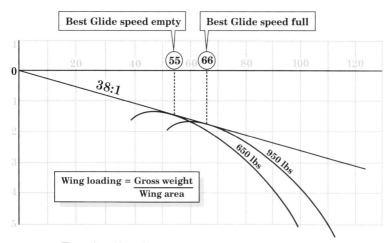

FIGURE 18 The polar with and without water ballast

The result is that the 'wet' best L/D remains virtually the same as the 'dry' best L/D (figure 18). The plus with water ballast is that best L/D now occurs at a higher speed, which means faster glides, higher average speeds, and greater range during any given period of good soaring. In bumpy conditions the higher wing loading can also mean a smoother ride. The downside, apart from the increased rate of sink, is that you have to calculate the values for yet another MacCready ring. This problem is easily solved by having the unballasted polar, so to speak, on one half of the ring, and a ballasted

See Appendix C (pp. 296–7).

polar on the other. It is then a simple matter to rotate the ring to use the appropriate scale. Label both sides clearly. If you fly 'dry' while using the 'wet' MacCready your flight will very likely be shorter than usual.

Dolphin and low loss flying

All of the foregoing discussion on speeds to fly has assumed that lift only ever occurs in discrete and fairly widely separated little packets, but that isn't always so. Wave is a perfect example of lift forming in long lines, and the best way to use it is not to circle. Previous discussion has also assumed, quite correctly, that you can't avoid having to climb at some point during a cross country flight. *Dolphin flying* and/or *low loss flying* are techniques which involve less circling and so result in much higher cross country speeds. There are no basic differences between the two techniques, but they address slightly different areas. Both are about energy management.

From all this it is clear that the route taken between areas of lift is important (figure 19). The pilot's next turning point lies somewhere off to the northeast of his present position, beyond point (B). The direct route ① would seem to be the quickest, and therefore 'the best', and the alternative routes ② and ③ seem to wander miles off course beneath clouds which may or may not produce any lift.

Despite the fact that routes ② and ③ are longer than route ①, both are likely to be more energy efficient and faster overall. Route ① is a straight glide to a distant cloud, very likely through an area of heavy and possibly continuous sink. The other routes take in clouds which are closer to the glider and each other. By slowing down in the lift under the clouds of route ② or ③ it may be possible to circle less and still lose little height on the way to (B), in theory, at least. Route ① will almost certainly require a circling climb somewhere near (B) to reclaim the height lost getting there.

Despite ① being the most direct route from (A) to (B), routes ② and ③ can give the highest average speed, and the glider may arrive at (B) at or near the height it had at (A). However, if ② and ③ divert too far off the direct course, and are not the result of tactical necessity, there will come a point when route ① is the best option, despite the possibility of a long climb at the end of it.

Whether you can continue to fly for mile after mile in a more or less straight line and lose little or no height overall, depends on the weather and the performance of your glider. Modern gliders have glide ratios which allow more efficient use of the available energy, and they can continue motoring on in conditions where older gliders have to take climbs. Older gliders can still make very substantial increases in cross country speed by adopting and adapting the techniques of dolphin and/or low loss flying. Unfortunately, the lower the performance of your glider the

FIGURE 19 Staying with the energy

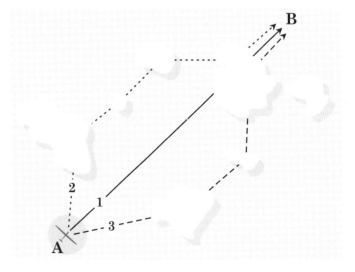

more important it becomes to fly at the correct speeds, which hardly seems fair, but there it is. The three basic messages are:

(1)   go where the lift/energy is and avoid the sink. Often easier said than done

(2)   slow down in lift. If you can't avoid the sink, fly through it faster, and accelerate before you reach it! The implication here is that you will be flying at the right speed for the circumstances, and that you can judge exactly when you ought to start speeding up – all of which is ridiculously easy to say, and very hard to get right

(3)   don't stop to circle.

If you follow the above advice to the letter, particularly the last item, your crew will get plenty of practice at retrieves. The best technique will depend, as always, on the conditions, how well you have assessed them, and, most importantly, whether you alter your strategy to suit conditions when they change. This is where most people tend to come unstuck, simply because they don't look or think far enough ahead.

Summary of chapter eight

Page	Subject	
230	**Best fit curve**	mean curve drawn through scattering of measured points.
231	**Best glide**	shallowest glide slope possible (in still air) and in relation to the air mass. Associated speed is *minimum drag speed*.
241	**Dolphin flying**	*low energy loss* technique.
229	**Glide angle**	term used (inaccurately) instead of *glide ratio*.
230	**Glide ratio**	determined by any of the following: (1) lift/drag (2) distance travelled/height lost (3) airspeed/sink rate (4) weight/drag.
233	**Lift**	**meteorological**: refers to any upward vertical component of air movement; caused by temperature differences (thermals), or obstructions to the wind (hill and wave lift). *See* chapter 10. **aerodynamic lift**: *see* chapter 3, p. 62.
241	**Low loss flying**	cross country techniques that reduces circling.
238	**MacCready ring**	speed to fly information displayed on ring round the variometcr.*
229	**Minimum drag speed**	*see* Total drag – chapter 3, p. 82. Also Appendix C, p. 296.
229, 231	**Minimum sink speed**	speed at which glider's sink rate is lowest.
230	**Polar curve**	performance curve – plots forward speed against sink rate.
236	**Rate of climb (ROC)**	**achieved**: overall climb rate **indicated**: instantaneous rate of climb.

*These days the 'ring' is incorporated into either the hardware of software of variometers, usually in conjunction with an audio unit.

Page	Subject	
233	**Sink**	opposite of *lift*.
236	**Speed to fly**	**theory**: optimising glide and climb to increase average speeds **ring**: *see* McCready ring.

CHAPTER 9
VARIOMETERS

CHAPTER CONTENTS ★ should know ☆ useful

9 VARIOMETERS

Variometers

In the early days of ballooning the aeronauts quickly realised that unless a balloon was already low, it was difficult to judge how fast it was climbing or descending. Given that balloons take a while to respond to more heat or less ballast, a visibly high descent rate was bad news. The aeronauts' solution to this problem was to tear up sheets of paper, throw the pieces out of the basket, and watch how swiftly they rose or fell.

While nowhere near as crude, a modern variometer does much the same job and is just as essential a part of a glider's instrumentation, helping the pilot make the best use of available lift and also indicating the sink. There's no point in having an inaccurate variometer – you might just as well stay on the ground and save yourself the frustration – but even when a variometer system works correctly, it has its limitations. A working knowledge of the individual instrument and the installation can be very useful, even if all that amounts to is knowing when and where to send it for repair.

The most basic variometer is a meter measuring the rate of flow of air through a small hole, or *capillary leak*. Despite the fact that the instrument doesn't measure the same things as the ASI and altimeter, it is nonetheless a pressure instrument. Figure 1 illustrates the three main pressure instruments. The ASI (figure 2) measures the pressure difference between the *static* port – open at right angles to the airflow – and the airflow's dynamic pressure at the normally nose-mounted *pitot* head. The altimeter compares the *ambient pressure* at the static – which may just be left open to the cockpit – with that in a sealed, flexible capsule. The variometer measures the flow rate created by any pressure gradient that exists between the static and a fixed *capacity*.

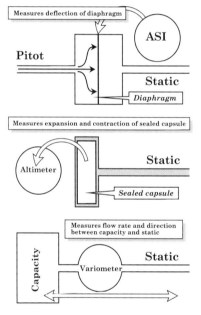

FIGURE 1 ASI, altimeter and variometer

CAPACITY

The capacity (figure 3, see over) is normally a vacuum-insulated container similar to a thermos flask, with an internal volume of around 420cm³ (0.42 litres), or nearly ¾ pint. In fact many gliders use a Thermos flask as a capacity, and they serve well enough even though making a leak-free seal in the bung at the flask's neck can be difficult. Regardless of the type of capacity, the variometer will have been calibrated to indicate specific rates of climb from specific rates of through flow, so the capacity needs to be of the correct volume. If it is too large, the rate

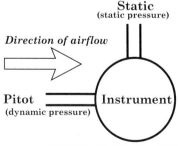

FIGURE 2 ASI, pitot and static

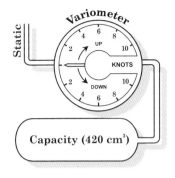

FIGURE 3 A basic variometer system

of flow will be greater than required and the variometer will over-read. Too small, and it will under-read.

The capacity is insulated to prevent tiny changes in its temperature, causing the air within to expand or contract. The variometer can measure extremely small rates of flow, so any additional changes due to temperature, however slight, could have a significant effect and again cause it to over- or under-read.

There is a similar problem with the tube connecting the variometer and the capacity. With the capacity located aft of the seat, the connecting tube could easily be five feet long, and given a bore of, say, 5mm, its volume will be 7% of the capacity's, big enough to introduce significant errors if the tube is heated or cooled. Ideally, the tube should be insulated, or the capacity should be behind the panel so that the system connecting tube is very short.

STATIC

The positioning of the *static ports* is critical. Pressure differences between the capacity and the ambient air are usually very small indeed, and the resultant flow between them the merest whisper. Any alterations to the static pressure caused by yaw or changes in speed could, by comparison, be very large, so it is important that changes in the static pressure caused by the glider climbing or descending are not influenced by anything else.

EFFECTS OF YAW ON STATIC PRESSURE

The usual way to minimise the effects of yaw and speed changes is to have two interconnected static ports paired symmetrically on either side of the fuselage (figure 4). Their exact positions may vary, depending on the glider type. Those on the K13, as, illustrated, work by averaging out any pressure differences on each side of the nose. For instance, if the aircraft yaws to the right, the pressure on the left side of the nose increases while that on the right decreases. Theoretically, the two should cancel each other out and so have no effect on the variometer readings and, up to a point that's what happens.

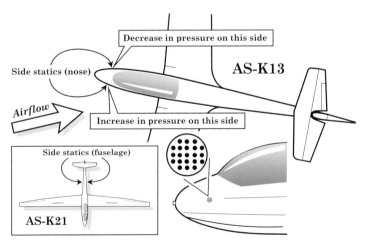

FIGURE 4 Location of the static ports on a K13

CLIMBING AND DESCENDING

As the glider climbs in lift, the pressure at the static falls, leaving the capacity pressure slightly higher. Air flows out of the flask, through the variometer, towards the static. The variometer needle registers the flow direction by deflecting upwards, indicating lift. When the glider descends, the static pressure is greater than the pressure in the capacity, so air flows back in through the static ports, through the variometer, and into the flask. The variometer needle points down, indicating sink. If there is any pressure difference between the static and the capacity, air will flow through the variometer towards whichever point is at the lowest pressure. The greater the pressure differential between capacity and static, the higher the flow rate and the larger the indication of lift or sink.

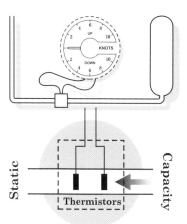

Electric and electronic variometers

The flow rate between the static and the capacity can be measured by mechanical or electrical means. The simplest form of electrical measurement involves placing either heated wires or *thermistors* into the capacity/static line (figure 5), and attaching them to a voltmeter. The electrical resistance of the thermistors or wires changes with temperature. The circuit is electrically balanced so that when both thermistors are at the same temperature and have the same resistance, no current flows and the voltmeter/variometer reads zero. When the glider climbs or descends, the flow between the static and capacity passes over and cools both thermistors. However, heat carried away from the upstream thermistor warms and alters the resistance of the downstream one. This unbalances the electrical circuit and creates a current which the voltmeter registers as up or down, depending on which thermistor was being warmed and by how much.

FIGURE 5 An electric variometer

Other systems measure pressure differences electronically, using pressure transducers.[1] As with all electrical/electronic variometers, the current can be harnessed to

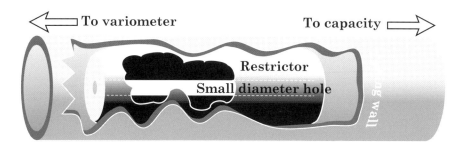

FIGURE 6 Restrictor

drive an audio unit. Electric variometers offer little resistance to the airflow and have few if any mechanical moving parts, so they respond rapidly, and to everything. The resulting display can become ridiculously jittery and full of what is, in the context, completely spurious information. Some form of damping is a must. This can be provided by inserting *restrictors* (usually metal plugs with a small diameter hole drilled through the centre (figure 6)) into the connecting tubing, or, in the case of electric variometers, using electronic damping to smooth out the signal.

IF THE ELECTRIC VARIOMETER DOESN'T WORK

You can't do much about an electric variometer that isn't working properly, unless you are an expert, or can take it to someone who is. The modern variometer is evolving into quite

[1] A pressure transducer converts pressure into an electrical signal, or an electrical signal into pressure. A microphone is a transducer, as is a loudspeaker.

a complex beast, able to average rates of climb which you previously had to guess – or use the altimeter and a stopwatch – and to share information with other electronic equipment. Despite these extras, the underlying operating principle of the modern electric variometer is the same as that of the mechanical variometer.

This chapter will concentrate on mechanical variometer systems because what goes on inside them is rather more obvious than what takes place in the obscure entrails of most electronic variometers.

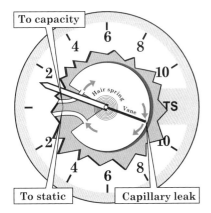

FIGURE 7 A vane type variometer

Mechanical variometers

THE VANE VARIOMETER

The most common examples of vane variometers are the Winter and PZL variometers. They are relatively cheap and robust, and most gliders have one or the other – usually as backup in the event of a battery failure or a component dying in one of the electronic boxes.

As air flows into or out of the instrument's case on its journey between static and capacity, it deflects a small vane attached to the indicator needle (figure 7). This deflection tensions a very fine hairspring – there to provide necessary resistance and return the pointer towards zero when the flow rate decreases. The instrument has to contain a 'leak' (actually, more of a miniature gate) to enable it to measure the flow rate. On some types of variometer this *capillary leak*, as it is called, is between the case and the vane, whereas on others the leak occurs through small ports on either side of the vane.

The mechanical variometer's design is simple. In steady conditions it reads accurately, but it responds rather slowly to changes. One reason for this is that by comparison with the tiny mass of the air moving in and out of the variometer, that of the vane and the pointer is large, so their inertia (and momentum) is fairly significant. Poor maintenance can result in a very sticky or sluggishly responsive instrument, as can corrosion or dust inside the case.

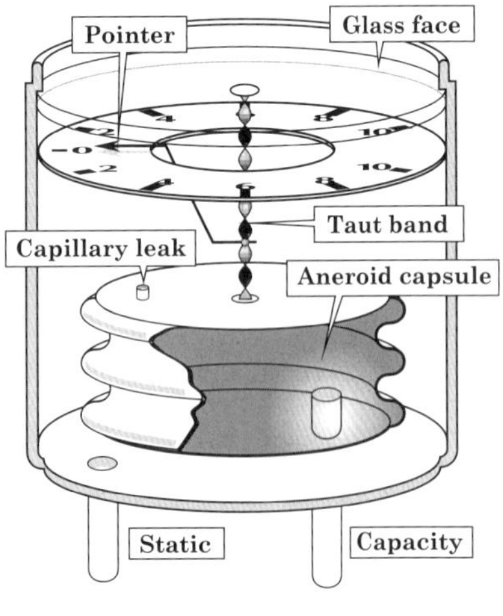

THE TAUT BAND VARIOMETER

Taut band variometers (figure 8) are manufactured by Schuemann and Bohli. These variometers overcome some of the inertial problems of the vane variometer and, as a result, respond more quickly. The capacity opens directly into an aneroid capsule, and the capillary leak is directly from the capsule into the case, which is at the static pressure. Any expansion or contraction of the capsule is translated to the pointer via a very fine, pretensioned (hence taut) and frictionless band, twisted and held firmly at both ends. To keep the mass of the moving parts to a minimum, the taut band is very thin and the pointer is constructed from a very fine fibre. When the glider climbs, the capsule expands slightly and the tension in the band is relaxed, causing it to twist and deflect the pointer upward. The opposite happens as the glider descends.

Though taut band variometers are faster and more accurate than vane variometers, they are expensive to manufacture and easy to damage. Since they too work by restricting airflow, there is always a measurable lag in their

FIGURE 8 A taut band variometer

response. Inertial effects and mechanical friction still figure. The instrument can take up to four seconds to respond to changes, and a poorly maintained one connected to a badly plumbed system can lag much more than that, and end up being worse than useless.

GLIDER INERTIA

When a glider flies from still into rising air it takes a short while to accelerate upwards, unlike a feather or a speck of dust which would react instantly. The heavier the glider and the higher the wing loading, the greater the delay. Whether circling in lift or cruising between thermals, the pilot has to remember and allow for all these extra seconds. Inter-thermal speeds in modern gliders are often very high, so the lag of a mechanical vario-meter can be a significant disadvantage during the first few moments of pulling up in lift and then trying to centre in it. As a result, electric or electronic variometers with faster response times are the first choice, with the mechanical variometer acting as a backup.

Total Energy (TE)

At any time when a glider is flying, its *total energy* consists of *kinetic* (speed) and *potential* (height) energy. Total Energy = Kinetic Energy + Potential Energy (this is identical to the formula $K = P + V$ in chapter 3, *see* p. 65). It is important to remember that a basic variometer measures only the rate of flow between the capacity and the static. This is entirely dependent on the difference in pressure between the two points – nothing else – and if the static pressure is altered by effects other than changes in altitude, then the basic variometer won't distinguish between any of them.

FIGURE 9 'Stick lift' as indicated by a basic variometer

When a glider is flying at a steady speed its kinetic energy remains constant. Potential energy, on the other hand, is nibbled away as the glider descends, so the total energy possessed by the glider gradually decreases. The basic variometer system will indicate a steady rate of descent (figure 9 (A)), which is exactly what's happening. When the glider's nose is lowered to, say, the attitude illustrated in example (B), the reduction in the AoA leads to a reduction in lift, and until the glider has accelerated to the speed appropriate to the new attitude (example (C)), it will sink at a slightly higher rate than usual. In terms of the variometer reading at (C), (B) appears to have over-read. This flight sag (*see* chapter 4 p. 106) is why, when you leave a thermal, it's a good idea to start speeding up before you reach the sink.

If the nose is then raised (example (D)), and the glider makes a short climb to convert some of its speed into height, the variometer will once again over-read. Nose-up (example (E)), there is

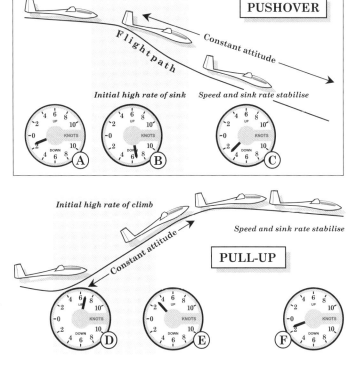

251

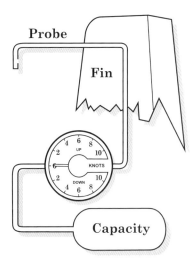

FIGURE 10 A total energy probe

no sustainable constant speed/sink situation as there was in the descent. When the glider levels off again and the speed has stabilised (example (F)), we are back to (A) again, but lower and therefore with less energy in total.

Because the variometer can measure minute rates of through-flow, relatively small changes in speed can have large effects on the readings of a basic, uncompensated variometer. The practical result is that when a glider pulls up into a thermal and then levels out, the basic variometer will indicate an initially heroic rate of climb (example (D)). Once the glider's speed and sink rate have stabilised, the indication will fall to something less encouraging. The basic variometer is telling the truth about the transient high rates of sink or lift, but only in terms of potential energy because that is all it can measure. The phenomenon is known as *stick lift*, and it makes the basic, uncompensated variometer a very poor aid to soaring.

Additionally, gusts can create static pressure fluctuations, and the weight of the air in the 'system' tubing can be affected by vertical accelerations. The variometer will register both of these as changes in lift.

Total Energy Compensation

So how to cancel out the effects of stick lift? The simplest way to do this is take some account of the kinetic energy changes and alter the pressure gradient between the static and the capacity; in other words, we've either got to blow some air into the system, or suck it out, and in exactly the right amounts.

Total Energy Compensation is a clever and simple idea (figure 10), which enables the variometer to indicate only total energy gains or losses. So that even if potential and kinetic energy are being swapped constantly one for the other, the variometer will respond only to their sum, which remains near enough constant over a short period of time.

The requisite Total Energy Compensation can be provided by any of the following devices: a probe, a venturi, a diaphragm, or by using electronic compensation.

PROBES

Most probes are more or less L-shaped tubes with holes or slots cut into the downwind side of the L's foot (figure 11). The slotted end needs to be placed well away from local pressure fluctuations caused by the airframe. For example, if the probe is mounted on the top leading edge of the fin, as most are, but is too short, then using the elevator and/ or the rudder could affect the variometer readings. The other end of the probe is connected to the static side of the variometer via yards of tubing running down the fin and along the fuselage.

Increases in static pressure caused by increasing speed are cancelled out by increasing suction from the probe, and vice versa. As a result, a probe-equipped variometer will indicate what the glider's sink rate would be if its speed at that instant were constant.

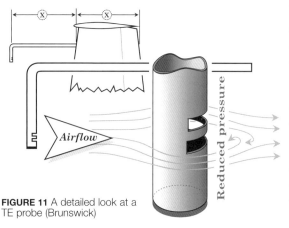

FIGURE 11 A detailed look at a TE probe (Brunswick)

VENTURI

We know from chapter 3 (p. 66) that changes in airflow speed through a venturi produce changes in pressure. A venturi attached to the static side of a variometer can provide compensation by suction, as did the L-shaped probe (figure 12).

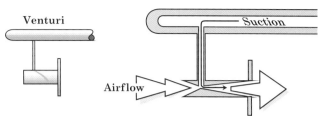

Like most total energy systems, the venturi has its disadvantages. Where it is located on the airframe is far more critical than for something like the Irving probe, for example. Fuselage-mounted venturi, in particular, tend to suffer from blanking by the wing and fuselage at high AoAs. Probes are also prone to handling damage. Venturi tend to be far more sensitive to yaw than probes. The pressure reductions in the throat cause the air to cool, and if conditions are right ice will form and block the venturi. If water enters probe- or venturi-driven variometer systems they can seriously misread or just stop working altogether.

FIGURE 12 The venturi as a total energy device (Irving venturi)

Electronic compensation integrates airspeed and the climb or sink rate, and is adjustable from the cockpit. You probably won't be looking out too much when making the adjustments, and having lots of things to twiddle and fiddle to get the compensation right can also mean an equal number of opportunities to get it wrong.

With or without a venturi, probes must produce very precise amounts of suction and operate accurately over a wide range of speeds. The length of the metal tube, its diameter, the size of the holes or slots and their radii and are all critical to correct operation.

FIGURE 13 TE using a diaphragm

TE COMPENSATION USING A DIAPHRAGM

Total energy compensation can be provided by using a rubber or thin metal diaphragm in a capsule T'd into the capacity side of the variometer. The other side connects to the pitot (figure 13).

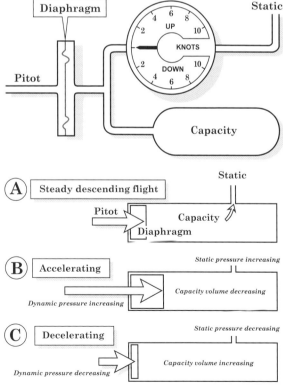

At a steady forward speed, the membrane's deflection remains constant and the variometer indicates a normal descent rate (figure 13 (A)). If the glider accelerates, air flows more quickly into the system via the static (B). On the pitot side, the increasing speed raises the pressure and bends the diaphragm towards the static side. This reduces the capacity's overall volume and slightly raises its internal pressure, partially balancing the increasing pressure from the static side and lessening the gradient between them. The variometer readings are now lower than they would be for a similar uncompensated variometer.

If the glider decelerates, the diaphragm is deflected towards the pitot side, marginally increasing the capacity's volume and slightly lowering its pressure. The readings are then somewhat lower than they would be for the uncompensated variometer.

The diaphragm needs to be carefully matched, in terms of size and elasticity, to the variometer it is driving, and to the capacity's volume. Only one variometer can be served at a time, so multiple variometers require multiple capsules and capacities.

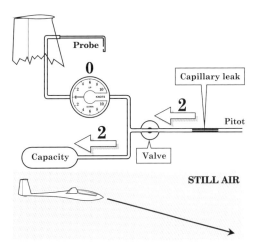

FIGURE 14 Gliding in still air

FIGURE 15 Flying through 3kt of sink, Netto in use

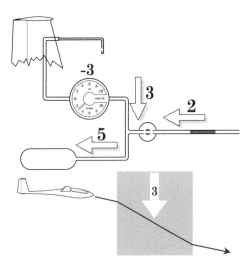

Compensation by diaphragm has several drawbacks:

(1)   it is accurate only at one particular altitude

(2)   it is sensitive to G and must be mounted vertically if it is not to interpret manoeuvring accelerations as lift or sink

(3)   rubber perishes and its elastic properties change with age. It can develop holes and splits. A metal membrane is unaffected by the problems of ageing and perishing.

The Netto variometer

Each of the compensation systems so far described will indicate the glider's overall sink rate – the vertical speed of the air mass plus that of the glider – at any airspeed, but there are many occasions when it would be more useful to know what the air alone is doing. Say that the glider enters sinking air and the variometer registers 4kt down. The MacCready ring indicates that you should fly at 70kt, but the moment you start to accelerate, the variometer needle runs off ahead to a yet larger value, say 5.5kt, where the speed to fly is correspondingly greater. 'Move and miss' gets a bit irritating after a time, and while it isn't that important to fly at exactly the speeds indicated, and the IAS will eventually catch up with the ring, there has to be an easier way to get to the right speed without having to plot an intercept course in advance. If we could subtract the glider's own sink rate from that of the air mass, we could target the appropriate airspeed immediately without having to chase it round the MacCready ring.

When the air is genuinely still the glider descends inexorably and the variometer says as much. What we want is a working variometer which indicates zero in the same situation, and somehow cancels out the sink due to the glider. The so-called *Netto* or *Net* variometer set-up does exactly what's required. The solution it adopts is, crudely, to ignore the variometer completely and pump up the capacity side to the same pressure as the static. There is then no flow between them, and the variometer reads zero. This feat is achieved by dribbling air from the pitot side into the capacity, bypassing the variometer via an extremely carefully calibrated capillary leak (figure 14). The capillary is usually an hypodermic needle cut to a specific length and sealed into a tube from the pitot side, but the same effect can be produced electronically.

In the example in figure 15, our glider is now flying through 3kt sink. In this case the total sink rate is 5kt. Without the leaked input from the pitot side the variometer would read 5kt down, so 2kt worth of the flow – the glider's sink rate – must come into the capacity via the leak, with the remaining 3kt worth coming through the instrument from the static.

In figure 16 our glider flies through 3kt of lift. The Netto will indicate +3kt, but in this particular instance you really do want to know the glider's actual climb rate, which will be the upward movement of the air mass less the glider's sink rate. Quite a few pilots have forgotten or not realised that the variometer has been set to Netto, and have gradually thermalled downwards with the variometer registering up! In this instance a Netto reading of +3 is an actual rate of climb of +1kt, so a Netto reading of +1 would in reality be a sink rate of –1kt. The more sophisticated variometer/navigation/make-the-tea-systems in modern gliders assume that if you are flying at less than, say, 55kt, then you are in lift, so the Netto cuts out, leaving you with a standard TE variometer.

Assuming that you stick with Netto, then the example in <u>figure 16</u> requires 1kt worth of air to flow out of the capacity, and 2kt worth to come in through the capillary and exit through the variometer, making up the required 3kt total which is the sink rate of the air mass.

NB Make absolutely sure that the capillary is *not* in the direct line from the pitot to the ASI (<u>figure 17</u>)!

Calibration of the capillary depends upon the performance of the glider and its wing loading, as well as the variometer system in use and the volume of the capacity. A mechanical variometer with Netto will only give true air mass readings at one wing loading. Adding water ballast changes the wing loading, and the Netto will need a larger and suitably calibrated capillary leak. It is usual to add one to a switchable bypass in the pitot line, or to use electronic compensation. A TE variometer is best for soaring, so a pneumatic switch may also be added to the pitot line to toggle between Netto and TE modes, as appropriate.

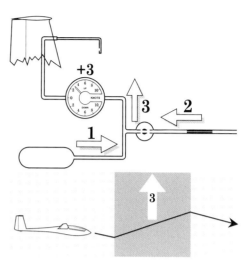

FIGURE 16 Flying through 3kt of lift, Netto in use

EFFECTS OF RAPID CHANGES IN PRESSURE

If the glider zoom climbs 300ft, say, the flow from the capacity is swift enough to cause a sudden drop in pressure, cooling the air by about 1°C. At the same time, the walls of the flask, the tubing, and so on, won't cool quite as quickly and some of their heat will be transferred to the contained air, causing it to expand. This process is fairly leisurely, so the additional flow it creates will rise gradually to a peak and then die away. It may be a minute or more before the temperatures equalise, and during that time the variometer won't be giving entirely accurate readings. The flask's internal temperature can be stabilised to some extent by introducing small amounts of a non-corrosive material that retains heat well. Copper pan scrubbers are ideal. While such methods reduce any delays caused by temperature differences, they affect the variometer readings by changing the flask volume and reducing the mass flow.

FIGURE 17 Capillary location critical

THINGS NOT WORKING RIGHT?

A bad variometer set-up will give you information which is at best misleading, and will probably be working at odds with the vital seat-of-the-pants sensations you need to be able to thermal well. This will put your workload up, and quite likely at the same time the glider will just carry on going down! Save yourself the frustration by making sure your variometer works properly. Don't assume that because it's electronic, links into your GPS and has 73 multi-function buttons, as well as telling you the number of angels currently dancing the Fandango on the head of a pin, that it's accurate. The more complicated a variometer system is the more likely it won't be operating optimally! Appendix E, p. 298, looks at variometer problems and their solutions.

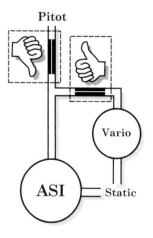

Summary of chapter nine

CHAPTER 10
METEOROLOGY

CHAPTER CONTENTS ★ should know ☆ useful

CHAPTER CONTENTS   ★ should know   ☆ useful

10 METEOROLOGY

Meteorology – the study of the weather and atmospheric phenomena – is a subject of such legendary complexity that this chapter has no realistic chance of covering it in great depth. However, in common with many complicated things, the weather is driven by the interaction of a number of relatively simple processes, and here we will look at some of the basic mechanisms.

Forecasting errors

Weather forecasters are a dedicated breed, and have to be able to deal with the whims of the weather and the often wholly unrealistic expectations of some of their clientele but, despite all the computing power now thrown at the weather, are accurate forecasts actually possible? Those which state the obvious are easy. 'After it gets dark it will get light again' stands an excellent chance of being right. Any forecast which lacks detail, such as 'tomorrow's' weather will be much the same as 'today's' is very likely to be right when a high pressure area grinds to a halt, because, on average, very slow, gradual change is the nature of such situations.

Unfortunately, small changes to the overall situation can turn what was a good forecast into an indifferent gliding/flying day. To be fair, today's forecasting inaccuracies tend to occur, not so much in the type of weather that is approaching – though there can occasionally be big surprises – as in the timing of its arrival. Either way, the culprit hides in the nature of change, and it is this which makes long range forecasts of dubious value.

Not so very long ago it was thought that accurate forecasting was difficult simply because we lacked sufficient information, and up to a point that is still true. Like most science before *quantum mechanics*, meteorological theory was based on the reasonable premise that weather processes must have some logic behind them. Perhaps we don't know everything right now, we said to ourselves, but when we do forecasts will be better. That comfortably clockwork view still persists, but the reality is more like wrestling with jelly. For a start, we are not dealing with a sterilised laboratory process, but with a planet-wide 'thing' that has grammar, so to speak, but no punctuation, and whose overriding constant is continuous change (<u>figure 1</u>).

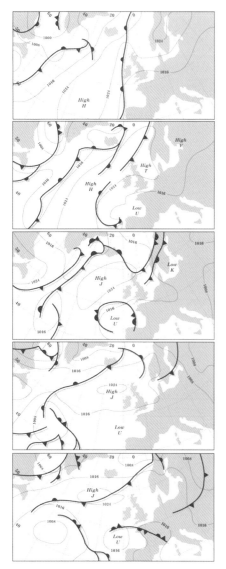

FIGURE 1 Atlantic forecast charts, 01–05 August 1995

Current theories give the weather at least some of the wayward characteristics of chaos, which doesn't mean that the weather is without logic or rules – just not quite the ones we'd like. One rule of *chaos theory*, contradictory as that may sound, is that very small, perhaps undetectable changes in a given set of initial conditions can result in dramatically different outcomes. For example, you could set 25 identical experiments going at the same instant, and within five days have 25 different sets of results, most very similar, but with a few beating very different paths. In terms of satisfying the demands of glider pilots trying to decide when to go on holiday, one consequence of chaos is that accurate long range forecasts are, and will probably remain, largely matters of chance. Oddly enough, this may not apply to forecasting general trends in the global climate over periods of tens of years. As for the short-term 'next day and perhaps the one after' forecasts, while they are better than they used to be, they can still promise good days (in gliding terms) and deliver dross instead.

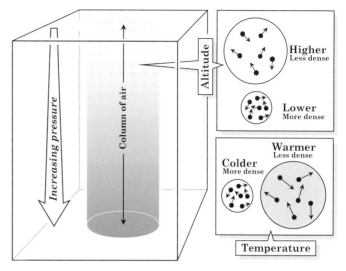

FIGURE 2 Temperature, density and pressure

RECAPITULATION

Points relevant to meteorology that have been made in previous chapters (figure 2) include:

(1) atmospheric pressure, measured in *millibars* in the UK, decreases with height

(2) overall temperature falls with height, though there are height bands where temperature actually increases with height

(3) 'parcels' of air that are relatively warmer than the surrounding air (12°C as against 11°C, or –35°C as against –36°C) are less dense. This gives them positive buoyancy and they will rise. Parcels of relatively colder air are more dense, have negative buoyancy and will descend. Neutral buoyancy results when the parcel is effectively indistinguishable from the surrounding air. Density is the critical factor in buoyancy

(4) raising the temperature of a gas causes it to expand, and vice versa

(5) when either temperature, pressure or density change, at least one of the others will be affected

(6) all energy systems, the weather included, create flow as they try to seek a state of equilibrium.

FIGURE 3 Weather machinery

RELATIONSHIP BETWEEN TEMPERATURE, PRESSURE AND DENSITY

By definition, parcels of air contain a fixed number of air molecules, but are 'elastic' and so able to expand or contract freely. If the temperature within the parcel rises, the energy levels of the air molecules increase and they drive each other further apart, lowering the parcel's density (mass divided by volume). If the parcel were a fixed size container, like the aerosol can in chapter 1, then increasing the temperature only increases the pressure; the volume and mass can't change in this particular example, so neither does the density, and as a result buoyancy is not affected. When a 'free' parcel is heated, however, it expands until the external and internal pressures are equal – if they differed the parcel would expand or contract further – and will rise if the temperature change has reduced the density.

THE PRODIGAL SUN

Immense torrents of energy flood out of this nuclear fireball and vanish into space, apparently wasted, but enough arrives on earth to support life, the weather, and just about everything else (figure 3). Most of the sun's energy comes in forms which have little direct effect upon us. Of those that do, there is one which we cannot do without, and it is not light, important as that is, but radiant heat. Without heat, either from the sun or from geothermal sources within the planet, the earth would be lifeless and weatherless.

The start button for almost all meteorological processes is heat, and heat has two major effects:

(1)   it maintains the atmosphere as a gas. Without it the various gases that comprise the atmosphere would have turned to liquids, or lie frozen solid on the surface

(2)   it creates the temperature/density/pressure differences which are responsible both for *convection* and the circulation systems that exist in the atmosphere at every scale, from the very small to the very large.

Temperature

HEAT AND ITS TRANSFER

About a third of the solar energy which reaches the earth makes it through to the surface, while the rest is either reflected back into space or scattered in the upper atmosphere. Our atmosphere is rather unusual in that it acts both as a filter preventing the sun's more life-threatening radiation from seriously injuring us, and as a window through which light and the infrared wavelengths can reach the surface.

Heat is a form of vibration. The sun's infrared energy doesn't warm the air directly, but pumps energy into the atoms of any suitable surface upon which it falls, heating it up. Energy flow is always 'downhill' (from the greater to the lesser), so once the atoms of the material are sufficiently agitated their excess energy is transferred to the air molecules by direct physical contact or by radiation (figure 4).

CONVECTION

Few large surfaces are completely uniform, and some absorb more heat than others. Hot spots readily develop, acting as trigger points for the tiny balloon-like parcels of warmed air that, to start with, are little more than small scale turbulence and micro-gusts. The surrounding air is cooler and denser and displaces the warmed parcels upwards, out of the way, flows underneath them and is then warmed in its turn. By accumulation, this convective process involves larger and larger volumes of air which eventually, but not inevitably, rise into the sky as *thermals* that can be used by gliders. We'll be looking at thermals in slightly more detail later. Convection can also occur over the sea, but the mechanism is slightly different as there are no hot spots as such.

INSOLATION

The convective process is dependent on the amount of solar energy reaching the ground, a process known as *insolation*, and defined by Chamber's Twentieth Century Dictionary as 'exposure to the sun's rays, received solar radiation'. Insolation depends on:

- *the angle at which sunlight strikes the ground*. The Earth's rotational axis is tilted in relation to its orbit around the sun, so the arc described by the sun across the skies of the northern hemisphere's mid latitudes is high and long in summer, and low and short in winter. Potentially, therefore, more energy falls upon a given square foot of ground during summer than winter (<u>figure 5</u>). The slope of the ground also has a significant effect, with sun facing slopes receiving more direct heat than others.

  At night the heat absorbed by the ground during the day radiates away into space – a process known as *nocturnal cooling* – and convection then cools the air near the ground. Winter's longer nights and shorter days allow far more time for what little heat the ground has absorbed during the day to dissipate, so winter tends to be colder than summer!

- *the amount of cloud cover*. The deeper and more extensive the cloud, the more solar radiation is scattered or reflected back into space. By the same token, cloud at night can reflect back to the ground the heat radiated by nocturnal cooling with the result that, on a clear night, the temperature will dip lower than when cloud is present.

  Amounts of cloud are measured in *oktas*, or 'eighths' of sky, three oktas (or 3⁄8 *cumulus*), would mean that just

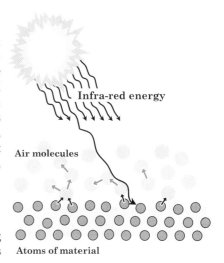

FIGURE 4 Transfer of heat energy

FIGURE 5 Sun's heating effect on a flat surface

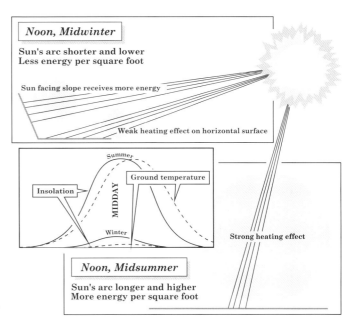

under half the sky was covered by cumulus cloud (figure 6). Cloud amounts may also be described as *scattered* or *broken*. On any given day different layers and levels of cloud can cover different amounts of sky. Aeronautical forecasts refer to cloud amounts in terms of oktas and the type of cloud, for example, 'three oktas scattered cumulus at 1,500ft; eight oktas stratocumulus at 3,000ft'.

- *the clarity of the atmosphere*. This is affected by the number and size of the dust particles suspended in the air, and to a lesser extent, by the amount of water vapour present. Visibility will be good if the air is clean and dry; poor if it contains large concentrations of smoke particles or is very humid. Clarity is usually referred to in terms of *visibility*, measured in either nautical miles or kilometres. Insolation is affected by the amount of murk in the atmosphere.

- *the colour and texture of the surface*. Dark coloured surfaces absorb more heat than light coloured surfaces. A snow-capped peak will reflect most of the energy that falls upon it, whereas a ploughed field and a conifer forest will absorb large amounts. The depth and volume of the forest may mean that the absorbed heat won't be released until late afternoon, and then only slowly. The ploughed field can remain a good source of thermals throughout most of the day, depending on the type of soil. In the lee of lines of trees and similar obstacles there may be little or no wind (*wind shadow*) to blow away the small parcels of warmed air before they've gathered together. If the sun is able to reach into such sheltered areas, the air temperature there is very likely to be a lot higher than elsewhere, so they can be a good source of often powerful thermals.

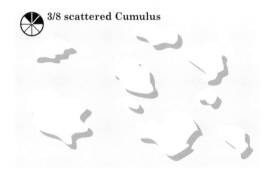

3/8 scattered Cumulus

FIGURE 6 Looking down on scattered cumulus

LAYERS OF THE ATMOSPHERE

Above the lowest layer of the atmosphere, the troposphere (figure 7), are several other layers, their depth defined more or less in terms of their temperature profiles. For example, in the *stratosphere* (top of troposphere to about 160,000ft) the temperature increases with height (figure 8). The stratosphere contains the ozone layer which, when it's there, absorbs a large part of the sun's damaging ultra violet radiation. In the *mesosphere* temperature falls with height, but increases with height in the *thermosphere*. In the *exosphere*, the final tenuous layer that fades discretely into the vacuum of space, the temperature eventually drops to within a few degrees of *absolute zero* (−273°C). Pressure from ground level to the farthest edge of the exosphere does not reduce uniformly with height, but falls off rapidly within the first 20,000ft or so, and less quickly above the *tropopause*, which is the variable altitude dividing line between the troposphere and the stratosphere.

GOING UP?

For gliders, the crucial ingredient in staying airborne for any length of time is weather that in one way or another creates usable rising air. Meteorological as opposed to aerodynamic lift is generated in three ways:

(1)   by hills and ridges obstructing the wind, giving rise to hill/ridge lift and also wave

(2) by convection and instability, resulting in thermals

(3) by the meeting of air masses on almost every scale, from the very large to the very small. We'll be looking at frontal systems later, but not at related phenomena such as convergence zones, sea breeze fronts and line squalls (*see* Bibliography p. 307–8) for further information).

For the majority of glider pilots, convection is the primary source of lift. As described, convection can be a very small scale process indeed, so for usable 'lift', each air parcel, or thermal, must be wide enough for a circling glider to fit inside it, and rising sufficiently fast to carry the glider upwards. If cross country flying is to be attempted, then convection needs to rise to at least 2,000ft above ground, and thermals be spaced close enough to allow the glider to get from one to the other without arriving at very low altitude, or not at all. Practical experience shows that thermal strengths change during the day and by location, which has something to do with the degree of insolation, and that the depth of the *convective layer* varies. In the morning this layer may be very shallow, and can occasionally remain that way throughout the day, so more is involved in the creation of usable convection than just the sun warming the ground.

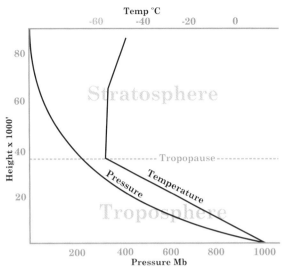

FIGURE 8 The lower atmosphere

STABILITY AND INSTABILITY

Since convection is due to differences in density between a parcel and its surroundings, any changes in the temperature of the surroundings, due to height, say, will have an effect on how buoyant any given parcel is likely to be. For example, if the whole atmosphere were at a constant temperature of 10°C (figure 9), then a parcel of air which stayed at 15°C and never cooled with height (A) would always be buoyant, wherever it was, and would rise as far as the atmosphere extended. Parcel (B), however, at a constant 10°C, would always stay where it was put, whereas parcel (C), at 3°C, would always sink to the ground. Luckily, the air temperature in the troposphere, though falling overall with height, is nowhere near as uniform as figure 8 implies.

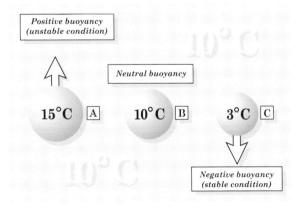

FIGURE 9 Positive, neutral and negative buoyancy

Exosphere

The layers of the atmosphere

Thermosphere

(265,000ft)
Mesosphere
(160,000ft)
Stratosphere
Troposphere

FIGURE 7
Layers of the atmosphere

These variations in temperature either encourage or discourage convection, with the air being either unstable or stable respectively. There can be multiple 'sandwiches' of unstable and *stable air* in the troposphere, and this layering is one of the requirements for wave, detailed later.

DRY ADIABATIC LAPSE RATE (DALR)

Normally air contains some water in vapour form, but unless the air becomes *saturated* (*see* p. 269) this has no obvious effect on how the parcel behaves. Assuming for the moment that the parcel contains no water vapour, lifting it vertically upwards causes it to expand (figure 10) as the surrounding atmospheric pressure decreases. The larger volume gives the enclosed air molecules more space in which to move around, and effectively dilutes their heat energy. As the pressure drops, therefore, the parcel cools. This cooling process is described as *adiabatic* (heat does not enter or leave the 'system'), and is entirely due to the parcel's expansion, and not to any mixing of the contents with the surrounding air. Theoretically, a rising parcel of unsaturated air will cool at the *Dry Adiabatic Lapse Rate* (DALR) of 3°C/1,000ft. This 'cooling line' can be verified by experiment.

Three points about the adiabatic process should be mentioned:

(1)   it is two-way, so a descending parcel of dry air will increase in pressure (i.e. compress due to the increasing height/weight of the air column above it) and warm instead of cooling at the DALR

(2)   whatever a parcel's initial temperature, the DALR is constant, so a plot of temperature against height will be a straight line. For example, if a parcel's initial temperature is 25°C (figure 11, line (A)), then by the time it has risen to about 8,300ft it will have cooled to 0°C. With a lower initial temperature of 5°C (line (B)), it will have cooled to 0°C at 1,500ft, and −10°C at 4,500ft

(3)   though a thermal is a parcel of sorts, its edges are far less well-defined than those of, say, a hot air balloon. Thermals cool at the DALR in the way described, but some mixing with cooler surrounding air – a process called *entrainment* – is unavoidable. As a result, their overall rate of cooling is usually slightly greater than the DALR.

ENVIRONMENTAL LAPSE RATE (ELR)

The DALR may be fixed, but the *Environmental Lapse Rate* (ELR) (the real-world temperature of the air at any given height) certainly isn't, and varies from day to day, even from hour to hour. These variations occur for a number of reasons which include nocturnal cooling, where the air mass has come from, and cloud cover. Whatever the exact reasons for these changes, the difference between the DALR and the ELR is crucial because it determines whether convection will occur, how deep it is likely to be (*depth of convection*), and to some extent the strength of any thermals or the likelihood of wave (*see* p. 280)

FIGURE 10 Expansion and cooling

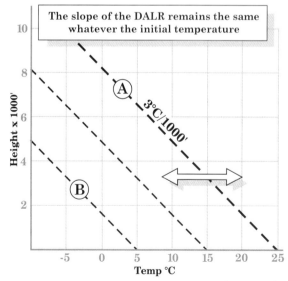

FIGURE 11 Dry Adiabatic Lapse Rate (DALR)

The temperature/pressure data (an *ascent*) required to plot the ELR is gathered by aircraft or radiosonde balloons. Figure 12 shows temperature/altitude plots for two separate days. Plot (D1) shows the temperature falling initially with height, rising between 3,500ft and 5,000ft, and then falling thereafter. Plot (D2) shows a very rapid increase up to about 1,800ft. Thereafter the temperature falls gradually until, at just over 6,000ft, it stays constant for a while before starting to fall again.

Given the ELR's wayward slope, a parcel rising and cooling at the DALR can't fail to run up against it eventually. For instance, a parcel with a ground-level temperature of 20°C (figure 12, line (B)) will meet the (D2) ELR at about 1,000ft, and will then have the same temperature and density as its surroundings. Momentum may carry the parcel slightly higher, but it will eventually sink back to the level at which it has neutral buoyancy and is indistinguishable from its surroundings. By contrast, in the first thousand or so feet where the (D1) ELR slopes to the left, a parcel with a ground level temperature of 15°C (line (A)) will come to a halt at about 2,500ft. Had the parcel's initial temperature been 20°C (extension of line (B)), then it would have reached 4,500ft before hitting the ELR.

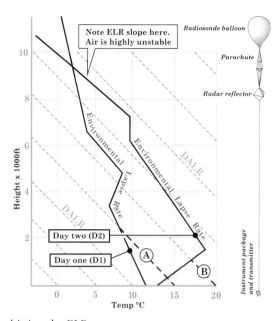

FIGURE 12 Environmental Lapse Rate (ELR)

INVERSIONS

If the slope of the ELR was always less than that of the DALR – like the (D2) ELR slope above 7,000ft – any rising parcel would become more and more buoyant, and accelerate unchecked to who knows what altitude. Various stable layers in the atmosphere prevent this, acting as sturdy lids on what would otherwise be a violently boiling cauldron of perpetual and gigantic storms.

These lids or layers are either *isothermal* – the temperature remains constant with height – or *inversions* – where the temperature, contrary to the general trend, increases with height. The stratosphere, for example, is more or less all inversion. Though inversions in the troposphere are very much shallower – varying from a few hundred to several thousand feet deep – the temperature gradient within them can create equally effective lids that limit or entirely prevent usable convection.

Figure 13 is a 3D representation of the (D2) ELR from figure 12. A low-level inversion stretches from ground level to about 1,200ft and there is a medium-level inversion (an isothermal layer) between 6,000ft and 7,000ft. The lower inversion is the more important of the two, because if the ground-level

FIGURE 13 A low and a medium-level inversion

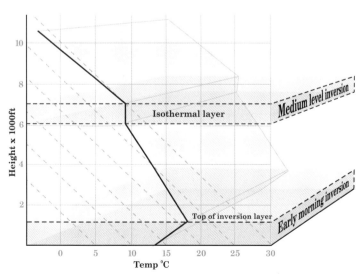

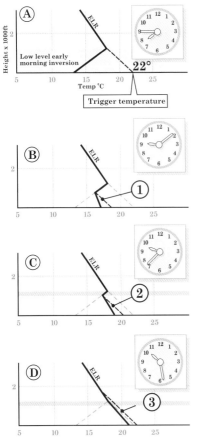

FIGURE 14 Breaking down of low-level inversion

temperature never rises high enough to allow a thermal to get past the 'elbow' at 1,000ft, then useable convection will not occur.

TRIGGER TEMPERATURE AND THE BREAKDOWN OF INVERSIONS

When a gliding forecast refers to a *trigger temperature* (figure 14), it is talking about the ground-level temperature required to give a parcel sufficient buoyancy to push it through an inversion. The usual expression is to 'break down the inversion', but what actually happens is much more like erosion.

The low level early morning inversion in figure 14, (A) is quite strong, and the ELR slopes well to the right. Let's say that at 07.45hrs the ground-level temperature is about 13°C, and that the temperature at 1,000ft is about 18°C, a difference of +5°C. For a ground-level parcel cooling at the DALR to reach 1,000ft, the trigger temperature has to be at least 22°C, i.e. not a difference of +5°C, but +9°C because, as it rises, it cools at the DALR and 5°C won't get it there. It doesn't mean that the parcel, or any thermal come to that, has to be 9°C warmer than the surrounding air, since only very small differences in temperature/density set convection going.

Convection is a slightly messy process and splashes heat energy around and about, gradually raising the air temperature below the inversion and changing the shape of the ELR (figure 14, (A) to (D)). Successive thermals push higher and higher, gradually nibbling away at the inversion until finally one of them reaches the trigger temperature, 'breaks through', and the inversion evaporates.

Just how long this takes depends on a number of factors, not least the strength of the inversion and the solar energy available. In June, say, it might take six hours or more from sun-up to produce the 9°C rise in groundlevel temperature needed to break down the lower inversion in (A). Once that's happened, the slope of the ELR above it requires a further rise of only 4°C (figure 15, lines ① and ②) to deepen the convective layer from 1,500ft to 5,000ft. Any thermal which is going to reach the base of the upper inversion has to start off at 27°C (figure 15, line ③), plus a further 3°C to break through. Though the upper inversion is much weaker than the lower one, in energy terms it is last in the queue. Shortly after midday the sun passes its zenith and insolation starts to decline. The trigger temperature required to break the upper inversion is 30°C (27°C + 3°C), which is high for the UK, though not impossible.

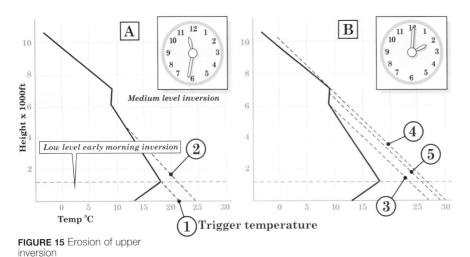

FIGURE 15 Erosion of upper inversion

The chances are that the upper inversion won't break. Given the slope of the ELR above 7,000ft, this is probably a good thing because any parcel that passed the 7,000ft mark would find its buoyancy rapidly increasing.

The presence of even minimal amounts of water in vapour form will at some altitude and/or temperature affect the lapse rate and the air's stability, so the result of a parcel of moist air passing the 7,000ft mark in the example just given could be large shower clouds, or possibly thunderstorms. We'll look at why in a moment.

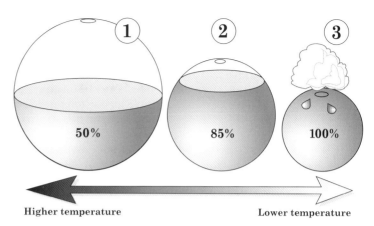

FIGURE 16 Relative humidity and temperature

Moisture (humidity)

Absolute humidity is a measure of the amount of water vapour in the air by weight, while *relative humidity* expresses the water vapour content as a percentage of the maximum that the air could contain invisibly at its current temperature; warm air can hold more than cold. Relative humidity has a significant bearing on cloud amounts and cloud base, and so is far more useful in respect of weather forecasting. Very cold air can have 100% relative humidity but contain almost no water vapour, whereas warm tropical air can contain much larger amounts, but have a relative humidity of only 50%.

Each of the round parcels in figure 16 contains the same number of air molecules and an identical amount of water vapour. The parcel's size represents the air temperature/density, so larger means warmer. Parcel ① is warm and has sufficient space between the air molecules for the vapour, with some space left over, and the relative humidity is, say, 50%. When the temperature falls the air molecules lose energy, move closer together and the parcel contracts, leaving less room for the vapour. The relative humidity rises to, say, 85% ②. If the air continues to cool, the parcel will contract further and eventually the relative humidity reaches 100% ③. The air is then said to be *saturated*, and if the temperature drops any further there will be too much water vapour for the available space, and the excess will pop into view as cloud, fog, mist, or even steam.

CONDENSATION

In normal circumstances water vapour can only become visible if it is able to find something upon which to condense. The atmosphere contains countless *condensation nuclei* which fit the bill perfectly: minute specks of dust and volcanic ash, soil fragments, small flakes of biological detritus, various industrial effluvia and exhaust pipe emissions, even sea salt.

A suitable surface will also serve. Take bathroom tiles. The bath water is hot and the air full of vapour. The moment the saturated air comes into contact with the cold tiles, its temperature container, so to speak, is rapidly cooled and 'shrunk' as the tiles absorb some of its heat energy. The relative humidity leaps to 100%, and the excess vapour condenses onto the tiles and runs as water droplets to the floor.

FIGURE 17 Origins and names of air masses

AIRMASS ORIGINS AND HUMIDITY

Land masses tend to change temperature more often and more quickly than the oceans, which operate as a vast heat sink helping to steady the global climate. In addition, approximately 90% of the water vapour in the atmosphere is picked up by air masses travelling over the seas and oceans. The origin, track and speed of an air mass will therefore have an important effect on its humidity. The *Maritime Tropical* (figure 17) air mass arrives in the UK from the Azores, and is warm and humid after having travelled a long way over a relatively warm Atlantic. Soaring conditions won't normally be good and visibility may be poor.

Continental Arctic, on the other hand, will have come from the pole, passed over Sweden and Norway – where some of its water content will have been lost as rain or snow – and arrive in this country as a very dry, cold, and usually clear air mass. Soaring conditions and visibility can be very good. Likewise *Continental Polar*, except that it can sweep up large amounts of pollutants and general murk during its travels over the industrial areas of Eastern Europe. For the UK at least, the best direction appears to be *Direct Maritime Polar*.

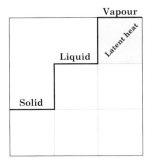

FIGURE 18 Latent heat and phase change

LATENT HEAT

Latent heat is 'hidden' heat. Put a saucepan on the stove to boil some water, and at normal air pressures the water's temperature will rise to 100°C and stay there, no matter how much steam is produced or how much heat the hot plate keeps pumping out. This temperature plateau is a characteristic of *phase changes*. Phase changes represent major alterations to the state of a material. Water, for example, can exist as ice, or as steam (a vapour). Another characteristic of phase changes is that, in the case of steam and the boiling water, both are initially at the same temperature. The hot plate's energy fuels the phase change (figure 18), and passes into the resulting vapour as latent heat, which can be thought of as the extra energy needed to keep the water in the vapour state. The energy step can be taken in either direction, up or down, so latent heat will be released when the vapour condenses back into water.

The oceans don't have to boil before water vapour passes into the air above, and *evaporation* from the surface occurs even at normal temperatures. If the air above is not already saturated, and depending on the temperature difference between the air and the sea, the resulting vapour is swept up and increases the air's humidity. If there is minimal convection or turbulence, then the result can be the formation of a moist layer of air close to the surface, with much drier air at higher altitudes.

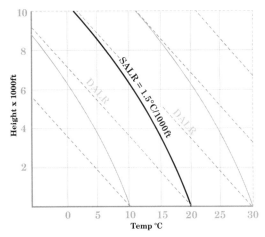

FIGURE 19 Saturated Adiabatic Lapse Rate (SALR)

THE SATURATED ADIABATIC LAPSE RATE (SALR) AND CLOUDS

As moist air is carried upwards it cools, eventually becoming saturated. Cloud forms. The consequent phase change (vapour to water) releases the latent heat which enabled the water to become vapour in the first place. This warms the rising air and makes it slightly less dense and therefore even more buoyant. Within the first few hundred feet of cloud forming, the release of latent heat alters the rate at which the air cools, from the DALR value to about 1.5°C/1,000ft. This new lapse rate is called the *Saturated Adiabatic Lapse Rate* (SALR) (figure 19).

The release of latent heat is a gradual process, so the lines representing the SALR (known as the *wet adiabats*) begin with a slope of 1.5°C/1,000ft – this corresponds to a decrease in stability – and then curve slowly back to the 3°C/1,000ft slope of the DALR, as all the available latent heat (for that phase change) is released. The practical result of the altered lapse rate is that if you take a climb into cloud, the lift starts to increase when you enter the base.

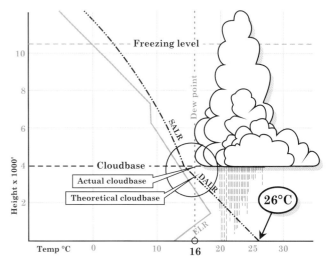

FIGURE 20 Dew point and the formation of cloud

DEW POINT TEMPERATURE

The temperature at which a given airmass will become saturated is known as its *dew point*. For example, if we assume a dew point of 16°C (figure 20), a parcel heated initially to 26°C ought theoretically to rise to about 3,400ft before it has cooled sufficiently for its relative humidity to reach 100%, and for cloud to start to form. Experience shows that, for whatever reason, cloud bases tend to be higher, and the empirical formula which covers this requires you to subtract the dew point temperature from the surface temperature and then multiply the result by 400. In this case, 26 – 16 = 10, and 10 × 400 = 4,000ft. Given the ELR it is also possible to work out the likely depth of the cloud.

THE FREEZING LEVEL

The ELR also indicates the *freezing level*, which is the height at which the ambient air temperature reaches 0°C. Once cloud extends into the freezing level ice crystals begin to form. In some circumstances they may not do so and water droplets can remain unfrozen (*supercooled*) to temperatures as low as –40°C. If ice crystals form they are carried upwards by the rising air, and grow by gradual accretion until they are too heavy to be supported. They then fall back down through the cloud, initially as hail or snow, and pass back through the freezing level, melt, and continue to fall as raindrops.

If you know the freezing level and have the ELR, it is possible to work out the likelihood of showers. For example, the freezing level in figure 20 is just over 10,000ft, but the difference between the ELR and the SALR above 7,000ft actually increases, so any clouds that do develop are likely to be very big, very active, and thundery. The freezing level depends on the airmass and on the seasons, so it tends to be lower in winter, as you would expect, and higher in summer.

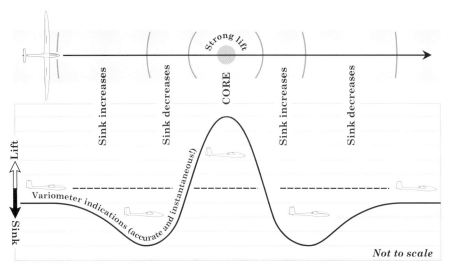

FIGURE 21 Thermal profile

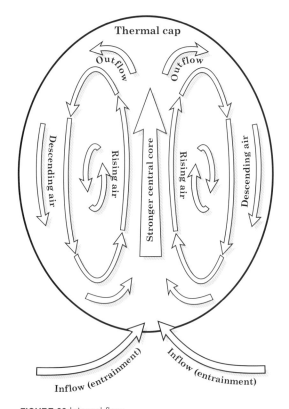

FIGURE 22 Internal flow pattern; vortex ring

THERMALS AND CIRCULATION

There's not a lot to be said about thermals that hasn't been said already of the various parcels of rising air. However, one very significant difference between them is that the parcel, being a theoretical contrivance, has a uniform temperature throughout and no internal flow pattern. Flying straight through the middle of a thermal reveals sinking air first, followed by rising air which increases to a peak (the *core*), and then decreases until the glider is back in the sinking air again (figure 21). Any theory of thermals and how they work has to take these changes in the air's vertical velocity into account, and tie them up with the fact that gliders don't invariably fall out of the bottom of every thermal they enter, which they certainly would if each was completely uniform and every part rose at exactly the same rate.

Practical experience demonstrates beyond any doubt that – pilot skills apart – gliders don't drop out of every thermal, that the pattern of lift and sink is as described, and that the core area, and indeed, a large part of the air in a thermal, must be rising faster than the thermal as a whole. The theory behind this has to be mechanically and 'energetically' sound, following the principle of 'you can't get something for nothing' which has appeared in many guises throughout this book. Further, if the thermal is to maintain its identity as it rises, any internal flow pattern must also be fairly tightly self-contained. In other words, up-flow has to be balanced by a related down-flow, and the two have to be physically connected in some way.

The only flow pattern that satisfies all the above criteria and has the appropriate degree of self-containment, is the *vortex ring* (figure 22). This can 'leak' in various ways, and not every thermal will look like the one illustrated, but there has to be a circulatory flow of some description no matter how misshapen the result.

The same general principles of circulation apply at virtually every scale in the atmosphere, from microscopic to planet wide.

CIRCULATION CELLS

Insolation is greatest at the equator, and humidity there is high. The conditions in the air mass are generally unstable, and the warmed air rises to the edge of the troposphere – which is deeper at the equator than elsewhere (figure 23) – and creates plenty of thunderstorms and rain. The high level air then flows a long way north (there is an equivalent flow southwards), cools, descends, and flows back towards the equator at the surface, to repeat the whole cycle. The result is two huge doughnut-shaped circulation cells ringing the earth, one just north of the equator and the other to the south. These are the *Hadley cells* and lie between Latitude 0° and 30° (N or S). Taking the northern hemisphere alone, there are two further circulation cells, one above 30°N and the other wrapped over the pole.

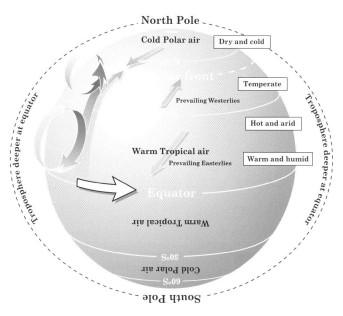

FIGURE 23 Circulation cells

Pressure, isobars and the wind

GRADIENT FLOW

Variations in atmospheric pressure act like hills and valleys, and in exactly the same way that water, driven by gravity, flows downhill to seek equilibrium, so too will air attempt to flow downhill from an area of high pressure to one of lower pressure (figure 24, (A)).

The air at the equator is warmer and less dense than at the poles, so that a particular pressure level of, say 300Mb, will be about 32,000ft above ground at the equator, and less

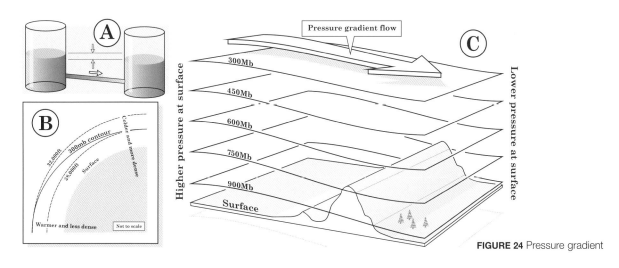

FIGURE 24 Pressure gradient

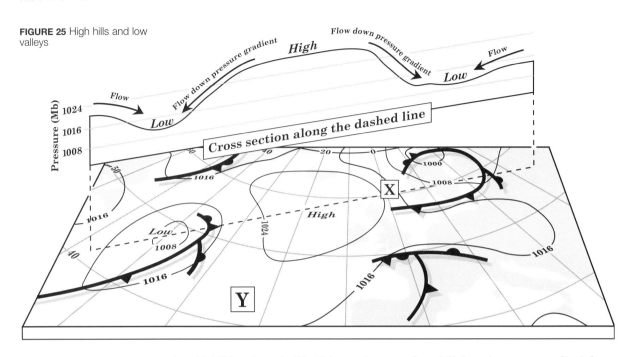

FIGURE 25 High hills and low valleys

than 28,000ft at the pole (B). This translates to a downhill slope (a *pressure gradient*) from the equator to the pole of about 8,000:1, which is not very steep. In reality, the slope isn't uniform and the circulation and pressure changes created by the huge convective cells mentioned previously can steepen the pressure gradient considerably. The results help set airmasses moving and create wind (C).

On a *synoptic chart, isobars* are lines joining points of equal pressure, in the same way that joining points of equal height on a map creates the contour lines. Like the hill contours, where the isobars are closest together, the pressure gradient is steepest. For example, at (X) in figure 25 there will be a moderate northerly wind, whereas at (Y), where the isobars are hundreds of miles apart, the wind is correspondingly light or non-existent.

While in principle the flow of air is downhill from a high into a low – as shown in the cross section of figure 25 – the winds which result from the pressure gradient are influenced by other factors, such as the *Coriolis effect* (*see* Appendix F, p. 305).

Figure 26 is a more accurate representation of the patterns of flow that develop. Near a low the surface wind blows more towards the centre than at altitude, whereas the opposite is true of a high. The reasons for this are discussed later. At altitude the winds blow more or less parallel to the isobars, rarely at right angles.

In the northern hemisphere air flows anti-clockwise into a low pressure area at the surface, rises, and at altitude flows outwards. In a high pressure area the air flows in clockwise at altitude, descends, and then flows out at the surface. In a low, the upflow has a destabilising effect on the air which in practice makes the weather worse. In a high, the air gently descends (*subsidence*), which tends to warm it and prevent, or at least limit, the formation of cloud. During the summer, if the high persists over several days the cloud disappears completely. The weather may then be 'nice', although not for gliding because the convective layer can be shallow, thermals 'bitty', and visibility bad.

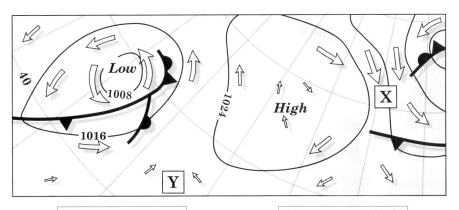

FIGURE 26 Wind directions around lows and highs

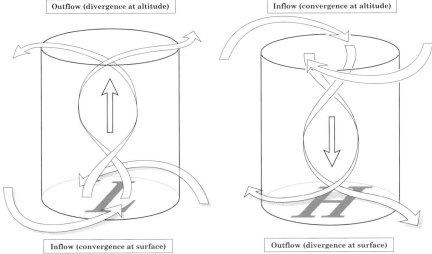

Outflow (divergence at altitude)

Inflow (convergence at altitude)

Inflow (convergence at surface)

Outflow (divergence at surface)

THE CORIOLIS EFFECT AND GEOSTROPHIC WINDS

On a non-rotating world an air mass that rolled down the general pressure gradient from a northern hemisphere mid-latitude would continue north to the pole. On a rotating world like our own the Coriolis effect causes moving air masses to turn to the right in the northern hemisphere, and to the left in the southern hemisphere. This effect is most marked near the poles and non-existent at the equator (*see* Appendix E, p. 298).

In time, the path of the air at altitude runs more or less parallel to the isobars, and a balance is then reached between the pressure gradient pulling downhill and the Coriolis effect trying to turn it uphill (figure 27). This balanced wind is known as the *geostrophic wind*, and its velocity is related to the closeness of the isobars which, as previously described, indicates the steepness of the pressure gradient. The

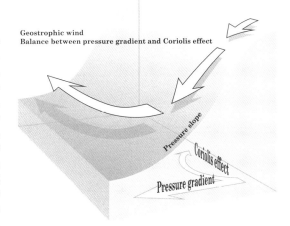

Geostrophic wind
Balance between pressure gradient and Coriolis effect

FIGURE 27 Balance between pressure gradient and Coriolis effect

relationship between the isobar spacing and the strength of the geostrophic wind varies with latitude, so that, for example, a spacing which gives a wind speed of 50kt at latitude 70° would result in a wind of 94kt nearer the equator, at latitude 25°.

The lower level wind is seldom exactly in balance in terms of the pressure gradient and the Coriolis effect, for the following reasons:

(1)   The earth, like a wing, has a boundary layer, and within the first 3,500ft or so of the surface, friction with the ground has a significant effect on the wind, both slowing and changing its direction. Typically, a geostrophic wind of 270° and 30kt at, say, 3,000ft becomes more like 240° and 20kt at the surface. The change is more marked over land than sea, particularly at night.

(2)   Vertical motion of the air. The horizontal component alters if the air moves up or down.

(3)   When the isobars curve round a *depression*, the outward acting centrifugal force reduces the inward pull of the pressure gradient, effectively weakening it and decreasing the wind speed. The opposite occurs round a high.

(4)   Non-parallel isobars. When the isobars narrow (in relation to the wind direction) the air accelerates to fit the steepening pressure gradient, and tends to turn and 'dive' across the isobars towards the lower pressure area. When the contours spread out the air slows down and tends to turn 'upslope'. Either of these effects can alter the wind direction by as much as 40° from the contour alignment.

(5)   Pressure changes. The wind direction turns towards the region where the pressure is falling fastest.

THE FORMATION OF FRONTS AND DEPRESSIONS

A *front* is the interface between two air masses of differing temperature and/or humidity. Some of the air from the mid-latitude cell (figure 23, p. 273) runs northwards at the surface and meets cold polar air flowing south, forming a *Polar front* which circles the planet. The exact position of this front depends on the relative temperature and density of the two air masses. In general, it lies further north in summer than in winter; figure 23 shows it in a summer position.

At the polar front the colder and denser polar air undercuts the less dense and warmer tropical air, pushing it upwards (figure 28) and setting in motion one of the processes which create what we know as *weather fronts*, or *frontal systems*, and their associated *depressions*, or areas of low pressure. Their common interface (figure 29, (A)) develops a slight bow, and the warm air starts to slide up the interface slope and develop a *cyclonic twist* (B), which helps to crease and fold the frontal surface further. This marks the initial stages of a developing low, or depression (C).

This upward movement of the air is not solely due to differences in density between warm and cold air. An often far stronger effect can be created by upper winds accelerating away and acting rather like a vacuum cleaner sucking up the air below the nozzle. A surface low starts to form below this 'suction region'. Once pressure falls, the pattern of isobars surrounding the new low creates a cyclonic circulation of the winds at low level.

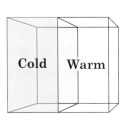
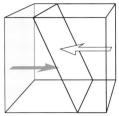
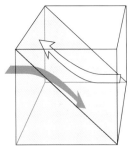

FIGURE 28 Overriding and undercutting

Cold   Warm

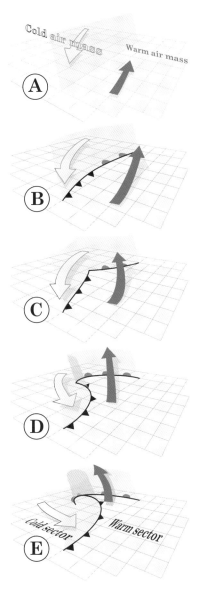

FIGURE 29 Developing low and fronts

The new circulation then starts to buckle the frontal surface, which affects the flow at altitude and may temporarily increase the 'suction' effect, speeding the low's development. The cyclonic circulation gradually works its way higher until it is as deep as the troposphere. The low then slows, becoming almost stationary. The fronts become wound round the centre of the low, with the cold airmass lifting the warmer mass clear of the surface (E), forming an *occlusion* (figure 30).

As more and more of the *warm sector* is lifted clear of the ground, the supply of fresh warm and cold air is gradually cut off. The pressure within the low then starts to rise (the low 'fills') and the associated frontal systems slowly disintegrate.

The frontal interface is also a mixing zone where cloud forms, with the cloud depth and characteristics dependent on the relative temperature/humidity differences between the air masses, as well as the interface slope. Huge amounts of cloud can be produced. The results spread for hundreds of miles ahead of the mixing zone and herald the type of front which is approaching.

THE JET STREAM

The *jet stream* is a narrow, snakelike tube of very strong winds – they can exceed 150kt – associated with the polar front, which wriggles its way round the globe at high altitudes, and has a very significant effect on the creation and the track of depressions and the associated frontal systems, as well as on the development of wave. It isn't really necessary for a glider pilot interested in the weather over the next day or so to know the location of the jet stream and the polar front. The reason is straightforward. Take any one of the synoptic charts from the first page of this chapter and assume that it is the forecast chart for tomorrow. That forecast should be based upon today's *actual* (what's really happening), which, virtually by definition, must already include the influence and location of the jet stream and the polar front,

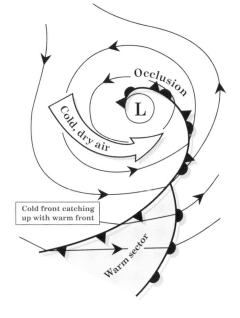

FIGURE 30 An occlusion

FIGURE 31 Cross section
through a warm front

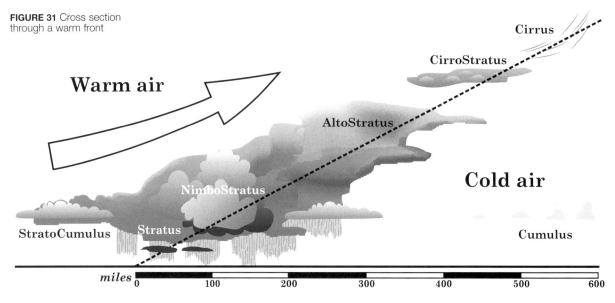

wherever they are. In other words, you can already see the effect they're having, and even though the possibility cannot be entirely ruled out, dramatic changes to the unfolding pattern are unlikely to occur by tomorrow.

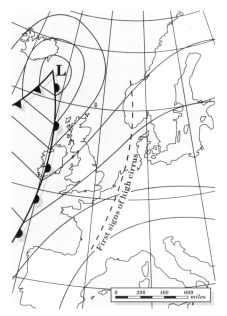

FIGURE 32 Warm front
approaches the UK

The warm front and warm front weather

The warm front marks the boundary between a warm airmass and the colder one it is replacing. Because it is less dense, the warmer air gradually rides up over the denser cold air along a shallow wedge whose slope can be anywhere between 1:100 and 1:200, sometimes greater, giving a frontal zone 300 to 600 miles wide. High cirrus is the precursor cloud for warm fronts, forming at the literally thin end of the wedge of warm air. The scale on the map will give some idea of just how far this influence can extend.

As the front approaches, cloud gradually thickens from the top down, to become CirroStratus, AltoStratus, and finally NimboStratus. Heavy rain may be followed by continual drizzle. When the front has passed, the low-level Stratus trailing behind (figure 31) gradually rises to form StratoCumulus. Warm fronts can be slow to clear, so this cloud may persist for a long time.

The wind usually *backs* (swings anti-clockwise) before the front arrives (figure 32), so a north-westerly will become more westerly and continue to back and increase in strength. As the front passes through, the wind usually *veers* (swings clockwise).

Soarable conditions can persist for quite a long time beneath the thickening high cover. If the front arrives late in the day, or the air ahead of it is particularly unstable in the lower levels, or there has been strong sunshine during the period just before its arrival, thermals may continue right up until the moment it begins to drizzle.

WARM SECTOR WEATHER

The warm sector is the area between a leading warm front and a trailing cold one (figure 33). The weather in this sector depends upon your distance from the associated low, the barometric pressure at your location, and whether it is rising, falling or remaining steady. The farther you are from the low the less cloud there is, the higher the pressure, and the better the chance of good weather.

The cold front and cold front weather

The cold front is steeper, faster moving and a great deal more vigorous than the warm front. A steep wedge of colder air replaces warmer air, lifting it upwards. The slope of the wedge is about 50:1, giving a mixing zone somewhere between 100 and 200 miles wide. Cloud along the leading edge of the front is usually convective, and made more so by the increased instability of the warmer air being forced up the interface (figure 34).

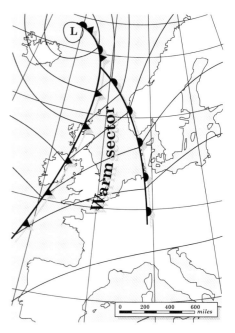

FIGURE 33 Warm sector over the UK

FIGURE 34 Cross section through a cold front

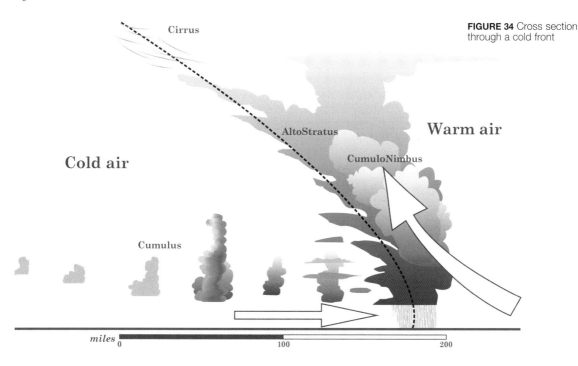

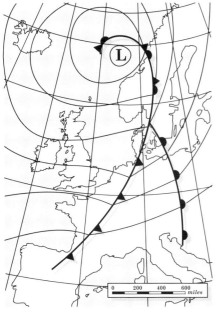

The clearance of a cold front is much more abrupt than the warm one, and a sharp, well-defined edge may well mark the transition. If the air behind the front is very unstable (the ELR slopes well to the left) then showers can persist for some time after the front itself has passed through, at least until rising pressure and subsidence cause the air to dry out.

As a cold front clears (<u>figure 35</u>), visibility improves and the air is dry and buoyant. If a ridge of high pressure builds behind the front, good soaring conditions usually follow, unless the isobars have a *cyclonic curvature*, when showery conditions can prevail. Where the cold air has travelled a long way over the sea the extra moisture may produce spread-out cloud beneath the inversion. This is more of a problem in the UK – Ireland in particular – than it is in the drier regions of the Continent.

Very active cold fronts are the result of marked differences between the airmasses involved, and they can be preceded by a belt of exceptionally strong wind, strong lift along the frontal edge, and sudden and occasionally torrential rain. Once a cold front has passed through, the wind will veer and reduce in strength.

Wave

FIGURE 35 A cold front clears the UK

When the wind blows against a ridge or a hill, a band of lift is created by the air running up the upwind side. On the lee side there is a cascade of sinking air. Quite a lot of the time 'up one side and down the other' is all that happens, but given the right atmospheric conditions the sinking air on the lee side can bounce up again and create a train of *standing*, or *lee waves*, which can reach very high altitudes.

Five conditions usually have to be fulfilled before wave can occur:

(1)　a layer of unstable air at low level

(2)　a stable layer above that

(3)　another unstable layer above that

(4)　a wind of 15kt or more over a ridge or hill

(5)　increasing wind speed with height.

The best wind direction will usually depend on where you are in the country, but whichever direction is best it should not alter with height by more than 25°, and preferably not at all. Approaching warm fronts can trigger wave.

The stable layer is represented in <u>figure 36</u> as a weight suspended between two springs which represent the unstable layers. This combination rises up the face of the generating hill, and at the top the inertia and momentum

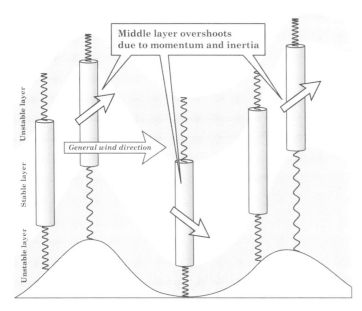

FIGURE 36 Creation of wave

of the non-springy stable layer cause it to overshoot. The springs cause it to rebound, and on the descending side of the hill everything accelerates downwards. Again inertia and momentum cause the stable layer to overshoot, squashing the lower layer and then rebounding. Though the analogy is flawed, wave does require the air mass to oscillate vertically, and the movement does resemble a series of bounces. Alternatively, one can view the stable layer's attempts to push into the unstable ones as having much the same result as trying to push the balloon into the bath in chapter 2 – it just keeps bobbing out again.

In a completely stable airstream there will be hill lift (figure 37, (A)), but no wave, though in some circumstances a half-hearted one can form downwind (B) if the hill is smooth and not too steeply curved on both sides. In wave conditions the first or *primary wave* (C) from a hill or ridge is the strongest. The amplitude of each succeeding wave in the downwind train that results gradually lessens, until 50 miles or so away, often very much further, it dies away to nothing. In hilly regions the pattern of wave is more complicated. Downwind hills can either be in phase with the wave from their upwind neighbour – in which case the wave can be boosted to a greater height and strength – or out of phase – in which case the wave can be cancelled out. A not uncommon effect is for the downgoing part of the wave to suppress ridge lift, occasionally killing it completely (D).

Some of the cloud patterns associated with wave are shown in figure 38, although lenticular clouds, which are often pointed out as a classic symptom of wave, don't have to be there for wave to be present. The wave orientation will be downwind of whatever hill is triggering it off, as in figure 39 (see over), and the lift follows a pattern similar to the shape and height of the generating hill. The illustration takes some account of in- and out-of-phase wave, but not of the fact that if the wind blows onto a ridge or hill at a sufficiently oblique angle it may simply go round rather than over the top. Wave systems can be very complex, and may have several vertically

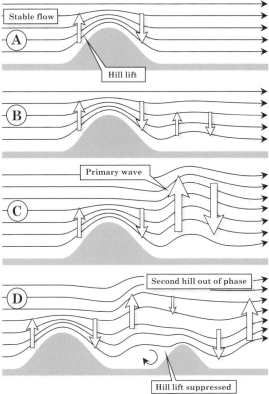

FIGURE 37 Relation of hill and wave

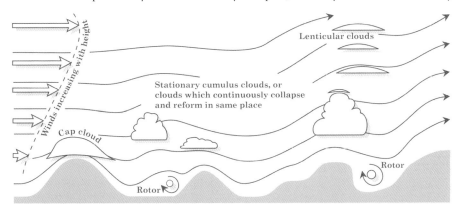

FIGURE 38 Clouds associated with wave

FIGURE 39 Wind
direction and wave
orientation

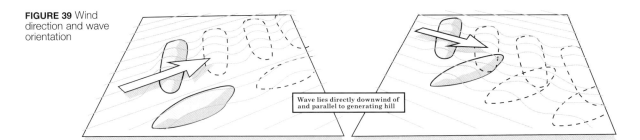

Wave lies directly downwind of
and parallel to generating hill

separated systems with no direct connection between any of them except, perhaps, at certain nodal points. Moving up from one system to another may prove difficult.

Apart from killing ridge lift, a further effect of wave can be to enhance thermals which have formed under the wave, and to damp down those attempting to form where the wave descends. Normally the wave doesn't dip deep into the convective layer, but it is often possible to thermal up to cloudbase, push to the upwind edge of a cloud and contact wave there. Wave does not need a solid hill to set it off. In the right conditions a thermal protruding through an inversion into a layer where the wind speed is markedly higher, or in a completely different direction, can set off usable but not always strong or very big wave.

Depending on the terrain and a number of other factors, wave can give rise to *rotor* – a rapidly rotating, horizontal and stationary vortex of air – usually fairly low down and beneath a wave crest. Any cloud that appears to be ragged or spindle-shaped, and is either rotating or changing shape rapidly, is best avoided, as conditions can be rough enough to cause structural damage or loss of control. Depending on where the rotor is, it can have a dramatic effect on the wind direction and strength at ground level, sometimes switching it through 180° and producing almost anything from much stronger winds than the wind speed for the day, to dead calm. The change from one to the other can occur within a few hundred feet vertically or horizontally.

Obtaining weather information

Even the most basic assessment of the weather requires accurate information, and this can be quite difficult to get. The general public only want to know how warm it is going to be, and whether it will rain or not. There are gliding forecasters who can provide a glider pilot with the information needed to assess the day, and make more or less accurate predictions into the bargain. In the long run, though, it is probably easier to avoid disappointment by regularly monitoring and observing the weather systems for yourself, and making up your own mind about what's likely to happen. Many newspapers provide good forecast charts and, occasionally, though more and more rarely, the actual from the day before. The early morning weather forecasts on BBC1 provide a detailed synoptic chart which you can and should make a practice of interpreting for yourself. The chart is usually on screen for about five seconds if you're lucky, so record it if you want to study it.

Information is also available via fax and telephone from the main meteorological offices, and from the Internet. Don't forget that there are specific gliding meteorology books available, written by experts in the field (*see* Bibliography, p. 307).

Weather (to go to the airfield or not) skills

The information you might need for a given day would be some, if not necessarily all, of the following:

(1)   where are the frontal systems and which way and how quickly are they moving?

(2)   what sort of fronts are they (warm, cold, occluded) and where did their respective air masses originate (clue to humidity, how vigorous they are likely to be, and visibility and cloudbase)?

(3)   is the pressure rising or falling?

(4)   how close are the isobars (wind strength)?

(5)   what's the dew point and/or the trigger temperature?

(6)   an ascent for today (ELR).

Most of the information above was provided and interpreted for you in a daily forecast chart for glider pilots from the Meteorological Office (figure 40). This service has been

FIGURE 40 Meteorological Office forecast chart

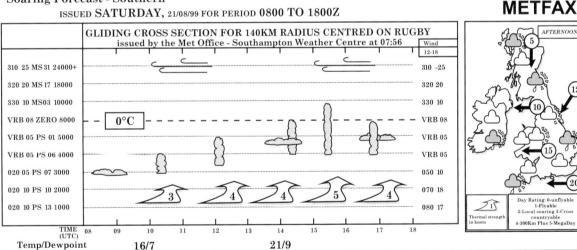

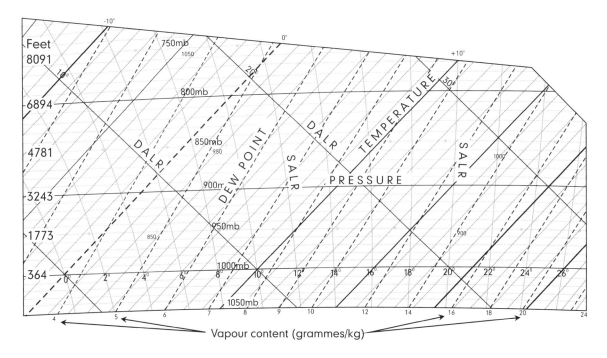

FIGURE 41 A tephigram

discontinued but something similar may be available elsewhere. Try the Internet. A simple way to test a forecast's broad predictions is to look out of the window in the morning. Where did all that high cirrus come from? Forecast thermal strengths are for air movement only. In other words, +1kt on the chart equates to zero sink in a glider whose minimum sink rate is 1kt, so the moment this glider turns or changes speed it will lose height! Times are given in *UTC* (Universal Time Constant) which is Greenwich Mean Time, so your watch may be an hour out.

Many glider pilots only turn up on the days they think are going to be excellent, either because the forecast says so – which is no guarantee – or more rarely because they have the experience and knowledge to stand a better chance than most of picking the good days. Being a fairweather pilot is ultimately self-defeating, even though people now seem to have so little time available that they sometimes can't afford to be anything else. The most likely result of trying to be a fairweather pilot is that without the practical experience provided by flights in less than perfect conditions, your forecasting skills will not improve. You will also reduce your chances of making the best of deteriorating or poor weather, which can be sprung on you even on the supposedly good days. You're also far more likely to land out.

If you're very dedicated you can put all the information from an ascent onto a chart like the above and be your own weather forecaster (figure 41). While the tephigram (pronounced teefygram) it isn't quite as complicated as it looks (allegedly), most of us will get more for less effort from some of the other sources already mentioned.

It is a regrettable fact of gliding, wondrous sport though it is, that anyone who wants to be good at it has to work hard, both physically and mentally.

Sources of meteorological information

AIRMET

Needs a fax machine. Aimed at power flying, but good for winds and major weather systems/events.

FAX

Useful, but can be expensive and FAX machines don't seem quite as ubiquitous as they were. The services include:

ASSEX – Actual, as seen on television (given what's happened fairly recently to TV forecasts, may not be much use any longer).
FSSX – forecast chart for 24 hours ahead. Long range forecasts available.

INTERNET

Since most TV forecasts have reduced the genuine information/brain exercise content to a level that wouldn't tax a gerbil, they are of little use. The Internet is by far and away the best source of weather information. There are many good sites with forecast charts up to five and, in some cases, ten days ahead. Like FSSX, though, okay for a day or two ahead, but not beyond.

There are several sites dedicated to gliding forecasts, but you need to make several weeks of invidious comparisons between what actually happened and what each site forecast before you decide which ones to trust. Whilst none of them will ever be 100 per cent accurate, some are more right more often than others. Tephigrams are also available on the Net. They look complicated (see figure 41, facing page) and need enlarging to be of much use. Choose an ascent from a weather station somewhere near the area where you are going to be flying – anything else is pretty pointless. Synoptic charts are three a penny, often in colour, sometimes animated, and can be downloaded from a number of official sites. The new RASP/blipmaps forecasts are computer based, but seem pretty good even though the level of detail can be a trifle obsessive (the meteorological equivalent of a digital watch's "18:43 and fifteen sixteenths of a second...approximately") and require a certain amount of genuine weather sense for their interpretation. However, having said that, they have forecast a few weather quirks, which just about everyone else missed, so they would seem worth a look.

NATIONAL OR LOCAL PAPERS

Not much use if you don't get your daily paper early. Depending on the paper, they can be a useful source of comparisons between actuals and forecasts. Atlantic synoptic charts are probably far more informative than UK only ones, but papers vary wildly in the detail and scope of the information they provide. You may also feel that buying the *Daily Hysteric* is a high price to pay for a half page, if that, of weather information consisting largely of five puffy clouds covering the entire UK. Go for the ones with proper synoptic charts.

SHIPPING FORECASTS

Good, but take practice to interpret effectively. The daily forecast after the shipping news is better. Sufficient information is provided for you to plot your own synoptic charts, but this requires a level of dedication which most of us simply can't, or don't, have the time to muster up.

VOLMET

These are actuals. Someone reads out wind strengths, directions, cloudbase and cover etc. for various places around the country. You don't get thermal strengths or anything like that, and they need practice to interpret well. The commentary is continuous and cyclic, so after twenty minutes or so it will return to the area where it was when you tuned in, having updated in the meanwhile if conditions have changed. Sometimes difficult to receive, but you can listen to it on your airborne radio if you feel inclined. Frequency 128.6.

Summary of chapter ten

NOTE: circulation directions are reversed in the southern hemisphere (e.g. Coriolis effect)

Page	Subject	
269	**Absolute humidity**	amount of water vapour by weight in the air (*see Relative humidity*); *see* also *Vapour concentration*.
264	**Absolute zero**	temperature at which all atomic movement ceases (−273°).
278	**Actual**	synoptic chart or meteorological information about conditions as they actually are (or more likely, were).
266	**Adiabatic**	no exchange of heat between a system and its surroundings.
–	**Adiabatic cooling**	cooling due to expansion or contraction of gas (*see Adiabatic*); *see* also *Lapse rates*.
270	**Airmass**	homogenous body of air usually extending hundreds of miles. Origin of (in UK): Maritime Tropical (SW) Continental Tropical (S) Continental Polar (E) Continental Arctic (NE) Maritime Arctic (N) Direct Maritime Polar (NW) Returning Maritime Polar (W).
–	**Anti-cyclone**	area of high pressure.
–	**Anti-cyclonic curvature**	(of *isobars*) clockwise curvature of isobars.
267	**Ascent, meteorological**	temperature/pressure plot (ELR) from radiosonde balloon or aircraft.
264	**Atmosphere, layers of**	from the bottom up: **troposphere**: 0–5 miles near poles, 0– 10 near equator **stratosphere**: top of troposphere to about 30 miles **mesosphere**: about 30–50 miles

APPENDICES

Appendix A

Vector sums

(A) is a small cluster of air molecules moving around at random velocities, as represented by the direction and length of the various lines. Vectors were discussed in chapter one, and a vector sum is just the sum of all the vectors. Faced by (A)'s random arrangement, however, where do you start? Doesn't matter. There are only 11 vectors so the resultant can be worked out graphically. (B) takes the vectors in a random order and links them all together, head to tail. (C) takes them in another order and does the same. Though (B) and (C) look different, they have identical resultants, and this would be so regardless of the order in which the vectors were linked, providing it was always head to tail. The circulation vector sum does something very similar but uses calculus instead to work out the resultant of measured values for pressure and velocity at a large number of points on the aerofoil's surface.

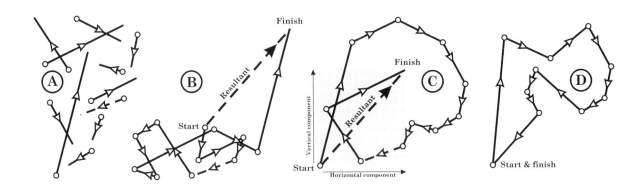

Appendix B

Calculating a glider's CG

The CG of a glider is calculated in relation to a fixed datum, usually the leading edge of the wing. According to the notes written by Cedric Vernon for the BGA, there are at least five different methods of weighing a glider, depending on its configuration. Whatever the method used, the weighing equipment must be accurate within the appropriate range of weights. Bathroom scales are often used for determining the tail weight (R), but the point loads of a tail skid can distort the weighing platform and cause it to collide with the mechanism beneath. If bathroom scales have to be used, they first need to be calibrated using a series of known weights within the appropriate 'R' range, plus the weight of any supports required at the tail, including any piece of wood needed to act as a 'load spreader' to prevent the platform distorting.

As described in chapter 6, the CG position determines the maximum and minimum cockpit loadings. Complicated arithmetic isn't involved, but obtaining accurate measurements of some of the distances, particularly the smaller ones, can be frustratingly difficult. The process of measuring and weighing may need to be repeated several times on the day, and an average taken of the results before any calculation is done.

Distances are measured on the ground with the aid of a plumb line and a rule. Strain gauges can be used if the glider is supported by slings, but only if the hangar roof trusses are up to it. The slings must hang vertically. The exact point of contact between them and the glider may be difficult to determine, particularly if the supporting strap is wide to prevent damage to the glider. Slings are not ideal for wooden aircraft, but if they are used they need to coincide with internal frames to prevent cracking the skin.

Apart from that, the process is relatively straightforward, and slow. Keep a notebook, a pencil and some chalk handy. If you aren't a BGA inspector you'll need the services of one to help with the weighing and the calculations.

Read the BGA notes mentioned above – they contain worked examples – and the appropriate section in the glider's handbook. This will tell you what you need to measure and from where. The glider may need to be weighed in a specific attitude, which the handbook will describe, and you may have to make a wooden wedge containing the appropriate angle. You will need a spirit level.

Rig the aircraft. Make sure it contains all its normal equipment, including radio, oxygen bottle (even if you don't use it very often), batteries, tail parachutes, and so on. Don't include your main parachute or yourself – they come under the heading of cockpit weights! Note the weight of any supporting blocks or platforms you are using. Make the required weight and distance measurements as accurately as possible. The datum will be detailed in the handbook.

Do the calculations. Remember that the weighing is to determine the glider's empty weight, then, given the AUW in the handbook, to calculate from the information you have gathered the maximum and minimum cockpit loadings such that the CG stays within the specified range. Double check the calculations. If you get odd answers, particularly very low minimum cockpit weights, you've probably made a mistake. With older gliders the minimum cockpit weight can work out either extremely close to the maximum cockpit weight, or above it! Take advice on this.

It will probably put the aircraft in the non-aerobatic category, but it may not be un-flyable.

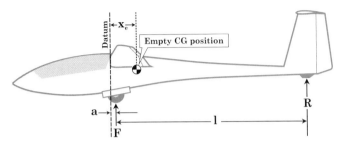

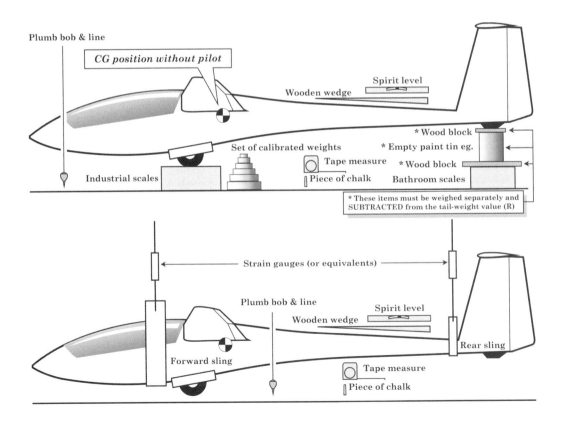

Appendix C

Water ballast

Water ballast affects a glider's performance in the same way that having heavier pilots, or pulling G does. The key is in the way the profile and induced drag curves respond to increases in weight. Total drag is the sum of profile drag and induced drag. Profile drag is independent of weight. Induced drag is not.

So far as the wetted area and displaced volume are concerned, a glider's shape remains constant. Whatever its AUW (within very broad limits), and excepting the use of airbrakes, if glider X flies at a steady 53kt, let's say, the airframe always creates exactly the same amount of profile drag. This link between a specific speed and a specific drag value applies throughout the speed range, so we can regard the profile drag's position on the graph (see figure) as fixed.

Let's now say that glider X's best L/D speed, **unballasted**, is also 53kts. Adding water ballast increases the wing loading. This has three negative effects; (1) an increase in the minimum sink speed (2) an increase in the stalling speed, and (3) a higher minimum drag speed. The important one is (3) and the reason is as follows: if the now **ballasted** glider continues to fly at a steady 53kt the additional lift needed to support the increased all up weight (AUW) can only come from an increase in the AoA, so the induced drag and the total drag increase. The glider then starts to sink faster and the L/D gets worse. Flying slower than 53kt makes things far worse. However, even though flying faster than 53kt will increase the profile drag, the lift is now generated more by the speed than by the AoA, so the AoA and the related induced drag decrease. The total drag will be higher than before, but the increase in profile drag isn't large enough to cancel out the reduction in the induced drag, and the result is that at some speed higher than 53kt – let's say 64kt – the total drag will again be at a minimum. Glider X's ballasted best L/D speed is now at 64kt, not 53kt (the new value depends on the amount of ballast carried), and if the best L/D at 53kt was 46:1, its still 46:1 at 64kt.

Increasing the AUW pushes the polar curve off to the right and down on the graph, which is exactly what happens when there are heavier pilots on board or you pull G. In theory the ballast induced polar shift allows faster average speeds. Think of the glider as being a different and heavier one which must be operated at higher speeds for optimal performance. Additionally, all the McCready values are higher (see chapter 8).

The usual fly in the consomme is the weather. If the thermals are weak and you have water ballast on board, your cross country speed is very likely to be slower than it would

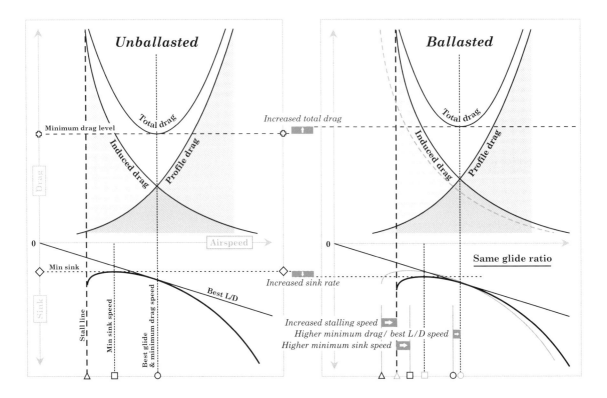

be without it, and there's a greater chance of landing out. Water ballast is usually something for good days, but lift distribution on a weak or indifferent day could be the deciding factor on whether to tank up or not. Even feeble streeting might make discrete amounts of water ballast worthwhile. The point is that if you're airborne and have it you can get rid of it, but if you're airborne and don't have it, you can't pick it up if conditions improve. You don't see too many gliders skimming the surfaces of reservoirs and lakes.

A sometimes useful consequence of water ballast and higher wing loadings is a slightly less rodeo-like ride in rough conditions.

Ballasted or not, the best thermalling speed is somewhere between minimum sink (best rate of climb), and best glide (minimum drag), taking account of the load factor. Circling at min sink is bad tactics: (1) the glider's near the stall and the smallest increase in the AoA, howsoever caused, has a large negative effect on the sink rate, (2) the controls, particularly the ailerons, are sluggish at minimum sink in straight flight, let alone a turn, so controllability's an issue, (3) it's easy to spin. You'll end up flying too fast if you choose best L/D speed instead. Say that in unaccelerated straight flight best L/D speed is 55kt, then at 45 of bank (load factor 1.41, see fig 13, p. 111) it becomes 1.41x55, or 78kt! Even novices don't thermal at that sort of speed! Choose a speed and bank where control is comfortable (we can manoeuvre), the circle's not too wide, and the variometer says good things (we are climbing well). In practice and for smooth conditions, that speed is about a third to halfway between minimum sink and best glide.

Appendix D

Ground effect

There are several explanations for how ground effect works, but the generally accepted one, at least as far as gliders are concerned, is that a reduction in the wing downwash caused by the aircraft's proximity to the ground, results in a reduction in induced drag. A number of ground effect craft have been built over the years, from the giant and enormously fast Russian Ekranoplan to the slow and stately manpowered Gossamer Albatross and Gossamer Condor.

For gliders, ground effect works best at relatively low speeds, so a glider doing a fast and very low final glide won't gain much (if any) advantage from it because, at speed, induced drag is a very small proportion of the total drag – profile drag dominates here. Ground effect becomes more noticeable as the glider slows and the AoA starts to increase, i.e. as induced drag increases. During the round-out and hold-off it is strong, but goes unnoticed because it's part and parcel of the landing process. However, ground effect can become very obvious if the brakes are suddenly closed during the round-out, and the glider can then float on for hundreds of yards before finally touching down.

The Ekranoplan, given its high speeds (200kt+), probably made use of additional effects, possibly ramair, to skate over the surface.

A potentially disastrous result of ground effect is that it can allow underpowered/overloaded aircraft to take off, but then not to climb away. As ground effect starts to decrease, the induced drag increases to the point where, at some usually very low altitude, the total drag is such that the aircraft can neither accelerate nor climb. E. K. Gann's book *Fate is the Hunter* contains a blackly comic example from real life, where he nearly demolished the Taj Mahal after taking off from a nearby airfield in an accidentally overloaded Liberator.

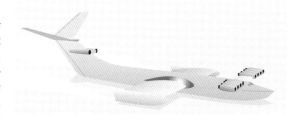

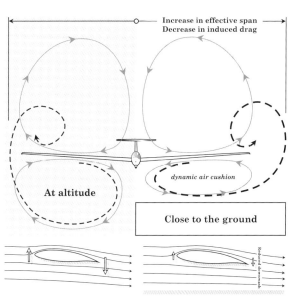

Increase in effective span
Decrease in induced drag

At altitude

dynamic air cushion

Close to the ground

Appendix E

Variometer problems and their solution

A variometer has to be very sensitive to measure what are minuscule rates of flow. It is vital that the pipework and fittings are completely leak free. Poor instrumentation is one of the main reasons why pilots can find soaring difficult, particularly in club aircraft, but even private owners are not immune. They can spend thousands of pounds on glider make and marque, comparing carefully and in great detail relative performance, and measuring precisely how much everything costs, and then more or less nail their gliders to the ground with poor variometer systems.

System leaks are a major problem. Finding them is important but often time-consuming. A lesser, but nonetheless frequent, cause of problems is the variometer's general condition. If it is not serviced every two to three years, the accuracy and response time deteriorate. A sluggish or sticky internal vane or a weakened hair spring will make the instrument unreliable, and it will then need recalibration and readjustment, as well as cleaning and lubrication. These are jobs for an expert with the correct tools, facilities, and a good understanding of the problems. Some variometers (probably the majority) have never been serviced since they were bought, so it is hardly surprising that after many cubic feet of the UK's atmosphere have blown back and forth inside them, that they can become unreliable.

MAKING THE VARIOMETER SYSTEM WORK PROPERLY: SERVICING

Next time you take a winch launch on a calm evening, watch the variometer after release and time its return to a sensible indication. If this takes longer than 5–8 seconds, the variometer needs servicing and calibrating.

FINDING LEAKS/CHECKING OUT THE TE COMPENSATION

A simple air test can detect a leaking system. On the same calm evening, when vertical movements of the air are not going to upset the readings, do the following tests:

(1)   fly for ten seconds at the minimum sink speed, or the stalling speed plus 5kt. The variometer should indicate the glider's minimum sink rate

(2)   push forward steadily – accelerometer somewhere between 0.2 and 0.5G – until the glider reaches a 10° to 15° nose-down attitude. If you don't have an

accelerometer, you should feel some reduced G, but not so much that the dust rises off the cockpit floor. The variometer needle should climb almost to zero. The weight of the air column in any vertical section of the tube between the probe and the instrument changes with the load factor, and adds to the variometer reading, but rarely more than +1kt

(3)   keep the pitch attitude. Keep an eye on the variometer, but not at the expense of lookout, and . . .

(4)   *before* reaching V_{NE}, smoothly pitch the glider up to between 10° and 15° nose-up

(5)   keep the attitude until the glider reaches the previous minimum speed.

During stages 3–5 the variometer may have done one of the following:

(A)   given an initially increased down reading during the pull-up, and then changed steadily and smoothly to a new 'up' figure, with no tendency for excessive up readings

(B)   as you accelerated to the new speed, the variometer indicated a large amount of sink which increased the faster you went. Then, as you climbed, it indicated lift

(C)   did something midway between (A) and (B)

(D)   as you accelerated, the variometer indicated climb. When you slowed down it read sink

(E)   had a bias towards lift, either reading it when it wasn't there, or over-reading.

  (A) is actually correct, so don't waste time trying to get rid of the initial down reading. It is telling you that the compensation is working properly. If the variometer behaved as in (B), (C) or (E), then there is a leak *into* the system – i.e. into an area where the pressure is *lower* than ambient. This will give you some clue as to its approximate location. For example, if the variometer behaved as in (B) or (C), then the leak will be somewhere between the variometer's static connection and the TE probe. It is as if the probe is producing insufficient suction, so the variometer is undercompensated.

LIKELY SOURCES OF A PROBE SIDE LEAK:

Probe/fin connection
Some probes are a slide fit while others are sealed with an O ring. Seals must be airtight. Check the O ring and replace it if it is perished. A thin smear of Vaseline can help make an airtight seal, but use soft, flexible tubing which fits tightly round the join if you can. The connection can be sealed with wing tape, but always use fresh tape and stretch it during application.

T-pieces
Choose a size to fit the tubing. Too small and leaks will occur at the connections. Badly made connectors can have moulding hairs (flashing) that encourage leaks. Carefully shave them off flush with a very sharp knife. 'T' or inline connectors can crack.

Tubing

The softer and more flexible the tubing you can use, the better. Rubber tubing perishes and cracks. Avoid it and use modern PVC or silicone tubing instead. Make sure tubes aren't kinked and that all the joints are airtight, preferably sealed with double, not single twist wire locking – take care, the wire can cut into the softer tubing – or silicon sealant for the more awkward locations. Annular constrictors (pig castrators) are good for squeezing tubes to connectors, but sometimes difficult to fit.

Multi-connectors

When it comes to removing the instrument panel, multi-connectors make life a lot easier, but on reassembly make certain the two halves match correctly. Good multi-connectors have an asymmetric layout of holes and locating lugs, and can't be fitted together incorrectly. Avoid cross-threading the screws that hold them together and don't do them up too tight. Cheap multi-connectors can be prone to leaks, plastic ones especially. Good quality machined metal connectors are worth the extra cost. The O rings with which they are sealed need regular maintenance.

Gust and dust filters

If fitted, make sure that they are leak free and that all connections are good. Some variometer systems are fitted with small, soft plastic bottles which act as gust filters. These are prone to leaks and should be replaced with ordinary car fuel filters, which will damp down gusts and filter the air.

Instrument connections

Should be airtight, but they can work loose. Be very careful not to overtighten them and crack the case.

If the variometer behaves as in (D), then it is overcompensated – the probe is creating too much suction, possibly because it's in the wrong place. The probe should not be anywhere it is going to be affected by the airframe, either through turbulence, local pressure fluctuations, or downwash. If you have to relocate a probe or venturi, consult an expert before cutting any holes in the glider. Don't make the probe yourself unless you know exactly what you're doing. If not, buy a probe!

A variometer that reads more up than it should, as in (E), is particularly annoying – good for morale, certainly, but not good for performance in the real world. In this case air is leaking into the system, on the capacity side of the plumbing, and increasing the volume of air flowing through the instrument, hence the optimistic readings. It is easy to confuse this problem with the one caused by overcompensation.

LIKELY SOURCES OF A CAPACITY SIDE LEAK:

Instrument

Apart from the connection, the case may be cracked. The instrument also happens to be a sealed unit, with the face glass held against a rubber seal by a screw bezel around the inside lip. This can work loose, or the seal can perish. If you don't have the correct tools, be very careful when tightening the bezel.

Tubing, T-pieces and multi-connectors

Remember that the pitot side may contain a capillary leak which should be checked, if only to rule it out as the leak's source. The pneumatic switch toggling the capillary into or out of the circuit is a common trouble spot.

Capacity

Before installing a capacity, check the connector is tight. If there is a stopper in the top, check it is properly sealed. Commercially manufactured capacities are best, but avoid plastic ones. Don't fit a capacity where a heavy landing will rattle it as it is quite likely to break, and, obviously, a broken or holed capacity is useless.

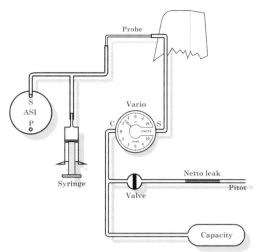

E1 A test set-up to check for system leaks

Test equipment

Producing a leak-free system is not always straightforward. A system may contain several leaks, the symptoms of which will depend upon the location of the largest, as well as their total size. In any case, you will have to start at the back of the glider and work your way forwards, sealing each potential leak as you go. Then test again.

Air testing every attempt at sealing could prove expensive. It is far easier and cheaper to test on the ground, using a syringe to provide suction via a T-piece connected to the static side of the ASI, and the probe (figure 1). A small piece of locking wire inserted into one of the holes of the probe will establish sufficient free passage to develop the required suction. Make sure that the test equipment itself is free of leaks, and that the pipework, T-pieces, syringes and ASI are all sound. Once you are sure that there are no leaks, slowly draw out the syringe and watch the ASI and variometer(s). Stop suction at 60kt. The ASI should stay at 60kt and the variometers drop very gradually back to zero.

Problem	Remedy
The variometer does not return to zero, or takes more than 10 seconds to do so.	(1) Check the various tubes aren't blocked or kinked. Cloud flying can fill the system with water. (2) Have the instrument serviced.
The ASI drops quickly when suction ceases, or won't sustain pressure.	There is a massive leak. If, during the test: (1) the variometer needle hardly moves or is very sluggish, there is a probe- side. (2) the variometer needle reads excessive 'up', the leak is on the capacity side.
Once suction is stopped, the ASI falls slowly back to zero.	There is a slight leak only. It will be significant. If the variometer: (1) reads excessive up while suction is applied and then returns slowly to zero, the leak is on the capacity side (2) reads up during the test but the needle swings quickly past zero to indicate down, and then slowly returns to zero when suction ceases, then the leak is on the probe side.

Problems with water ingress

If gliders are left outside during a shower or overnight, or fly through cloud or rain, water can find its way into the tubing and cause the variometer to misread. Water tends to collect at the lowest point in the pipework, and even drops a great deal smaller than the one illustrated (figure 2) can have an effect, causing the variometer to gulp and/or the needle to quiver, or just stop the tube working altogether. Purging the system can be difficult, but *water-traps* can be added in line at the lowest point and cleared if water ingress is suspected. These traps can be a source of additional leaks.

Traps are not the whole answer, so if water has got in, disconnect the pipes and blow air through them. Take care! If you just connect up a compressor and blast high pressure air through the system it is very likely to blow every joint apart. If the hidden connection to the probe in the fin gets blown off, it can require major surgery to get it back on again. Less obviously, a blast of high pressure air shatters the water droplets into tiny particles which cling by surface tension to the walls of the tube. The majority of these move so slowly that they never really clear the system, and when your 'hurricane' is turned off, these tiny particles quietly recoalesce into large droplets.

Never blow air through the tubing at more than two psi, and make sure it is as dry as possible, and slightly warm. Don't blow into the tubes yourself as all that does is to introduce even more moisture.

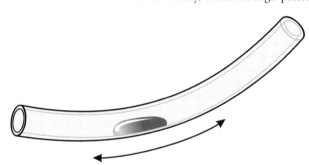

Water droplet in a tube

★ WARNING! Before connecting any pipe to an external air supply, make sure that the other end is open to the atmosphere and not connected to any instrument(s). ★

Total energy dump

Some instrument panels are equipped with a pneumatic switch or tap connected to the TE suction tubing. Closed, the switch has no effect. When open it connects the TE line to the cockpit static.

This achieves two things:

• if the probe becomes blocked by ice or water and the variometer dies, opening the tap connects it to cockpit static and it will then function as an uncompensated variometer

• if there is water in the plumbing, the probe may be able to clear it by sucking air through from the cockpit static.

Fitting such a tap and all its joints and connectors can add up to five extra potential sources of leaks!

Appendix F

The Coriolis effect

In the northern hemisphere the Coriolis Effect turns air masses to the right. The opposite happens in the southern hemisphere. A rotating world like our own may be solid, near enough, but the surrounding atmosphere certainly isn't, and frictional contact between the two is low. The example below assumes that there is no friction.

RELATIVE MOTION

Chapter 1 went into some detail about frames of reference (p. 21) and the Coriolis effect is a classic example of one. We'll look at a two dimensional example to outline the basic principle.

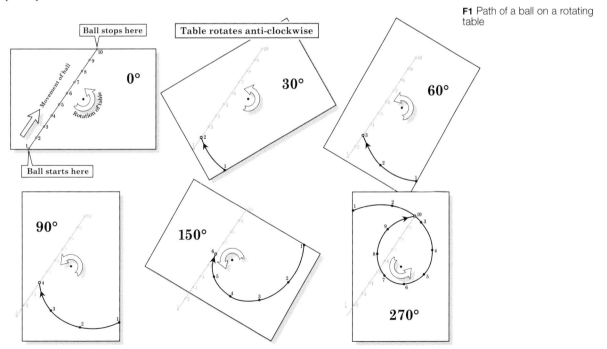

F1 Path of a ball on a rotating table

303

Imagine a billiard table, or something similar (illustration on previous page). A ball is cued and runs across a stationary table, from 1–10, as illustrated. To the player, and to a small insect at the centre of the table, the ball travels in a straight line. If the table rotates smoothly by 30°, as the ball passes each 'way point', it still seems to the player that it travels in a straight line, as indeed it does in relation to his external frame of reference. But to the insect the ball appears to follow a curved path which loops back upon itself. In short, from one point of view the ball runs straight, from the other it doesn't and it would appear that some unusual force is acting upon it. (If you are in any doubt about how this happens, draw it out.)

Unfortunately, though something very similar happens to moving air masses, the linear velocity of a globe's surface-changes with latitude (see illustration below). An airmass moving north from a midlatitude appears to accelerate to the right, to the East, because it maintains the eastward velocity component of its starting point as the surface underneath starts to slow down. A southward moving air mass, also diverting to the right (West) appears to decelerate for the same reasons.

At some point both air masses end up running parallel to the equator. The situation is made rather more complicated by the gyroscopic forces created by the earth's rotation, and the fact that the velocity changes are taking place in three dimensions, not the two of the billiard table. The result is that if other forces permit, the air masses will try to curve back towards their starting latitudes.

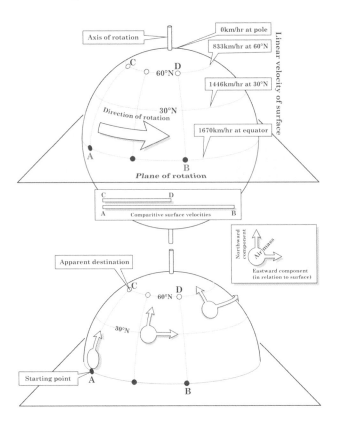

BIBLIOGRAPHY

The following books and publications were referred to in the writing of this book.
   (OP = Out of print)

Air Registration Board, *British Civil Airworthiness Requirements*, Section E, 1948
Boyne, W. J., *The Leading Edge*, Artabras, New York, 1991
Bradbury, T. A. M., *Meteorology and Flight*, A & C Black, 1989
British Gliding Association, *Sailplane and Gliding* (magazine)
CAA, *Joint Airworthiness Requirements*, Section 22, 1983
Carpenter, C., *Flightwise* (Volumes 1 and 2), Airlife, 1996 and 1997
Chambers Twentieth Century Dictionary, 1976
Chanute, O., *Progress in Flying Machines*, M N Forney, 1894
Concise Encyclopaedia of Science and Technology (3rd Edition), Parker/McGrawHill, 1992
Crystal, D., *The Cambridge Biographical Encyclopaedia*, Cambridge University Press, 1995
GibbsSmith, C. H., *The Aeroplane, an historical survey*, HMSO, 1960 (OP)
Hadley, D., *Only seconds to live*, Airlife, 1997
Harper, H., *My fifty years in flying*, Morrison and Gibb Ltd, 1956 (OP)
Harrison, J. P., *Mastering the Sky*, Sarpendon, 1996
HMSO, *Handbook of Aviation Meteorology*, 1994
Mouillard, L. P., *The Empire of the Air*, 1881, English edition 1893
OSTIV, *Airworthiness requirements for sailplanes* (1976 edition)
Piggott, D., *Understanding Gliding*, A & C Black, 1977
Pritchard, J. L., *Sir George Cayley*, Max Parrish, 1961
Reichmann, H., *Cross Country Soaring*, Thomson Publications, 1988
Rolt, L. T. C., *The Aeronauts*, Allan Sutton Publishing, 1985
Scull, B., *Soaring across country*, Pelham Books Ltd, 1979
Simons, M., *Model Aircraft Aerodynamics*, Argus Books, 3rd edition, 1994
Sutherland, A., *Basic Aeronautics for Modellers*, Traplet Publications, 1995
Wallington, C. E., *Meteorology for Glider Pilots*, J W Arrowsmith Ltd (OP), 1977
Weather, the ultimate guide to the elements, Collins, 1996
Welch, A., *The Story of Gliding*, John Murray (OP), 1980
Welch and Irving, New Soaring Pilot (Third edition), Pitman Press (2nd edition) (OP), 1977

FURTHER INFORMATION

Meteorology titles

Bradbury, T., *Meteorology and Flight*, A & C Black, 1989
HMSO, *Handbook of Aviation Meteorology*, 1994
Wallington, *Meteorology for Glider Pilots*, John Murray, 1977
Welch, *Pilot's Weather*, John Murray, 1973
Weather: the ultimate guide to the elements, Collins, 1996

Internet sources

These are too numerous to mention individually but my experience is that a great deal of caution needs to be exercised when using the net as a research source, as the information isn't always reliable. Google is one of the better search engines for queries like 'Sir George Cayley', or 'Evaporation', to name but two, and will usually provide more references than anyone's ever likely to want to trawl through. Generally speaking, the first three or four pages of 'hits' are enough.

British Gliding Association

Contact details:
Kimberley House
Vaughan Way
Leicester, LE1 4SE
Telephone: 0116 2531051
Facsimile: 0116 2515939
Email: bga@gliding.co.uk
Website: www.gliding.co.uk

INDEX